S0-ABU-569

LABORATORY MANUAL

To Accompany

BIOLOGY

LABORATORY MANUAL

To Accompany
BIOLOGY

Wessells
Hopson

Richard M. McCourt

RANDOM HOUSE NEW YORK

First Edition

9 8 7 6 5 4 3 2 1

Copyright © 1988 by Random House, Inc.

All rights reserved under International and Pan-American Copyright Conventions. No part of this book may be reproduced in any form or by any means, electronic or mechanical, including photocopying, without permission in writing from the publisher. All inquiries should be addressed to Random House, Inc., 201 East 50th Street, New York, N.Y. 10022. Published in the United States by Random House, Inc., and simultaneously in Canada by Random House of Canada Limited, Toronto.

ISBN 394-37595-5

Manufactured in the United States of America

Cover and text design by Victoria Van Deventer
Cover art: Broad-billed hummingbird (*Cynanthus latirostris*). Photo by Bob and Clara Calhoun/Bruce Coleman.

Artists: Albert Burkhardt, Mary Burkhardt, Pat Rogondino, and Bridget Carson.

Text and art credits: Table 11-1: Professor Frederick Mosteller. Figure 12-3: From Helena Curtis, *Biology*, 4th ed., Worth Publishers, New York, 1983, page 350. Figure 12-4: Redrawn and reproduced with permission from Kelly, T.E.: *Clinical Genetics & Genetic Counseling* 2nd. edition Copyright © 1986 by Year Book Medical Publishers, Inc., Chicago. Figures 17-15 and 17-10; From Bold, Alexopoulos, and Delevoryas, *Morphology of Plants and Fungi*, 4th ed, Harper & Row, New York. Figures 20-3a, 20-5, 20-6, 20-8, 20-9, 20-10, 21-1, 21-3, 21-4, 21-6, 21-7, 21-8, 21-11b, 22-1a, 22-2: From Sherman and Sherman, *The Invertebrates, Function and Form*, Second Edition, © 1976 by Macmillan Publishing Company. Figures 22-4b and 22-7b: From C. Eberhard, *Biology Laboratory*, Holt, Rinehart & Winston. Figures 26-1, 26-2, 26-3, 26-5, 26-7, 26-8, 26-9, 26-11, 26-13, 26-14, 26-15, 26-16, 26-17, 26-20, 26-21. From Theron Odlaug, *Laboratory Anatomy of the Fetal Pig*, 6th Ed., W.C. Brown, Dubuque, Iowa.

Photo credits: Figures 2-1, 2-7, 26-4b, and 26-6b: Grant Heilman. Figure 2-5: R. E. Litchfield, Photo Researchers. Figure 2-12: Jeremy Pickett-Heaps, Photo Researchers. Figure 2-13: Ross E. Huchins, Photo Researchers. Figure 7-1: Lee D. Simon, Photo Researchers. Figures 7-2, 7-3, 13-3, 16-2, 24-2, 24-6b, 26-6a, 26-10, and 26-19; Photo Researchers. Figure 12-5 and 26-4a: B.P.S. Figure 16-4: Asa Thoresen, Photo Researchers. Figure 26-6c: D. M. Phillips, Taurus.

CONTENTS

PREFACE

This laboratory manual is designed to accompany the text BIOLOGY, by Norman Wessells and Janet Hopson. The sequence of chapters and subjects covered follows that of the textbook. Each chapter is divided into exercises that emphasize different aspects of a common theme. The objectives—what the student is expected to learn—are clearly stated at the beginning of each exercise.

The laboratory manual is intended for a broad audience of college-level biology majors. As such, the exercises have been designed to require a minimum of expensive equipment or materials that are difficult to obtain outside a particular region. While covering the classic topics necessary in any biology laboratory course, the laboratory manual also includes some newer and relatively novel subjects (such as Chapter 28 on creating miniature biospheres). Wherever possible, students are encouraged to think about the rationale and design of experiments. In addition, student-designed experiments are a major part of a number of chapters, and these exercises require the student not only to design an experiment, but also to face the sometimes uncomfortable (but valuable) process of learning through "failed" experiments. In addition to learning a large number of facts about biological systems, students should come away from the laboratory with an appreciation of the scientific method and increased understanding of the many experiments they will encounter in future courses.

I would like to acknowledge the dedicated efforts of my editor, Beverly Fraknoi, whose many constructive criticisms clarified the writing in this volume. In addition I would like to thank the numerous colleagues and friends who have contributed ideas or criticisms of the material included here: Robert W. Hoshaw, Donald A. Thomson, Guy Hoelzer, Robert S. Mellor, Michael J. Donoghue, Nicholas P. Yensen, Clair E. Folsome, Robert Kull, and Cherie Wetzel.

Richard M. McCourt

The material in this chapter corresponds to Chapter 1 in your text.

1
INTRODUCTION TO BIOLOGY LABORATORY

As a scientist Charles Darwin had many virtues, but he is probably history's foremost biologist because he knew how to ask the right questions. This may seem curious to students, who are primarily concerned with getting the right *answer* to whatever question a teacher asks. However, as Darwin wrote in his autobiography, asking the right question is probably the most difficult and important part of being a scientist.

Laboratory work is an essential part of a course in biology. Laboratory exercises are the equivalent of behind-the-wheel lessons in driving: You can read all you want about driving, but until you are faced with steering, braking, double clutching, parallel parking, and so on, you cannot learn how to drive. Laboratory work also gives you a critical appreciation of how the science of biology is carried out. For any scientist, most professional knowledge is gathered from books, scientific papers, and lectures, because no one person can perform even a tiny fraction of the experiments that contribute to the core knowledge in a field. On the other hand, one cannot be simply a passive consumer of knowledge. Some experiments are better planned and executed than others, and none is perfect. To judge whether an experiment was done well or poorly, first-hand experience in the laboratory is essential. That first-hand experience begins with an understanding of the scientific method.

EXERCISE 1-1 THE SCIENTIFIC METHOD

Objectives To understand the nature of development and change in scientific theories and the relationship of data to theory testing.

The **scientific method** is an outline of how scientists work. The end product of a series of experiments is never final. A good experiment in biology produces information that either confirms *or* disproves part of a theory. The idea that some experiments are valuable because they force us to abandon cherished notions of how nature works may appear paradoxical, but the changeable nature of scientific understanding is crucial to our ability to improve that understanding.

Chapter 1 of the textbook discusses the elements of the scientific method in detail. Briefly, these elements are:

Observations Events and objects are observed with one's own senses and scientific instruments.

Inductive reasoning Based on a particular group of observations, a general explanation or **theory** is developed about the causes of the observed phenomena.

Hypothesis formulation A tentative explanation, called a **hypothesis,** is developed to explain a particular set of observations.

Prediction and hypothesis testing A hypothesis must be testable by experiment or further observation or else it is useless. Deductive reasoning leads to logical predictions based on the hypothesis; the predictions are proved true or false by additional experiments and observations. Experiments must be designed carefully to make sure they give an unequivocal answer. Guidelines for experimental design are discussed later in this chapter.

Theory modification When hypotheses are supported by experimental tests, the more general explanation or theory is also supported. If a hypothesis is disproved by experiment, one is forced to examine the underlying premises and logic of the theory. Theories constantly undergo modification as experimental evidence accumulates. It usually takes more than one failed hypothesis to dethrone an otherwise valuable theory. But occasionally theories are abandoned because so many of the hypotheses they generate are proved wrong. A new theory may take its place, but the new one must explain a set of observations better than the old one, and the new theory itself must then be tested just as rigorously. A good theory never rests—it continues to generate further hypotheses that are either verified or disproved by future experiments and observations.

Experimental Design

We experience many events in our daily lives, and as we do we consciously or unconsciously develop explanations for them and make predictions about future events. The car is misfiring; you suspect a spark plug is bad and a check confirms this. The cake you baked fell; maybe the recipe calls for too little baking powder, so you add more the next time and it turns out fine. Scientific experiments are also part of experience, but they differ from everyday activity. Why?

A scientific experiment is **controlled** experience. A series of procedures is carried out under carefully defined conditions and the results are observed. Take the example of the cake that fell. You might, if you had ingredients to spare, make a series of cakes, adding different amounts of baking powder while leaving the rest of the recipe unchanged. Many experiments function this way: One feature of the experiment is varied in a systematic way while the others are held constant. Any differences in results are probably due to the variation in that one feature.

A key feature of an experiment is that it allows you to compare things. Therefore, an experiment has at least two parts, a **control treatment** and an **experimental treatment.** The control treatment is the baseline set of conditions used as a comparison for the experimental treatment, in which one feature is varied and the others are held constant. In the cake example, the control treatment is the basic recipe; the experimental treatments are the recipes with more or less baking powder. In biology, the control treatment is often the natural or standard set of conditions in the laboratory or field. The experimental treatment is the changed set of conditions manipulated by the experimenter. For example, a pesticide is tested on some potato plants by spraying some plants growing in a field with the pesticide and spraying other plants in the same field with water or an inert chemical. The damage done by insects is then measured. The plants sprayed with water are the **controls;** those sprayed with pesticide are experimentals. The growing conditions are the same for both treatments; even the experience of being sprayed is the same. If *only* the pesticide affects the insects on the plants, the experiment should reveal this.

The difference between the results of experimental and control treatments is often expressed in a **null hypothesis.** A null hypothesis expresses the expected outcome of an experiment if the experimental treatment has no effect. In the pesticide example, one null hypothesis would be: Plants sprayed with pesticide will have as many insects on them as plants sprayed with water. If the plants sprayed with pesticide have fewer insects, we would say the null hypothesis is *rejected* and conclude that the pesticide had an effect. If insect numbers are the same on plants sprayed with pesticide and plants sprayed with water, we *accept* the null hypothesis and conclude that the so-called pesticide did not work (at least not for these insects).

Experimental procedures are usually performed more than once—often many times. This process of **replication** is important in experimental designs because it shows that a particular result was not a fluke and that the results of an experiment are reliable. For this reason, scientists carefully describe how their experiments are done so that other scientists can critique their procedures or repeat the experiment for themselves if necessary.

Some results are **qualitative:** the cake fell or it did not. But most results are obtained by counting or measuring, and statistical analysis of such **quantitative data** is usually necessary. For example, hens fed a certain diet may produce slightly larger eggs. This small difference may be important to the chicken farmer, and only a statistical analysis of a larger number of chickens and eggs would reveal if a slight size difference in eggs were due to diet or to chance.

- Your instructor will have several experimental setups on display. For each one you should be able to:

  1. Describe the experimental treatment and the control treatment.
  2. State in one sentence a null hypothesis for the experiment.
  3. State whether the experimental setup supports or disproves the null hypothesis.
  4. Describe what quantities would be measured or counted in the experiment.
  5. Describe how more replications of the experiment would improve your confidence in the results of the experiment.

Hypothesis Testing

- The following list includes a number of hypotheses, some of which are subject to scientific testing and some of which are not. Comment briefly on whether the hypotheses are testable by the method outlined above, and if so, explain how they might be tested.

  1. People with blond hair have blue eyes.

     Testable. Get a large no. of blond haired people and find out if all of them have blue eyes.

  2. People born under the astrological sign of Gemini are better at mathematics than are individuals born under the sign of Pisces.

     Testable. First test Geminis in math, then Piscis and compare the two.

3. Smoking causes lung cancer.

Testable. Get people who smoke, find out how many have lung cancer - make a strong ratio.

4. The world was created five seconds ago. (Also created at that time were your memories of a childhood that never really existed.)

Not Testable.

5. A person's soul is reincarnated after death.

Not testable.

6. The earth is approximately 4.5 billion years old.

Testable. Collect data and experiments that can confirm the age of the earth.

Being Right for the Wrong Reason

Even theories that appear to be valid should continue to be tested. Why? *Because they can be right for the wrong reason*. In the pesticide example, suppose the plants sprayed with pesticides had no insects on them. We might conclude that the pesticide had killed the insects. But there is an **alternative hypothesis.** Perhaps the pesticide had no effect on the insects but instead induced the plant to produce its own toxic chemicals that killed the insects. You can probably think of other alternative hypotheses that would explain the result of the pesticide experiment. That is why a theory must be tested over and over—by testing a variety of hypotheses based on the theory—to make sure that the predictions of the theory are right for the right reason.

It is rarely obvious that a theory has led to the right prediction for the wrong reason. The logic of a theory may be flawed or incomplete. Comment on how the following hypotheses could be right for the wrong reason.

Hypothesis The sun revolves around the earth from east to west. **Prediction** The sun rises in the east and sets in the west.

Maybe this experiment was only done in one area of US. The sun could rise & set a different way in another area.

Hypothesis Fresh water is attracted to sea water by a hidden force. **Prediction** All rivers empty into the sea. All water could run downhill, ∴ falling into the seas.

Hypothesis Frank is cheating on exams. **Prediction** Frank will get an A on the next exam.

Frank could get an A on the next exam - but maybe he studied this time or maybe just because Frank is cheating doesn't mean he'll get an A.

Hypothesis The college basketball team has been jinxed by a witch. **Prediction** The team will lose their next game. Maybe the jinx doesn't work, but, at the same time, the team has a bad night.

Looking Ahead

During the course of the laboratory exercises in this manual, you may occasionally refer back to this chapter to understand what you are doing in the context of the scientific method. In many cases you will conduct experiments that have been done by generations of beginning biology students. In the interest of time, you will conduct experiments that have a high likelihood of success. So, just as you may use a tried-and-true recipe to ensure that you only have to cook one dinner for your guests instead of two (or more), the exercises in this manual will probably yield some worthwhile results.

Unfortunately, this timesaving device obscures something of the true nature of science—both its tedium and its exhilaration. Practicing scientists often have to design their own experiments, and must do them over and over before they work. That can be tedious and frustrating. But the exhilaration comes when the experiment *does* work and the scientist uncovers something brand new, a fact or event that no one else has ever seen before.

To acquaint you with the frustration and excitement of nonrecipe experiments, some of the exercises will require you to design experiments of your own. In these cases, reference to this chapter and your textbook will help you ask the right questions. And even though the experiments you design may not work exactly the way you plan, if they are carefully thought out you will still learn a great deal from them. In the exercises for each chapter, learn the information presented, but try also to develop the habit of asking questions, to go beyond what is known, just as Darwin did.

The material in this chapter does not correspond to a chapter in your text.

2

MEASUREMENT, MAGNIFICATION, AND SCALES

Being a scientist means observing and describing events in the laboratory or natural world and explaining them in a logical way. The quality of the explanation depends in part on the quality of the observations on which it is based. Some observations are based on simple descriptions; for example, "Starfish in the intertidal zone of the ocean prey on mussels." But many—if not most—valuable observations are quantitative: "A starfish foraging for x amount of time must eat y mussels in order to obtain z calories for growth and reproduction."

To make quantitative observations, scientists need a common system of measurement based on units that are easy to use, and that are understood around the world. You are familiar with the U.S. Customary System, which includes measurements expressed in inches, feet, yards, ounces, pounds, and so on. But this system of recording length, weight, volume, and other quantities has several drawbacks for scientific use. For one, scientific work deals with widely varying amounts. Thus, if you were to use the U.S. Customary System to compare the weight of a mouse with that of an elephant, the mouse's weight would probably be expressed in ounces, whereas the weight of the elephant would likely be expressed in tons. Moreover, conversions between such units are often unwieldy. If you want to know how much your pet elephant weighs in ounces, you need to multiply by the awkward factor of 16 (1 pound contains 16 ounces). Another problem with the U.S. Customary System is that few other countries use it. You may have encountered problems driving on highways in other countries where the speed limits are posted in kilometers per hour.

Unlike the U.S. Customary System, the **metric system** is both easy to use and widely understood. The official name of the metric system is "The International System of Units," or "SI" (for *Système international*) for short. The metric system was first proposed by a Frenchman in 1670, and its official use in that country was fostered after the French Revolution. In the United States, use of the metric system was sanctioned by Congress in 1866. And although the public resisted using the system, the scientific community embraced it wholeheartedly. The reason is the metric system is a decimal system: All units can be derived from the basic units by multiplying or dividing by factors of 10. Thus, because our mathematical system is in base 10, conversions in the metric system are relatively painless. Also, because the metric system is used in nearly all countries, scientists everywhere can read articles and understand the procedures and results involved without referring to cumbersome conversion tables. (Of course the language barrier remains, but the units are the same.)

In these exercises, you will use the metric system to measure the length, mass, and volume of various specimens. You will also learn to use significant digits, to express numbers in scientific notation, and to calculate the magnification of illustrated specimens and construct scales for such illustrations.

EXERCISE 2-1 MEASURING LENGTH, MASS, VOLUME, AND TEMPERATURE

Objective To measure length, mass, volume, and temperature in units of the metric system.

Table 2-1 shows the names of metric system (SI) units commonly used in biology. Table 2-2 shows the names and symbols for multiples and submultiples of metric units. Use the information in these tables to perform the following exercises.

Table 2-1 Names and symbols of metric system units commonly used in biology.

Quantity	Unit	Symbol
length	meter	m
mass	kilogram	kg
volume	liter	L

Table 2-2 Names and symbols of multiples and submultiples of metric units.

Prefix	Symbol	Power	Numeric equivalent
tera	T	10^{12}	1,000,000,000,000
giga	G	10^{9}	1,000,000,000
mega	M	10^{6}	1,000,000
kilo	k	10^{3}	1,000
hecto	h	10^{2}	100
deca	da	10^{1}	10
deci	d	10^{-1}	.1
centi	c	10^{-2}	.01
milli	m	10^{-3}	.001
micro	μ	10^{-6}	.000001
nano	n	10^{-9}	.000000001
pico	p	10^{-12}	.000000000001
femto	f	10^{-15}	.000000000000001
atto	a	10^{-18}	.000000000000000001

Length

The basic metric unit of length is the **meter** (m). At one time the international standard for the meter was the distance between two marks on a platinum-iridium bar kept by the International

Bureau of Weights and Measures in France. In 1960, the standard was changed to a less practical but far more precise measurement: the length equal to 1,650,763.73 times the wavelength of the orange-red radiation in vacuum of krypton 86. Fortunately, for our measurement purposes, rulers manufactured by a reputable company will suffice!

- Use a ruler to measure the maximum length and maximum width of the various plant specimens provided by your instructor. Decide which unit (m, cm, mm) is appropriate for reporting the measurement of each specimen. Record your observations on the following chart and compare them with measurements made by other members of the class.

Chart 2-1 Measurements of plant specimens.

Specimen	Maximum length	Maximum width	
1. Rubra	23.7cm	13.7cm	
2. Rubra	25.1cm	15.1cm	251mm
3. Rubra	26.4cm	12.9cm	2.64m

- Referring to the measurements above, express the length and width of Specimen 1 in kilometers: .00237 length .00137 width km. Express the length and width of Specimen 2 in micrometers: 251,000 length 151,000 width µm. Express the length and width of Specimen 3 in gigameters: 2.64×10^{-9} length 1.29×10^{-9} width Gm.
- Table 2-3 shows the metric equivalents of common U.S. Customary units. How tall are you in feet and inches? 5 feet 4 inches. How tall are you in centimeters? 162.56 cm. In kilometers? .0016256 km. In millimeters? 1625.6 mm.

Table 2-3 Metric equivalents of some common U.S. Customary units.

U.S. Customary unit	Metric equivalent
inch	2.54 cm
foot	0.3048 m
yard	0.9144 m
mile	1.609 km

Mass

The basic metric unit of **mass** is the **kilogram** (kg). The standard for the kilogram is a prototype metal cylinder kept at the International Bureau of Weights and Measures in France. Biologists often use submultiples of the kilogram in their work, especially the gram (g) and milligram (mg) (Table 2-2). A gram of distilled water kept at 3.98 °C at sea level occupies a volume of 1 milliliter. Thus 1 liter of water in your laboratory has a mass of approximately 1 kilogram.

Mass can be measured with simple balances or with very precise analytical balances that read mass to the nearest microgram or less.

- Your instructor will provide you with a balance and instruct you in its use. Practice using it by measuring the mass of sample objects provided by your instructor. Record your measurements in the following chart and compare them with those of other students in the laboratory.

Chart 2-2 Mass of sample specimens.

Specimen	Mass (g)
1. styrofoam	.04 g
2. salt	3.02 g

Volume

The metric unit of volume is the **liter,** abbreviated L. By definition, a liter is the volume occupied by 1 kilogram of water at 3.98 °C at sea level. One liter is equal to 1.056 quarts. Many scientific measurements are made in milliliters (ml); as Table 2-2 shows, 1000 ml is equal to 1 L. In common speech, "milliliters" is often shortened to "mils." You may also see volume expressed in cubic centimeters (cc), especially in clinical medical practices. For practical purposes, 1 cc is equal to 1 ml.

- Your instructor will provide you with graduated cylinders, pipettes, and several types of containers to measure volume. Using these tools, perform the procedures described in the following paragraphs.

Graduated cylinders are glass cylinders marked off in units of volume appropriate to their size. Depending on the volume you wish to measure, you must choose the correct size of graduated cylinder.

- Your instructor will provide you with one or more graduated cylinders. Pour a small amount of water into one of the cylinders. Notice that the surface of the water is not flat (Fig. 2-1).

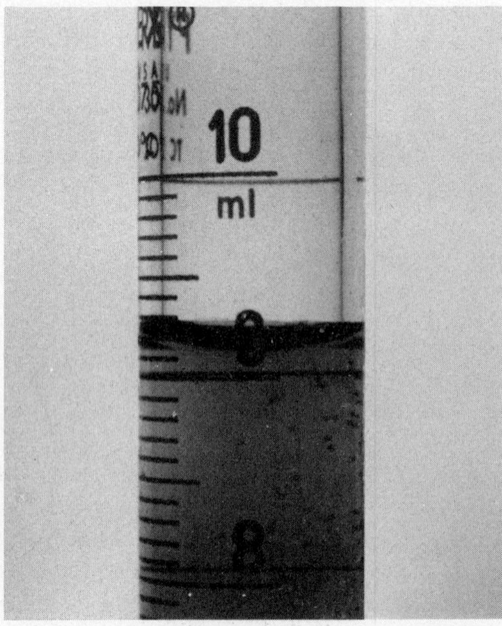

Figure 2-1 Meniscus of water in a 10-ml graduated cylinder marked in 0.1-ml increments.

This curved surface is called the **meniscus;** it forms because the water adheres to the glass and "climbs the walls" of the cylinder. When measuring the volume of a fluid that forms a meniscus, you read the level that aligns with the bottom of the meniscus; for example, the volume of fluid shown in Figure 2-1 is 9.1 ml.

- Your instructor will provide you with a list of volumes to measure in the graduated cylinders. Use the appropriate graduated cylinder for each measurement and fill it to the specified level. Have your instructor check your work.

Pipettes are used to measure small amounts of liquid (ml or drops). Liquid is drawn into the pipette using a bulb (Fig. 2-2). This process is called "pipetting the fluid." NEVER PIPETTE A FLUID BY MOUTH. What you think is water may be a harmful chemical. Besides, pipetting by bulb is far more accurate. Various types of bulbs or other pipette attachments are available for pipetting. Your instructor will show you how to use the ones available in your laboratory.

- Practice pipetting specified volumes of fluid in a pipette. Notice that a meniscus forms in the pipette. As in graduated cylinders, measure the level of a fluid at the bottom of the meniscus in a pipette.

Volumetric flasks are used to prepare solutions of specified concentrations. A volumetric flask has only one level marked on it, such as 1 L or 500 ml. The mark is on the narrow neck of the flask so that the specified volume can be more accurately measured (Fig. 2-3).

An experiment may call for a solution of a particular **concentration.** Concentration is measured in various ways. One way is to measure percent by weight of a compound dissolved in solution. Usually the compound is dissolved in distilled water, although sometimes alcohol or other solvents are used. A 10% solution of sodium chloride contains 10 g of sodium chloride in 100 g of mixed solution (sodium chloride plus distilled water). This is called a **weight percent** solution even though one measures the mass of sodium chloride. In practice, one assumes that 100 g of solution weighs approximately 100 g. So you make a 10% solution by dissolving 10 g of a compound in just enough water to make 100 ml of solution.

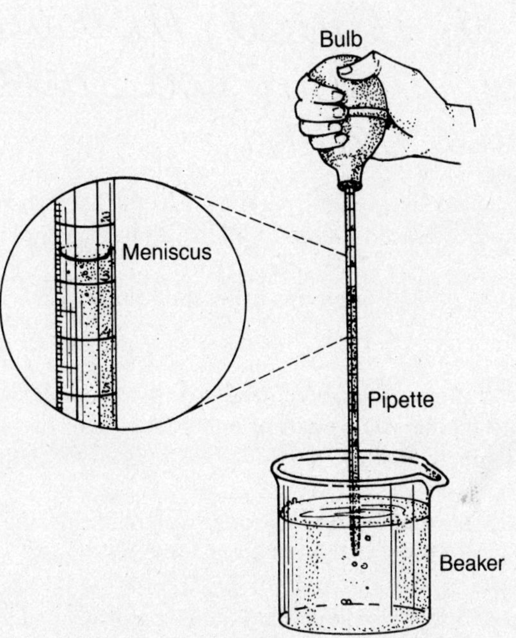

Figure 2-2 Method for pipetting fluids.

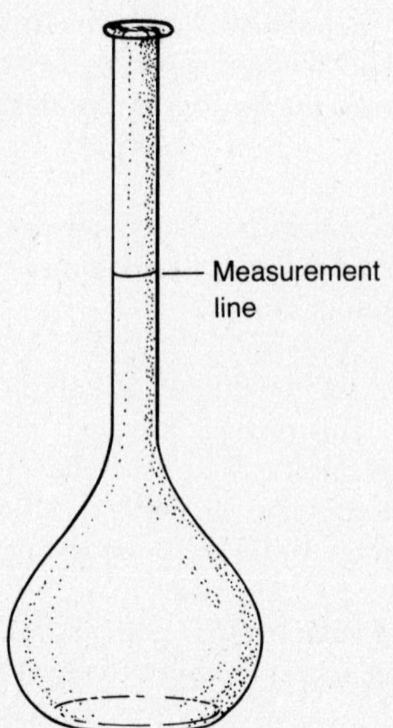

Figure 2-3 Volumetric flask used in preparation of solutions of specified concentrations.

- Practice making a weight percent solution of the concentration specified by your instructor. Use the volumetric flask or graduated cylinder provided. When dissolving powders or salts in a fluid measured with a volumetric flask or graduated cylinder, first add the necessary amount of dry chemical to the flask, then fill the flask about half full and swirl until the chemical is dissolved. In some cases, you may be instructed to heat the solution slightly. Then add fluid to the volume mark.
- A question to consider: Why should you add the dry chemical first and then fill the volumetric flask halfway instead of filling the flask to the volume mark and then adding the chemical?

If you fill the flask to the volume mark and then add the chemical, the volume is going to increase ∴ giving you more than what you actually wanted.

Volume percent is calculated like weight percent, except that two volumes of fluids are mixed. A 10% solution of absolute alcohol consists of 10 ml of absolute alcohol and 90 ml of distilled water.

- Practice making volume percent solutions using the solutions and measuring tools provided by your instructor.

A third important way of measuring concentration is by the **molarity** of the solution. One **mole** of a compound is equal to the atomic weight of one molecule of the substance in grams. Sodium chloride (NaCl) has an atomic weight of:

$$\begin{array}{cccc} \text{atomic weight of sodium} & + & \text{atomic weight of chlorine} & = \\ 22.99 & + & 35.45 & = 58.44 \end{array}$$

A 1 molar solution (written "1 M") would contain 58.44 g of NaCl in 1 L of distilled water. A 0.1 M solution would contain 5.844 g in 1 L of solution and so on.

- Make a solution of the molarity specified by your instructor. Show your calculations below and have your instructor check them.

If you have a concentrated stock solution of a given compound you can make less concentrated solutions by diluting a small volume of the original with more fluid. The volume (*V*) of the original concentrated solution needed is calculated as:

$$V = \frac{(\text{concentration desired}) \times (\text{volume desired})}{(\text{concentration of stock solution})}$$

Add *V* to a graduated cylinder or volumetric flask and then fill to the total volume desired with distilled water or the appropriate solvent.

- How would you make 10 ml of a 0.1 M solution of NaCl starting with a 1 M stock solution? Show your calculations below and have your instructor check them.

Temperature

Temperature in scientific studies is measured on the **Celsius** scale. Water freezes at 0 °C and boils at 100 °C. Human body temperature is approximately 37 °C (98.6 °F). To convert from the more familiar Fahrenheit scale to Celsius use the formula

$$C = \frac{5}{9}(°F - 32)$$

To convert from Celsius to Fahrenheit use the formula

$$F = \frac{9}{5}°C + 32$$

- Use thermometers provided by your instructor to measure the following temperatures:

room air = __________

ice bath = __________

outside air = __________

refrigerator compartment = __________

freezer compartment = __________

EXERCISE 2-2 USE OF SIGNIFICANT DIGITS AND ROUNDING OFF IN MEASUREMENT

Objective To understand the use of significant digits in making measurements.

As you measured some of the specimens in Exercise 2-1, you may have wondered how accurate the measurements should be. Accurate measurements depend in part on being careful, but they also depend on the smallest units you can measure with a given ruler or scale. The goal is to measure as accurately as possible without implying greater accuracy than you can be sure of.

Suppose, for example, that you want to measure the length of a leaf. And suppose that the only ruler you have is marked in centimeters. Upon measuring, you find that the leaf's length is greater than 5 cm but less than 6 cm. How should you record this finding? Simply writing "5 cm" or "6 cm" omits part of your observation because you know the true length is somewhere in between these two numbers.

This type of problem is solved by using the **significant digits rule:** A measurement should include all the digits you are sure of, plus an estimate to the nearest tenth of the next smallest unit.

The measurement of the leaf length would thus be 5.x cm, where 5 is the digit you are sure of and x is the estimate to the nearest tenth. The number of digits in a measurement is the same regardless of the unit of measurement; for example, 5.4 cm would be expressed as 54 mm, *not* 54.0 mm. When multiplying or dividing a measurement by another number, express the product or quotient with the same number of significant digits as the original measurement.

Rounding off is a procedure used when calculations yield a number with more significant digits than the rule allows. We commonly round off when we state our height in feet and inches; for example, you may be 5 feet 7.25 inches tall, but normally you would report your height as simply 5 feet 7 inches. Greater precision is not needed. To round off in the laboratory, use the following rules: If the last digit is less than 5, the previous digit is rounded down (that is, left unchanged; 5.43 becomes 5.4). If the last digit is greater than 5, the previous digit is rounded up (that is, add one to it; 7.26 becomes 7.3). If the last digit is 5, the measurement is on the borderline between rounding up or down. (Oddly enough, this *seems* to happen more often than it should by chance.) Several options are possible in this situation. Some scientists round up if the digit preceding the 5 is odd and round down if the preceding digit is even. Others use a random-numbers table to pick a number and then follow the same odd/even rule. Others flip a coin, and still others round down and just leave it at that. You can decide on the rule you wish to use, and discuss it with your instructor and laboratory partners. Make sure that your measurements of length, mass, volume, and temperature contain the correct number of significant digits.

EXERCISE 2-3 CONSTRUCTING MAGNIFICATIONS AND SCALES

Objective To understand and construct magnifications and scales for scientific illustrations.

Objects illustrated in scientific texts are rarely shown actual size. Instead, they are either magnified or reduced to fit onto a page. Microscopic objects must be magnified hundreds or thousands of times to be visible to the naked eye. This magnification of a figure in a text can be represented several ways. One popular way is to state in the figure legend that the object is magnified a certain number of times; for example, a magnification of 100X means the object is one one-hundredth as large as shown, and .25X means that the object is actually four times larger than shown. Objects pictured in texts can also be *reduced* rather than enlarged; that is, they are shown smaller than actual size. The amount of reduction can be expressed as a fraction: 1/2X, 1/4X, and so on. Magnification is calculated as:

$$\text{magnification} = \frac{\text{size of object in figure}}{\text{actual size of object}}$$

- Calculate the magnification of the objects shown in Figures 2-4 to 2-7 and record your answers in the following chart.

Chart 2-3 Magnification or reduction of objects in Figures 2-4 to 2-7.

Figure/Object	Actual size	Size of object in figure	Magnification/reduction
2-4/Pine cone	60 mm	73mm	1.22 X
2-5/Pollen grain	108 μm 10^{-6}	54,000 μm	500 X
2-6/Tree	67 m 11cm	.11m	.0016 X
2-7/Diatom	395 μm	90,000 μm	227.85 X

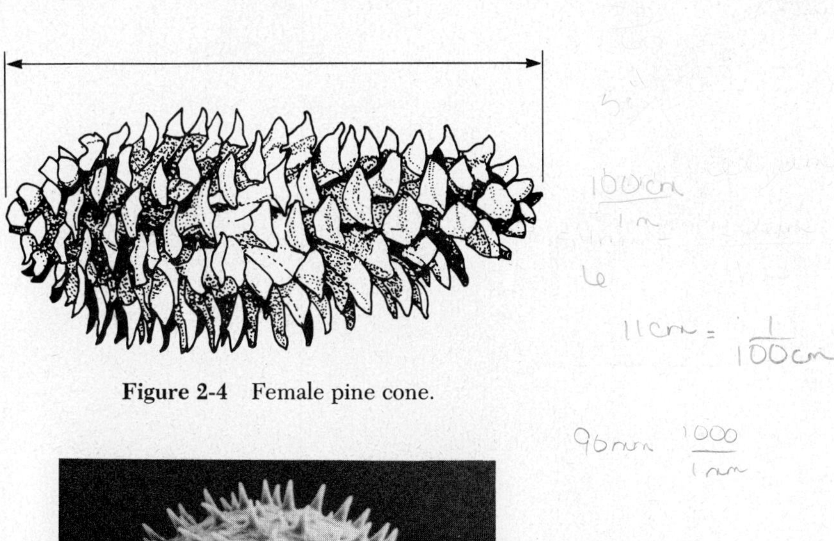

Figure 2-4 Female pine cone.

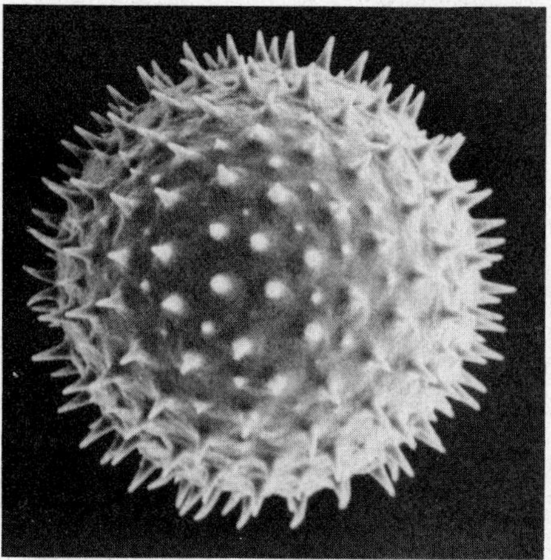

Figure 2-5 Electron micrograph of pollen grain from a flowering plant.

Figure 2-6 Sequoia.

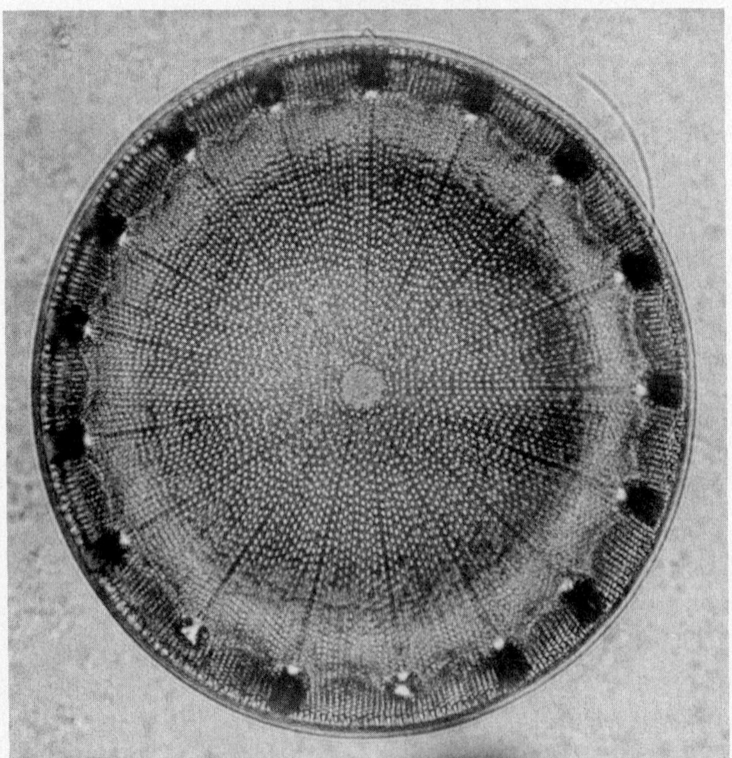

Figure 2-7 Photomicrograph of a marine diatom, showing ornamental cell wall.

The magnification of a figure can be used to calculate the actual size of the object. Rearranging the equation for magnification given above yields the following:

$$\text{actual size of object} = \frac{\text{size of object in figure}}{\text{magnification of object}}$$

- Calculate the actual sizes of the objects shown in Figures 2-8 to 2-11 and record your answers in the following chart. Express the size in the appropriate metric unit.

Chart 2-4 Magnification or reduction of objects in Figures 2-8 to 2-11.

Figure/Object	Actual size	Magnification/reduction	Size of object in figure
2-8/Perch	161.67 mm	0.6X	97 mm
2-9/Alga	.087 mm	850X	74 mm
2-10/Sea Palm	272.5 mm	0.4X	109 mm
2-11/Lichen	.686 mm	110X	75.5 mm

Figure 2-8 Freshwater perch (*Perca fluviatilis*).

Figure 2-9 Single-celled freshwater green alga (*Staurastrum*).

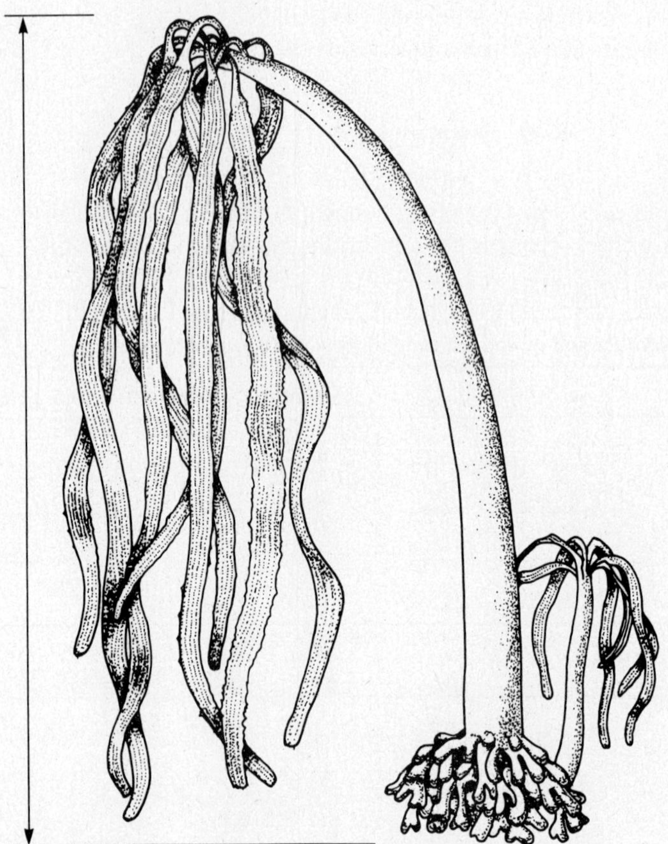

Figure 2-10 Sea palm (*Postelsia*), an intertidal seaweed from California.

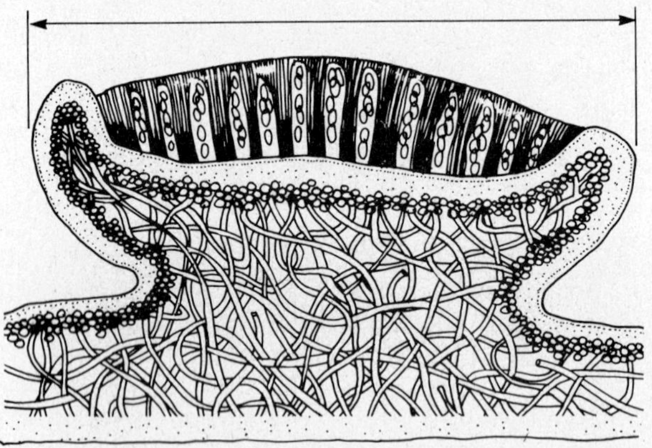

Figure 2-11 Cuplike fruiting body of a lichen.

Another popular way to show the size of an object in a photograph or illustration is to include a **scale** in the picture that represents some standard length, say 10 μm.

- Figure 2-12 shows a photomicrograph of a single-celled organism. Its actual width is 138 μm. Draw a scale bar next to the photomicrograph representing 100 μm.
- Figure 2-13 shows a photograph of a crab and a scale representing 1 cm. Estimate the width in centimeters of the main body of the crab (excluding the legs). 5½ ______ cm

Figure 2-12 Single-celled freshwater green alga (*Micrasterias*).

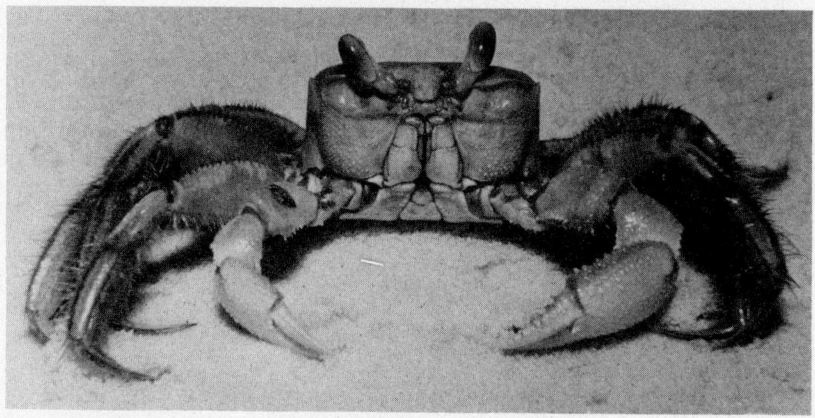

Figure 2-13 Marine crab.

The material in this chapter corresponds to Chapter 5 in your text.

3

MICROSCOPES AND THEIR USE

Many things change in the science of biology, some so rapidly that books are barely printed before the material in them is dated. But one thing a biology student of 50 years ago would immediately recognize in modern laboratories is the **microscope,** a device that magnifies objects too small to be visible with the naked eye. Like many technological marvels, the microscope is something even nonscientists take for granted. Today, the term "microscope" encompasses a much wider variety of instruments than it did when Robert Hooke used primitive microscopes to observe cells in the 1600s. From portable, hand-held field microscopes (which may have optics surpassing those of microscopes of just a few decades ago) to electron microscopes, the array of tools a biologist employs to see structure in the subvisible world is remarkable.

High magnification reveals greater image detail, but highly magnified images appear blurred. The limit to magnification with a light microscope is determined by the wavelength of visible light. Therefore, the smallest visible objects are approximately the size of the wavelength of visible light, 0.0004–0.0007 mm. In practice, the highest useful magnification is around 2,000X. Electron microscopes use electron rays, which have much smaller wavelengths than light rays and can reveal finer structural detail.

During this course you will see many photographs of microscopic images (photomicrographs). Some are from light microscopes, others are from electron microscopes. You will also spend quite a bit of time peering through a light microscope. This chapter outlines the care and use of two commonly used types of microscopes: the **compound microscope,** and the **stereoscopic** or **dissecting microscope.**

A word about caring for microscopes Inevitably, every student encounters a microscope that does not work quite right. The gears grind as they turn, the image is blurred, a lens is cracked. And of course the culprit, a former student, is long gone. Microscopes are precision instruments, and even ones that look as if they belonged to Louis Pasteur cost hundreds or thousands of dollars. Observe the following rules when using microscopes:

1. The major enemy of microscopes is dust. Each microscope has a dust cover, which should be kept on the instrument when it is not being used. Store microscopes in a closed cabinet or cupboard.
2. Always carry a microscope with both hands—one hand under the base and the other holding the microscope arm.
3. Do not use chemicals near microscopes; any liquid spilled on the instrument should be cleaned up immediately.
4. When finished with a microscope, remove the slide from the stage, center the stage, wind the cord around the base, replace the dust cover, and return the microscope to its cabinet.

As you use a microscope, think of it as a good friend's expensive camera and treat it accordingly. You, future students, and your instructor will all benefit.

EXERCISE 3-1 THE COMPOUND MICROSCOPE

Objective To observe prepared slides with a compound microscope, and to calibrate the ocular micrometer for future use.

The compound microscope magnifies images of specimens approximately 25 to 1,000 times and is useful for viewing specimens at the cellular level. Older compound microscopes are **monocular,** with one eyepiece, but newer models are **binocular** and have two eyepieces. Most people find viewing easier with a binocular microscope because it eliminates the squinting with one eye necessary with a monocular microscope.

- Take your assigned compound microscope from its storage cabinet and carry it to your desk, holding the curved **arm** at the back with one hand and the **base** with the other (see Figure 3-1 for a labeled diagram of a typical compound microscope). Place the microscope in an uncluttered work area and remove the dust cover; store the dust cover in a dry place.
- Compare the microscope diagramed in Figure 3-1 with your own and locate the labeled parts.
- Plug in the **light source** and turn on the power. The light should shine up from the light source through the **condenser** and a hole in the **stage** to the specimen. Briefly look through the

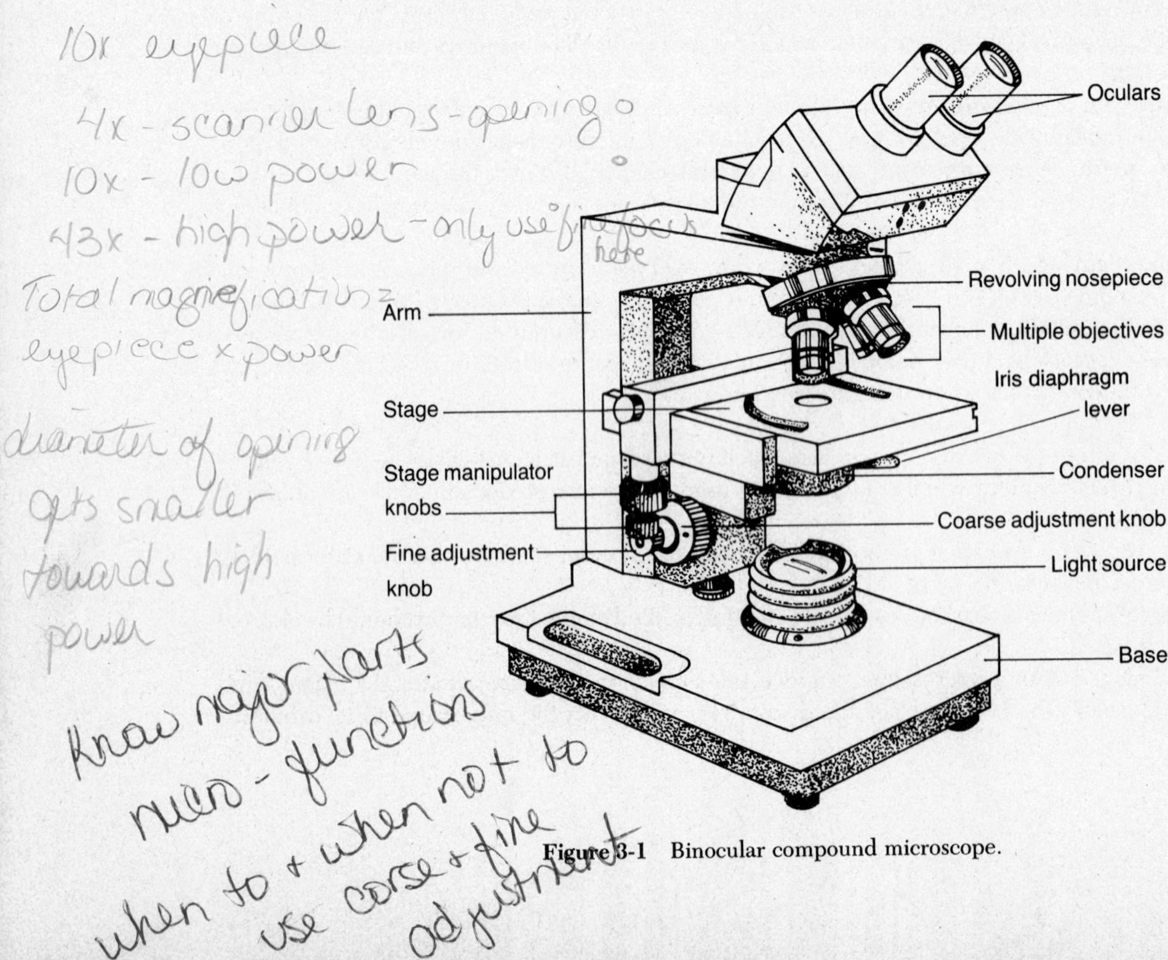

Figure 3-1 Binocular compound microscope.

oculars and make sure the circular **field of view** is lighted. If not, the **objective lens** may not be in place; gently turn the **revolving nosepiece** until it clicks into position.

- Obtain a prepared slide of a leaf or other specimen from your instructor. Gently place it in the **clips** on the stage.
- Before you look through the oculars, turn the **stage manipulator knobs** and observe the movement of the stage and slide. Move the specimen to a point beneath the objective. A circle of light from the condenser should shine through the specimen slide.
- Again, before looking through the oculars, turn the **coarse adjustment knob** and observe how the direction of turning moves the objective up and down. Raise the objective as high as it will go. Rotate the objective base until the low-power objective (usually 2.5X) clicks into place; lower the objective as far as it will go. Does the objective reach the slide? no. Now, raise the objective with the coarse adjustment knob and repeat the procedure for each objective. A word of caution: The higher-power objectives are longer than the low-power objective and it is possible to break the slide or damage the objective lens if you lower the objective too far. Which objectives could break the slide if you turned the coarse focus knob too far? 43x The higher-power objectives may be bayonet mounted or spring loaded at the tips. Up to a point, they will help prevent slide damage by collapsing on contact.
- Check the lens at the end of each objective for encrusted dirt or oil. Gently wipe the lens with clean, dry lens paper. Harsh rubbing will drag grit across the lens and scratch the lens surface. An inexpensive alternative to lens paper is to break a styrofoam packing peanut in two to expose a clean and exceptionally soft surface to wipe over the lens.
- Switch to the low-power objective and observe the specimen through the oculars. Use the coarse adjustment knob to focus on the specimen. Fine-focus the image with the **fine adjustment knob.** While viewing the specimen, move the slide around the stage and learn to make a visual search of the slide by turning the stage manipulator knobs. As you move the slide toward you what happens to the image?

  It appears as if the image is moving away as you look at it thru the oculars.

  What happens to the image as you move the slide left or right?

  When you move the slide left - it appears it is moving right as you are looking thru the oculars and vice versa

As you gain expertise, moving the slide with the stage manipulator knobs will become second nature.

- Locate the **iris diaphragm lever** extending from the condenser. This lever opens and closes the iris diaphragm, just as changing the f-stop on a camera adjusts the aperture. What happens to the image as you move the lever?

  gets lighter and darker

Specimens vary in thickness and translucency, and you can adjust the illumination with the iris diaphragm lever to obtain the optimal image for a specimen.

- Switch to the next higher-power objective (usually 10X). Your microscope may be **parfocal,** that is, specimens will stay in focus when you switch objectives. However, fine adjustment is sometimes necessary. At higher magnifications you may also have to increase the amount of light coming from the power source.
- Now, switch to the next higher-power objective (usually 40X). Turn the fine adjustment knob and describe how the image changes.

you can only see a smaller portion of the imag, but it is much more detailed than before.

The microscope focuses on a thin layer in the specimen. The thickness of this layer is called the **depth of field.** At higher magnifications the depth of field is less, so you see a thinner slice of the specimen. Because many specimens are translucent, you can observe different layers in them by focusing up and down. This technique allows you to visualize the three-dimensional structure of specimens.

Your microscope may have an **oil-immersion** objective. Light entering other types of objectives passes through the specimen, then through a layer of air before it reaches the objective. Higher magnification is possible if the light passes through a drop of oil between the cover glass and the oil-immersion objective.

- To use this objective, raise it clear of the slide or turn it slightly to the side and place a small drop of **immersion oil** on the cover glass directly below the objective. Lower or click the oil-immersion objective in place so that it touches the oil. The oil should seal the slide and the objective; this seal will be maintained even when the stage moves. Observe the specimen and note the degree of magnification (usually 1,000X) and the clarity of the image. The oil-immersion objective must be cleaned after use or the oil will form a crust on the lens. Clean the objective with lens paper or a broken styrofoam peanut as described before. Your instructor may provide you with xylol, a solution that dissolves oil. Never use water or any other cleaning fluid on an objective because such substances can damage the lens.

A microscope magnifies an image in two stages. The objective lens system magnifies the image 2½ to 100 times, depending on the power of the objective, and the ocular magnifies it another 10 times. The individual magnifying power of the ocular or objective is written on the outside of its barrel. To calculate the total magnification of the image with each objective, use the following equation:

$$\text{Total magnification} = \text{magnification of ocular} \times \text{magnification of objective}$$

For example, most oculars magnify 10X, and the low power objective usually magnifies 10X, for a total magnification of 100X.

The diameter of the field of view may be used to estimate sizes of objects, and may be measured with a **stage micrometer.** Here, the use of the term "micrometer" is different than its use as a unit of measurement (μm); in this case, the term means a ruler or scale for microscopes. The term for the unit is usually pronounced MY-crow-me-ter; the term for the ruler is usually pronounced my-CRAWM-uh-ter. The stage micrometer is simply a miniature ruler. The ruler lines on it are barely visible to the naked eye but show up clearly under the microscope. The distance between the lines is marked on the slide. Usually the ruler area is 2 mm long, marked off in 0.1-mm increments with 0.01-mm increments at one end.

- Obtain a stage micrometer from your instructor. Observe the stage micrometer with each objective and record in Chart 3-1 the diameter of the field of view at each magnification.

Chart 3-1 Magnification and diameter of field of view.

Magnification of ocular	Magnification of objective	Total magnification	Diameter of field of view
10x	4x	40x	4.8 mm
10x	10x	100x	1.75 mm
10x	40x	400x	.44 mm
10x	100x	1000x	.19 mm

- For future observations, use the numbers in the table to estimate the sizes of objects. A cell that is two-thirds the diameter of the field of view for the 25X objective would be two-thirds as wide as your measurement of the field of view for the objective. Estimate the sizes of structures or specimens your instructor provides and record the values in Chart 3-2.

Chart 3-2 Estimated sizes of specimens.

Structure or specimen	Objective	Fraction of field of view	Estimated size
leaf	10X	1/7	.25 mm

Your microscope may also be equipped with an **ocular micrometer.** This is a small ruler or scale visible inside the ocular (Fig. 3-2). The marks on the micrometer do not represent a standard metric

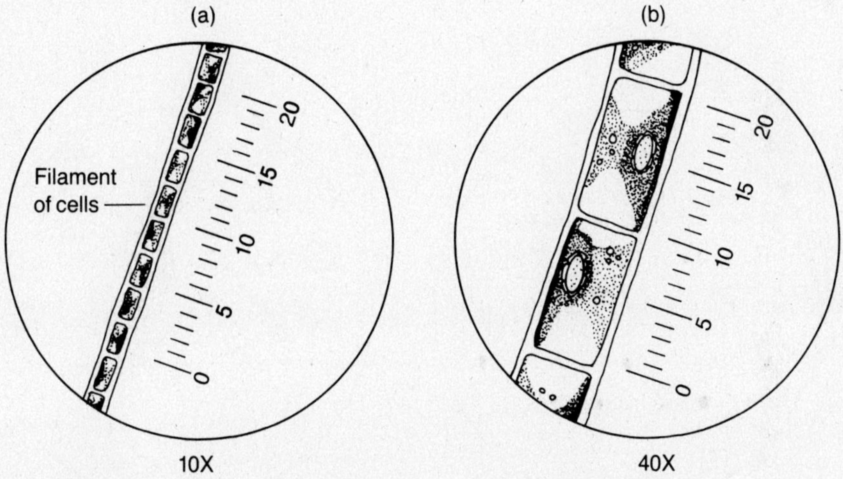

Figure 3-2 Ocular micrometer: views of an algal filament through (a) 10X objective and (b) 40X objective.

unit. The micrometer is located inside the ocular, which can be turned by hand to orient the micrometer as you wish. Notice that the micrometer spans the same length *relative to the field of view* regardless of which objective you use (Fig. 3-2).

- By calibrating the micrometer, you can use it to measure structures at any magnification. The stage micrometer is used to calibrate the ocular micrometer, as follows:

1. View the stage micrometer with the low-power objective. In addition to the ocular micrometer, you will see the stage micrometer as a series of vertical lines. The distance between these marks is usually written on the stage micrometer. Figure 3-3a shows a stage micrometer on which the large lines are 0.1 mm apart and the smallest unit is 0.01 mm (10 μm).
2. Turn the ocular until the ocular and stage micrometer markings are parallel (Fig. 3-3a). You could estimate the distance between ocular units directly, but there is a more accurate way of calibrating these units. The arrows in Figure 3-3b point to the place where two markings on the ocular micrometer line up exactly with two markings on the stage micrometer. The actual distance between these markings on the stage micrometer is 0.20 mm, so the two markings on the ocular micrometer span this distance as well. The equality of the distance as measured on the stage and ocular micrometers is shown in the equation:

$$10 \text{ units on ocular micrometer} = 0.20 \text{ mm on stage micrometer}$$

To calculate the length of one unit on the ocular micrometer, divide each side of the equation by 10:

$$1 \text{ unit on the ocular micrometer} = 0.02 \text{ mm}$$

So for the low-power objective, you can measure the size of a structure by superimposing the ocular micrometer over it, measuring its length in ocular units, and multiplying by 0.02 mm. Use the significant digits rule (Chapter 2) to measure structures at this magnification. For example, in Figure 3-3b you saw that the cell is 9.4 ocular units long under the low-power objective. Its actual length is:

$$9.4 \text{ ocular units} \times 0.02 \text{ mm/ocular unit} = 0.188 \text{ mm}$$

or 0.19 mm rounded to significant digits. For convenience, fractions of mm are often converted to μm by multiplying by 1,000.

$$0.18 \text{ mm} = 180 \text{ μm}.$$

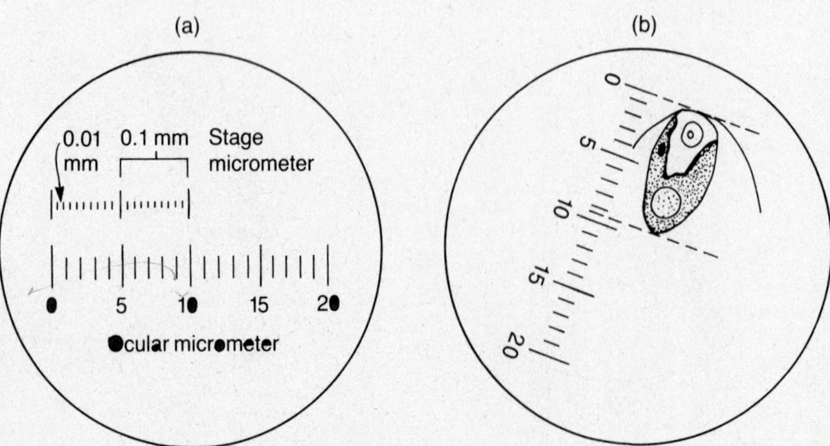

Figure 3-3 Calibrating the ocular micrometer.

In theory, an ocular unit at 25X should span a distance on the slide four times as long as the ocular unit at 100X. In practice, however, this is rarely true, because the optics of the microscope are not that precise. Therefore, the above procedure for calibrating the ocular micrometer must be repeated for each objective. Also, each microscope must be individually calibrated because of differences in optics and ocular micrometers.

- Perform these calibrations for each objective on your microscope and fill in Chart 3-3 for future reference. (Note: The numbers you obtain may differ greatly from those in the example.) Calibrate the oil-immersion objective last and clean the stage micrometer slide for the next student.

Chart 3-3 Ocular micrometer calibrations for microscope number ________.

Objective		Ocular micrometer unit length			
4	X (1.8/7)	.257	mm =	257	µm
10	X	.1	mm =	100	µm
40	X (.17/7)	.024	mm =	24	µm
100	X (oil)	.01	mm =	10	µm

EXERCISE 3-2 MAKING A WET MOUNT SLIDE

20 units

Objective To make a wet mount slide from a culture of living organisms.

Many organisms are grown or stored in liquid medium. They must be transferred to a slide along with a small amount of liquid in order to be observed with the compound microscope.

- The steps in making a wet mount slide are shown in Figure 3-4. First, obtain a clean microscope slide. Your instructor will provide you with a culture of *Euglena* or some other unicellular organism growing in liquid medium. Use a pipette to suction a small amount of liquid from the water surface in the culture tube. Squeeze out one or two drops so that a small bead of liquid forms on the slide (Fig. 3-4a).
- Next, hold a clean **cover glass** by the edges between your thumb and forefinger and place one edge on the slide near the bead of liquid (Fig. 3-4b). Slowly lower the cover glass onto the liquid as if you were closing the lid on a box (Fig 3-4c); you may want to lower the slide with a dissecting needle if your fingers get in the way.
- The liquid will spread out beneath the cover glass (Fig. 3-4d). If you have used too much liquid, the cover glass will float and slide from side to side. Remove excess water by touching a small piece of paper towel to the edge of the cover glass, first on one side, then on the other. If you have used too little water, air bubbles may form under the cover glass. If so, use the pipette to add a tiny bit of liquid to the edge of the cover glass. This liquid will flow under the cover glass and fill the air spaces.
- Holding the slide horizontal to keep the cover glass from slipping, place it on the compound microscope stage and observe under low power. *Euglena* cells are active swimmers, so you will have to be quick with the manipulator knobs to keep track of one. If your instructor has

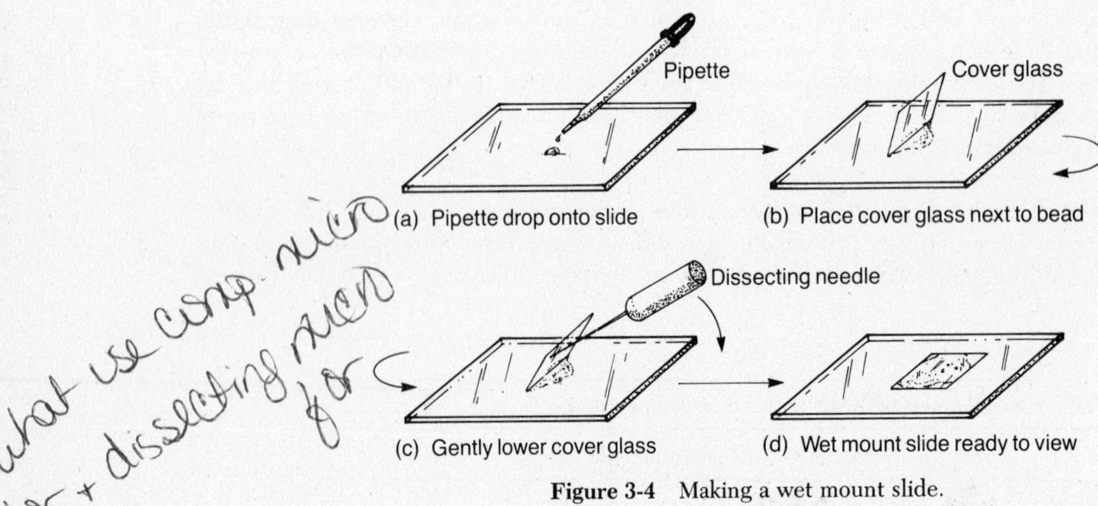

Figure 3-4 Making a wet mount slide.

provided you with a viscous solution of methyl cellulose, gently remove the cover glass, mix a half-drop of methyl cellulose with the liquid, and replace the cover glass. Observe the *Euglena* cells at both low and high power. The methyl cellulose will slow down the cells so you can see more details of internal structure and the beating flagellum at one end. (You will observe *Euglena* again in Chapter 16.)

Before you put your microscope away, clean the stage of debris or liquid and clean the objectives as described earlier. Replace the dust cover and put the microscope in the storage cabinet.

EXERCISE 3-3 THE STEREOSCOPIC OR DISSECTING MICROSCOPE

Objective To use the stereoscopic microscope to observe specimens under transmitted and reflected light.

The **stereoscopic** or **dissecting microscope** is generally used for observing at lower magnifications (10X–60X). This microscope is useful in dissection procedures because of the amount of working space between the objective lens and the stage. The term "stereoscopic" refers to the two oculars, which allow a three-dimensional view of specimens. Specimens can be illuminated with either **reflected light** from above or, on some microscopes with substage illumination, with **transmitted light** from below.

- Take your assigned stereoscopic microscope from its storage cabinet and set it in a clean working area on the lab desk.
- A typical stereoscopic microscope is shown in Figure 3-5. Compare the diagram to your own microscope and locate the labeled parts.
- Plug in the light source. Obtain a leaf or other specimen and place it on the stage. If the specimen is moist, place it in an open petri dish to protect the stage.
- Turn on the reflected-light source and look through the oculars. As with a pair of binoculars,

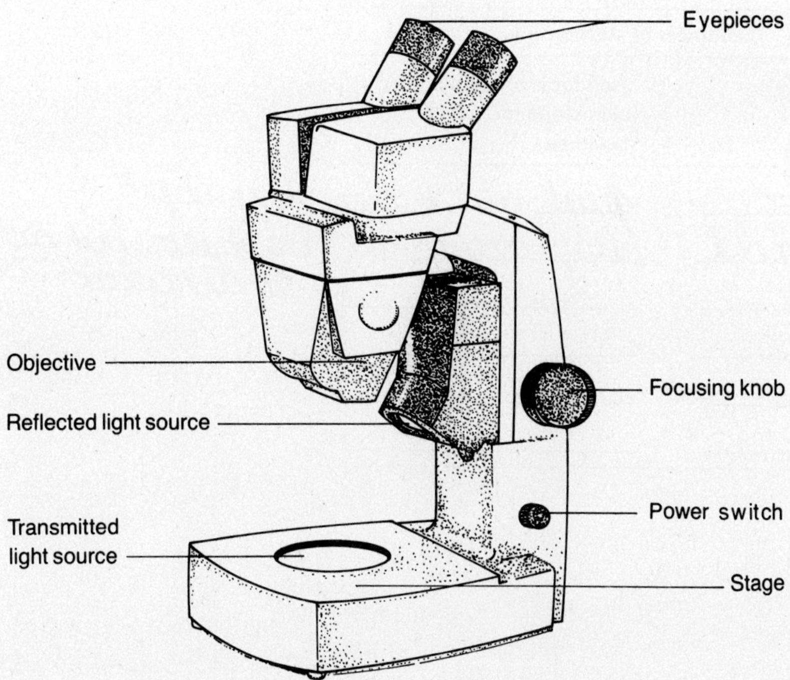

Figure 3-5 Stereoscopic or dissecting microscope.

you may need to adjust the interocular distance to match the distance between your pupils. To do this, look through the oculars and move them in or out until you see a single image. Next, turn the **focusing knob,** raising the objective until the leaf comes into focus. Move the leaf around the stage to get a feel for how the image moves as the specimen moves.

- Turn the **zoom knob** on top of the microscope and observe how magnification of the image changes.
- Switch from reflected to transmitted light. Describe the difference in the image of the leaf compared to the image you see with reflected light.

- Make a drawing of the leaf, based on your observations with both reflected and transmitted light. Place a ruler marked in millimeters on the stage to estimate sizes of structures and include a scale bar in the drawing.

- Observe several other specimens with the stereoscopic microscope—perhaps a newspaper photograph, fingernail clippings or cuticle, insects, hair, or other items provided by the instructor. Evaluate the usefulness of the stereoscopic microscope for viewing the various items, and record your evaluations in Chart 3-4.

Chart 3-4 Usefulness of stereoscopic microscope.

Specimen	Usefulness of stereoscopic microscope for viewing specimen
finger	great - able to view thick objects
leaf mold	okay - able to view big objects - but not too detailed

The material in this chapter corresponds to Chapter 3 in your text.

4

MOLECULES OF LIVING THINGS

Many of the special characteristics of living things derive from the nature of their chemical components. Life on Earth is based on the element carbon, and the unique and diverse properties that make carbon the basis of living systems are discussed in your textbook (Chapter 3). Carbon-containing compounds are called **organic** compounds, and the entire field of organic chemistry is devoted to their study.

But while carbon may be the backbone of organic molecules, it is only one of numerous important **bioelements.** The five other primary bioelements are hydrogen, nitrogen, oxygen, phosphorus, and sulfur. A convenient way to remember this list is to think of the acronym formed by their chemical symbols: CHNOPS (pronounced, roughly, chin-ups). Organic molecules are chemically reactive because clusters of bioelements are attached to them. These clusters are called **functional groups.** In this chapter you will examine the most important functional groups for biological systems—aldehyde, ketone, carboxyl, and amino groups.

The laboratory exercises in this chapter involve chemical tests that serve as markers of particular functional groups in various substances. You will conduct tests that reveal the presence of the functional groups peculiar to three major classes of large molecules unique to living things: carbohydrates, lipids, and proteins. A fourth major class of large molecules, nucleic acids, is discussed in the textbook but will not be covered in the laboratory.

Objectives To name the three major classes of biological molecules and identify their functional groups; to conduct and interpret qualitative tests that reveal the presence of these biological molecules.

In each of the following series of tests you will use one or more test substances and a control substance (distilled water). There are two reasons to use caution and clean laboratory technique in these tests: (1) except for the distilled water, many of the substances are potentially harmful to your clothing and to your respiratory system and other body parts, and (2) cross-contamination of stock bottles, test tubes, and pipettes will spoil the tests and lead to erroneous results.

test substances what they were used to test for functional groups also

EXERCISE 4-1 CARBOHYDRATES

Carbohydrates comprise a wide variety of monomers and polymers of saccharides, and no single test can be used as a marker for all of them. You will conduct two tests specific to two important classes of carbohydrates.

A. Benedict's Test for Reducing Sugars

Benedict's solution tests for the presence of two functional groups, aldehyde and ketone, present in many but not all sugars. Both functional groups contain an oxygen atom double-bonded to a carbon (Fig. 4-1). Sugars that contain these groups are called **reducing sugars.** Copper ions ($Cu\ 2^{+}$) in the blue-colored Benedict's solution take on electrons released by the oxygen in the sugar. In this reaction, the copper is said to be **reduced** by the sugar and forms cuprous oxide, a yellowish to red-colored substance.

Substances that form in a reaction between two solutions are called **precipitates.** Besides forming a precipitate, a reaction with a small amount of reducing sugar turns the solution green; a reaction with a large amount of sugar turns the solution red-orange. The reaction will not occur if no oxygen atoms are available in ketone or aldehyde groups on the sugar (that is, if the oxygen atoms are involved in the bond between monosaccharide units).

- Label seven test tubes a–g. Place 2–3 ml of the following solutions (see Fig. 4-2) in the corresponding tubes:

a. 1% glucose
b. 1% sucrose
c. 1% maltose
d. 1% starch
~~e. 1% ribose~~
~~f. 1% galactose~~
g. distilled water

- Add an equal amount (2–3 ml) of Benedict's solution to each tube.
- Place the tubes in a boiling water bath for several minutes. In Chart 4-1, note the formation of precipitate and any color changes, and interpret the result of each test regarding the presence or absence of reducing sugar.

Chart 4-1 Results of Benedict's test for reducing sugars.

Tube	Contents	Precipitate or color change	Interpretation
a.	Glucose	deep rust	lg amount reducing sugar present
b.	Sucose	lt blue no color change	no reducing sugar
c.	Maltose	deep orange	lg amount reducing sugar
d.	Starch	lt blue no color change	no reducing sugar
~~e.~~	~~Ribose~~		
~~f.~~	~~Galactose~~		
g.	Distilled water	lt blue no color change	no reducing sugar

- The chemical structures of the compounds tested are shown below. Benedict's solution reacts with sugars having free aldehyde groups (–COH groups in the diagrams). Circle the free aldehyde group in each chemical structure and state whether your test for each compound yielded the correct result. Suggest an explanation for any discrepancies.

(A) Aldehyde (b) Ketone

Figure 4-1 Functional groups present in some sugars: (a) an aldehyde group and (b) a ketone group.

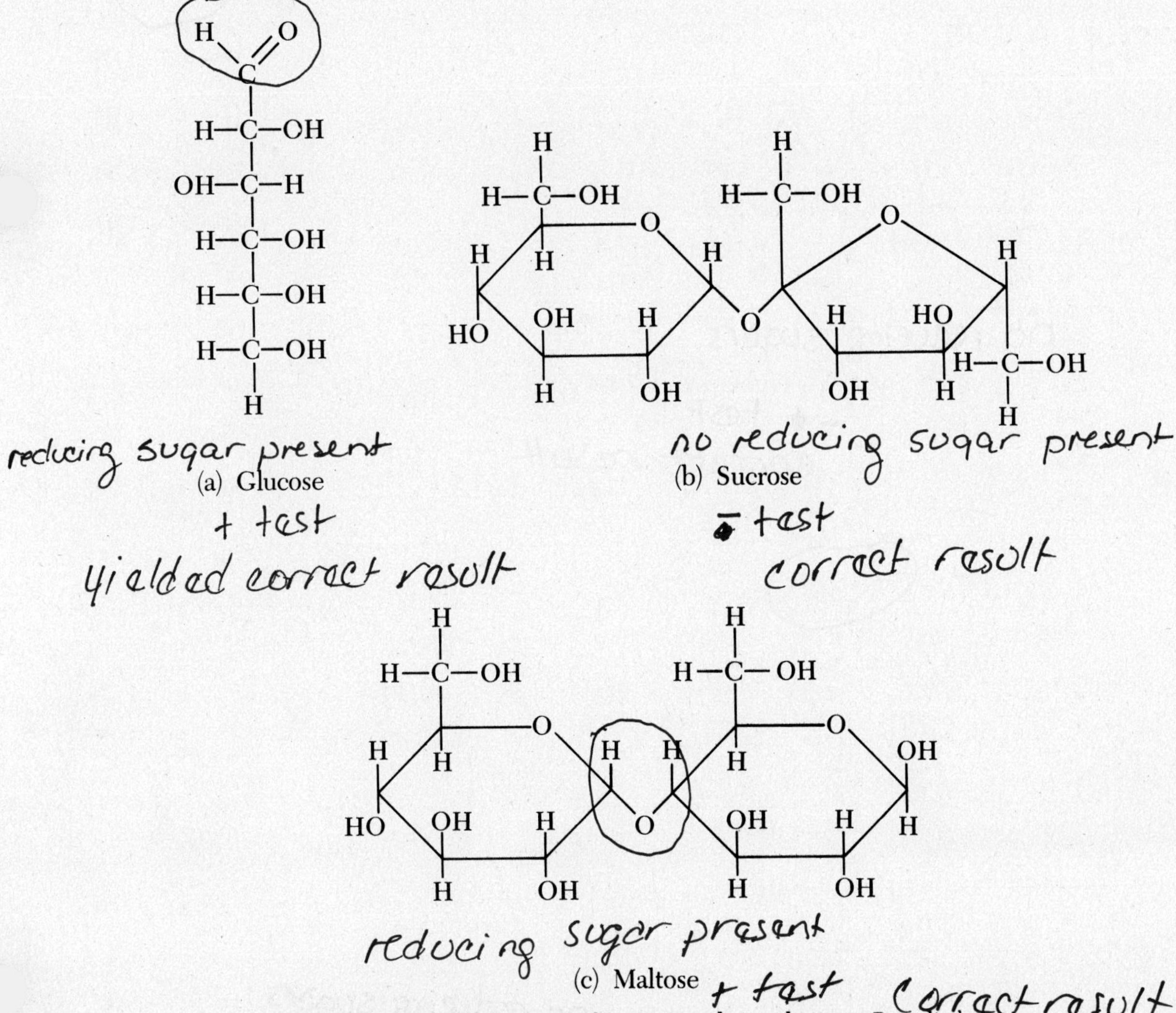

Figure 4-2 Chemical structures for compounds in solution in Benedict's test for reducing sugars (Exercise 4-1A).

Amylopectin

Amylose

no reducing sugars

(d) The two components of starch

– + test
correct result

(e) Ribose

(f) Galactose

no reducing sugars

(g) Water

+ test
–
correct result

Figure 4-2 Continued.

B. Lugol's Test for Starch

Long polymers of monosaccharides are among the most important molecules in living things. Starch is one such polysaccharide and is the major nutrient storage material in plants and their seeds. Starch itself is composed of subunits of two smaller polysaccharides, amylose and amylopectin, which in turn are composed of chains of glucose molecules. Lugol's test is an easy method for detecting the presence of starch. Lugol's solution contains iodine, which stains starch-containing material dark blue.

- Label five test tubes a–e. Place 2–3 ml of the following solutions in the corresponding tube:

a. 1% glucose
b. 1% starch
~~c. 1% galactose~~
d. 1% sucrose
e. distilled water

- Add an equal amount (2–3 ml) of Lugol's solution to each tube and shake the tubes.
- Record any color changes in Chart 4-2. Interpret the results of the tests and explain why color changes did or did not occur.

Chart 4-2 Results of Lugol's test for starch.

Tube	Contents	Color change	Interpretation
a.	Glucose	transparant yellow	no starch
b.	Starch	bluish-black	contains starch
~~c.~~	~~Galactose~~		
d.	Sucrose	transparant yellow	no starch
e.	Distilled water	transparant yellow	no starch

QUESTIONS

What was the purpose of the tube of distilled water in each test?

It functions as a control.

What would you have concluded if the tube of distilled water had show a positive reaction in either test?

Something in our experiment would have been contaminated.

What would you have done in this case?

Get out new supplies or clean the same ones again + then repeat the experiment.

What can you conclude about the difference in arrangement or bonding of the functional aldehyde or ketone groups in glucose as compared to sucrose?

The arrangement of glucose is in a chain w/ the functional group at one end (aldehyde) +

Some plants store food as sugar, some store it as starch. Suggest a test to determine which storage reserve is used in a vegetable you might find at the market.

Extract some of the juice from it and apply iodine, if it is a starch then it will react as dark blue or black.

EXERCISE 4-2 LIPIDS

Fats and oils are two important types of lipids found in living things. Chemically, fats and oils are very similar, being composed of the same two subunits: glycerols and fatty acids. The glycerol subunit is a chain of three carbon atoms, each with a long-chain fatty acid attached (Fig. 4-3). The combination of the glycerol "backbone" and the three fatty acid chains is termed a **triglyceride.** Humans employ all sorts of diet and exercise program to rid their bodies of fat, often to no avail. There is a good reason dieting is so difficult: Fats and oils are highly efficient energy storehouses, and only a small physical quantity of fat needs to be metabolized to produce the calories burned in vigorous exercise.

The main test you will perform to detect the presence of fats and oils does not identify a single functional group, as did Benedict's test for reducing sugars. The test uses a dye called Sudan black, which reacts with the long chains of carbon atoms in the fatty acid part of the lipid molecule. These long fatty acid molecules make lipids nonpolar and therefore immiscible with water. Sudan black dissolves in nonpolar substances like fats and oils and stains them red. Before performing the Sudan black dye test, however, you will carry out a simple visual test for the presence of lipids.

A. Visual Test for Lipids

- In a petri dish half-filled with tap water, place one drop of vegetable oil. Add the drop with an eyedropper or stir the water with a glass rod that has been dipped in the oil. Observe what happens at the surface of the water and record your observations below.

The oil beads up and does not mix w/ the water. It is insoluble in water.

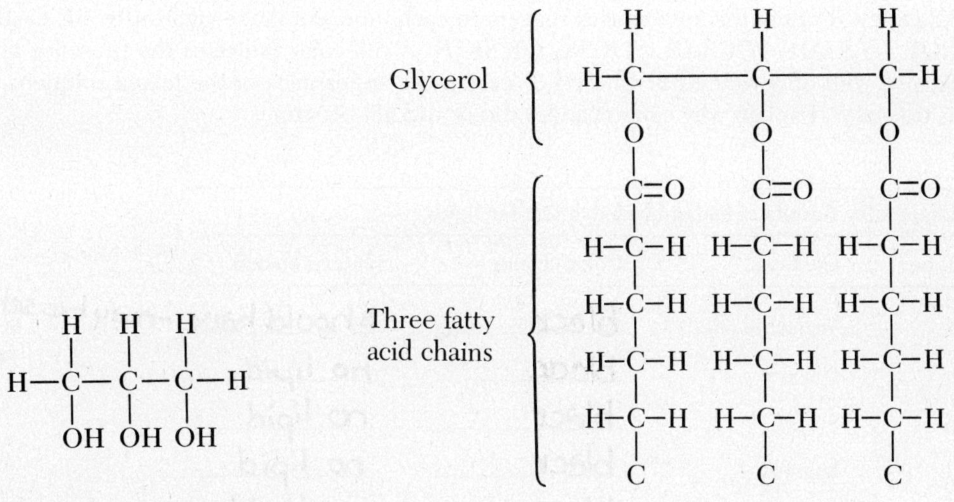

		H	H	H
	Glycerol	H—C—	—C—	—C—H
		O	O	O
		C=O	C=O	C=O
		H—C—H	H—C—H	H—C—H
	Three fatty acid chains	H—C—H	H—C—H	H—C—H
		H—C—H	H—C—H	H—C—H
		H—C—H	H—C—H	H—C—H
		C	C	C

```
 H   H   H
 |   |   |
H—C— C— C—H
 |   |   |
OH  OH  OH
```

(a) Glycerol

(b) Triglyceride

Figure 4-3 Functional groups in fats and oils: (a) a glycerol molecule and (b) a triglyceride.

- You may have observed this reaction of oil and water in everyday experience. Interpret your observations in terms of the structure of the vegetable oil molecule and its inability to hydrogen bond with water.

Oil molecule doesn't have any polarity so ∴ it cannot bond w/ a polar molecule such as water

- What can you say about the relative densities of oil and water?

Oil is less dense than water.

- In light of your answer to the previous question, what function, other than energy storage, does fatty blubber serve in a whale?

It helps them to float because of the difference in density.

B. Sudan Black Dye Test for Lipids

- Label five test tubes a–e. Place 2–3 ml of the following solutions in the corresponding tubes.

a. vegetable oil
b. 1% glucose
c. 1% starch
d. 1% sucrose
e. distilled water

- Add a few drops of the Sudan black reagent to each tube and shake vigorously. BE CAREFUL NOT TO STAIN YOUR CLOTHING OR SKIN. A red color indicates the presence of lipids. Record your observations in Chart 4-3, noting the appearance of the mixed solutions as well as the color. Explain why color changes did or did not occur.

Chart 4-3 Results of Sudan black dye test for lipids.

Tube	Contents	Color change	Interpretation
a.	Vegetable oil	black	should have - maybe sol. was wrong
b.	Glucose	black	no lipid
c.	Starch	black	no lipid
d.	Sucrose	black	no lipid
e.	Distilled water	black	no lipid

EXERCISE 4-3 AMINO ACIDS AND PROTEINS

Proteins are a diverse set of biological molecules that are the key substances in the structure and physiological functioning of living things. They are major structural components of muscle, skin, bones, leaves, and roots. In the form of hormones and enzymes they regulate the metabolism of plants and animals.

Amino acids, the building blocks of proteins, possess both a carboxyl group and a free amino group (Fig. 4-4). Proteins are polymers of amino acids linked through covalent peptide bonds involving the carboxyl group of one amino acid and the amino group of another.

A. Ninhydrin Test for Amino Acids

Ninhydrin is a reagent that reacts with the free amino group on an amino acid. When applied as a spray or solution to filter paper spotted with amino acid, the reagent turns violet.

- Label four strips of filter paper a–d.
- Place a drop of each of the following solutions on the corresponding strip of filter paper.

a. egg albumin (egg white) dissolved in water
b. 1% glucose
c. 1% starch
d. distilled water

(a) Carboxyl (b) Amino

Figure 4-4 Functional groups in amino acids: (a) a carboxyl group and (b) a free amino group.

- Working under a hood or in a well-ventilated area, spray the strips of paper with ninhydrin spray or stain them with a drop of ninhydrin solution. (Ninhydrin is a toxic substance: AVOID INHALING THE FUMES, AND DO NOT LET THE SOLUTION TOUCH YOUR SKIN OR CLOTHING.) The paper will need to dry for 20–30 minutes before the results are evident. Warming the paper with a blow-dryer, if available, will speed up the process. Record and interpret your results in Chart 4-4.

Chart 4-4 Results of the ninhydrin test for amino acids.

Tube	Contents	Color of spot after ninhydrin test	Interpretation
a.	egg albumin	faint ring violet	amino acid
b.	glucose	no change	no amino acid
c.	starch	no change	no amino acid
d.	distilled water	no change	no amino acid

B. Biuret Test for Protein

As noted earlier, **proteins** are large molecules composed of many amino acid units linked by **peptide bonds** (Fig. 4-5). A peptide bond forms through a condensation reaction of an amino group with a carboxyl group (see Figure 4-4). Biuret reagent (copper sulfate, $CuSO_4$) reveals the presence of the peptide bonds by turning a solution containing protein deep blue under alkaline conditions.

- Label four test tubes a–d.
- Place 2–3 ml of the following solutions in the corresponding tubes.

a. egg albumin dissolved in water
b. 1% glucose
c. 1% starch
d. distilled water

- Make each solution alkaline by adding 2–3 ml of 10% sodium hydroxide (NaOH).
- Add several drops of 1% copper sulfate solution to each tube and mix well.
- Record any color changes in Chart 4-5 and interpret the results.

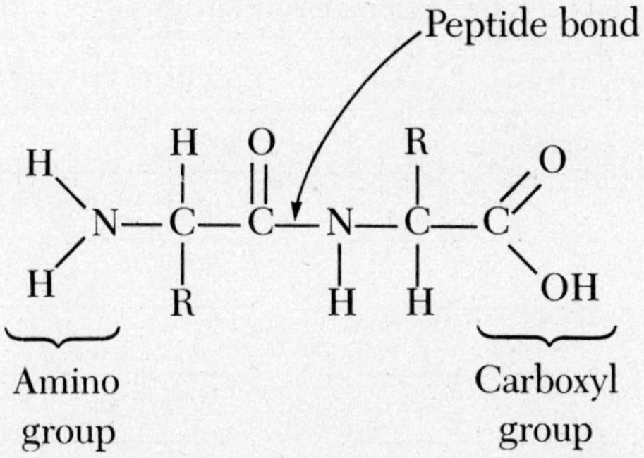

Peptide bond

Amino group

Carboxyl group

Figure 4-5 Amino acids linked by a peptide bond.

Chart 4-5 Results of Biuret test for protein.

Tube	Contents	Color change	Interpretation
a.	egg albumin	purple	peptide bond
b.	glucose	~~faint blue~~ no change	no peptide bond
c.	starch	no change	no peptide bond
d.	distilled water	no change	no peptide bond

QUESTION

If a substance gave a positive result with the ninhydrin reagent and a negative result with the Biuret reagent, what would you conclude about its composition?

It would contain amino acids but they would not form peptide bonds.

EXERCISE 4-4 TESTING THE COMPOSITION OF COMMON SUBSTANCES

Don't DO

Objective To use the techniques learned in the previous exercises to determine the presence of carbohydrates, proteins, and lipids.

- In our everyday lives we encounter many substances produced by living things. Your instructor will provide you with a selection of common substances and one or two unknown substances to subject to the tests you have used in the preceding exercises. Test each substance for sugar, lipids, and protein (Biuret test only). Record your results in Chart 4-6. If a large number of substances is available, you may be instructed to divide the activities with laboratory classmates, sharing data to complete the chart.

Chart 4-6 Testing the composition of common substances.

Substance or unknown	Results of the test for		
	sugar	lipids	protein
1.			
2.			
3.			
4.			

(continued)

Chart 4-6 Testing the composition of common substances.

Substance or unknown	Results of the test for		
	sugar	lipids	protein
5. ______	______	______	______
6. ______	______	______	______

QUESTIONS

Which substances were present in Unknown #1?

Which substances were present in Unknown #2?

The material in this chapter corresponds to Chapter 4 in your text.

5

ENZYMES

If enzymes did not exist, you would not be reading this page. You would be unable to digest what you had for breakfast this morning. You would not be able to breathe and provide oxygen to your cells. You simply would not *be*.

Enzymes are **catalysts** for the chemical reactions that take place in living things. As catalysts, enzymes do not *cause* these reactions. Instead, they speed up the rate at which chemical reactions occur, sometimes hundreds or even thousands of times. And as catalysts, enzymes are not used up in the chemical reactions they facilitate. They participate in the reaction and then emerge unscathed to be used again and again in the thousands of reactions that take place in living cells.

Nearly every enzyme is a protein with a complex three-dimensional structure. Within that structure is an **active site,** which binds with one or two chemical compounds called **substrates** to form an enzyme-substrate complex, or **ES** (Fig. 5-1). During a reaction, substrates are either broken down or combined with other substrate compounds. When the substrate binds to the active site, the shapes of the substrate and enzyme are changed. In this way, the enzyme lowers the **energy of activation** of the reaction and makes it occur more readily.

Although enzymes speed up chemical reactions, their ability to do so is affected by physical and chemical conditions in the cell. Factors that affect enzyme activity include temperature, pH, and the concentrations of the enzyme and its substrate. In the following laboratory exercises you will control these conditions in experiments with fruit and enzyme solutions inside test tubes. You will conduct a short series of experiments in which one condition is varied while the others are held constant. This will allow you to see how a change in a particular condition results in a change in the activity of the enzyme.

Thousands of enzymes are known, and each one is a catalyst for a specific reaction involving a specific substrate. This specificity is reflected in the enzyme's common name, which often ends in the suffix *-ase* and indicates the substrate, the reaction catalyzed, or both. For example, cytochrome

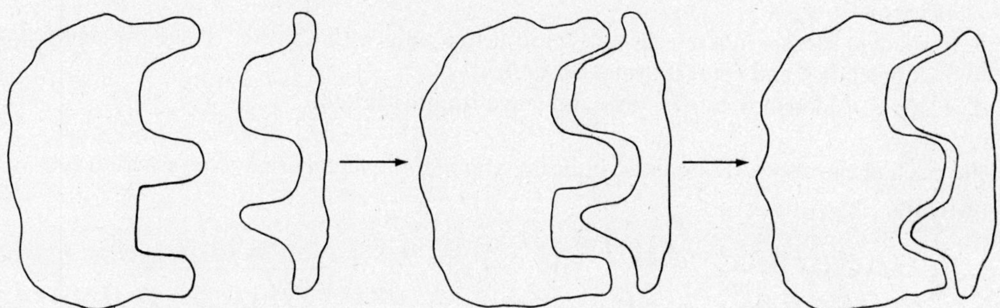

Figure 5-1 Binding of an enzyme and substrate to form an enzyme-substrate complex (ES).

oxidase catalyzes the oxidation of cytochrome. The enzyme you will use in the following exercise is called **catecholase**, an enzyme that causes bruised fruits to turn brown by catalyzing the reaction between catechol and oxygen. In the presence of catecholase, catechol is oxidized to form benzoquinone, which is a component of chemical compounds that give bruised fruits their red and brown colors.

To expedite the exercise procedures and keep track of timed reactions, your instructor will probably divide the class into small groups.

EXERCISE 5-1 THE EFFECT OF CATECHOLASE ON A CUT APPLE

Objective To slow down or speed up catecholase activity by changing the conditions of the reaction.

When you slice a juicy apple, you cut through many cell walls and release catecholase onto the white surface of the fruit. Left open to the air, the enzyme catalyzes the reaction of catechol with oxygen. The reaction produces benzoquinone, and the surface of the apple quickly turns brown. However, a few simple changes in conditions can alter the rate of this chemical reaction.

- Your instructor will provide your group with an apple or other fruit. Slice the apple in half, give one half to another group, then cut the remaining half into five smaller sections. Treat the apple sections as follows:

1. Place one section in a beaker of ice.
2. Place one section in a warming oven (about 40 °C) or on a window sill warmed by direct sunlight.
3. Place one section in a petri dish and squeeze lemon juice over the cut surfaces. During the course of your other activities, make sure that the cut surfaces are kept moist with lemon juice. Test the pH of the lemon juice with pH paper provided by your instructor.
4. Place one section in a petri dish and moisten it with distilled water; keep it moist with water as you did with lemon juice for the other section. Test the pH of the distilled water with pH paper.
5. Place one section in a mortar and mash it to a pulp with a pestle. Place the mashed apple in a petri dish and set it on your lab desk.
6. Place one section in a petri dish and leave it undisturbed.

- For each of the above treatments, indicate which of the factors that alter reaction rate you are changing.

1. ______ 4. ______
2. ______ 5. ______
3. ______ 6. ______

- Check the apple sections every few minutes for the first half hour while you prepare equipment for the next exercises. Note the time and intensity of any color changes in the apple tissue. Record the times and extent of browning (if any) of each section in Chart 5-1.

Chart 5-1 Color changes in apple tissue.

Apple section	Time of first browning	Time course of further browning
1. ice	~~[illegible]~~ no change	
2. heat	10 min	35 min
pH3 3. lemon	~~[illegible]~~ no change	
4. water	15 min	30 min
5. mashed pulp	2 min	25 min
6. alone	5 min	40 min

- After a half hour of frequent observation, check the apple sections periodically until the end of the laboratory period. You should be able to interpret the results in terms of how each treatment affected the activity of the enzyme in catalyzing the oxidation of catechol. In Chart 5-2, note the effect of each factor on reaction rate as evidenced by rate of color change in the apple tissue.

Chart 5-2 Effects of treatment in catalyzing the oxidation of catechol.

Apple section	Effect of treatment on enzyme activity
1. ice	slows activity
2. heat	~~[illegible]~~ slowed alittle
3. lemon	slows activity
4. dist. water	slows activity
5. pulp (mashed)	speeds up activity - released enzymes when cut
6. alone control	control - used to compare

QUESTIONS

Which treatment(s) is (are) the control for this experiment?

the undisturbed apple

Would an uncut apple also be a suitable control? Explain.

No. Because if it is uncut then we are not exposing anything to it in order for a reaction to occur ∴ it cannot be compared to apples that have been exposed to something.

EXERCISE 5-2 ENZYME CONCENTRATION

Objective To observe how changes in enzyme concentration affect enzyme activity.

In the previous experiment you observed the effects of various conditions on enzyme activity. But with a cut apple it was difficult to control the concentrations of the chemicals involved in the reaction. This experiment, which involves an enzyme in an extract of potato, will allow you to control more precisely the concentration of enzyme and to determine the effect of its concentration on enzyme activity.

The concentration of the enzyme catecholase from potato extract will be varied by diluting the enzyme with a **buffer** solution of pH 7. A buffer solution is resistant to pH change. Usually a weak acid itself, the buffer will take on or release hydrogen ions as they are added or removed during chemical reactions. By keeping hydrogen ion concentration relatively constant, the pH is held constant. Your instructor will provide you with a buffer solution or with directions on how to make a fresh solution.

Note The stock bottle or flask of potato extract must be kept on ice to maintain activity of the enzyme. Fill your tubes with extract from the stock bottle only when you are ready to proceed with the experiment.

- Mix the following solutions in three numbered test tubes.

Table 5-1 Contents of test tubes for enzyme concentration experiment.

Test tube	Drops of buffer (pH 7)	Drops of potato extract
1.	25	10
2.	15	10
3.	5	10

In which tube is catecholase concentration highest? tube 3 In which tube is catecholase concentration lowest? tube 1

- When catechol is added to these tubes, the color of the solution will change: The darker the color, the higher the rate of the reaction of catechol with the enzyme (catecholase) from the potato extract. When the tubes are ready, add 10 drops of catechol to each tube and shake once per minute for 15 minutes. *Add the catechol to all the tubes at the same time so the reactions in them can be easily timed*. Observe any color changes that occur at regular intervals after adding the substrate. In Chart 5-3, indicate the darkness of color in the tubes with a "+" for light color, "+ +" for darker color, etc. Terminate the experiment when all the tubes have turned the same dark color.

Chart 5-3 Results of enzyme concentration experiment.

Test tube	Color change and intensity after time intervals (min)							
	1	3	5	7	9	11	13	15
1.	+	+	+	+	++	++	++	++
2.	++	++	++	+++	+++	+++	+++	+++
3.	+++	+++	++++	++++	++++	++++	++++	++++

All reached equality at 33 min.

QUESTIONS

What are your conclusions regarding the effect of enzyme concentration on reaction rate? State your conclusions in a few concise sentences.

when the enzyme concentration is the greatest, the reaction rate increases because there are more enzymes to react ∴ react faster.

Why did you use buffer instead of distilled water to dilute the enzyme for this experiment?

We used the buffer to hold the pH constant so that pH cannot be a factor in this experiment only concentration of enzyme. (Buffer takes the concentration)

EXERCISE 5-3 SUBSTRATE CONCENTRATION

how affect reaction

Objective To observe how changes in substrate concentration affect enzyme activity.

Given a certain amount of enzyme, how does enzyme activity change as you add more and more substrate? The enzyme and substrate must combine to form an ES for the reaction to proceed. The more substrate added, the more ES that forms—up to a point. In this experiment you will vary substrate (catechol) concentration by diluting it with a buffer solution of pH 7.

- Mix the following solutions in five numbered test tubes.

Table 5-2 Contents of test tubes for substrate concentration experiment.

Test tube	Drops of buffer (pH 7)	Drops of catechol
1.	10	1
2.	10	5
3.	10	10
4.	10	15
5.	10	25

In which tube is catechol (substrate) concentration highest? tube 5 In which tube is catechol concentration lowest? tube 1

- You will provide an excess of the enzyme catecholase by adding 30 drops of potato extract to each tube at the same time. If enough test tubes are available, you may want to measure out 30 drops in each of five test tubes ahead of time, to quickly add the enzyme to the substrate tubes. Observe any color changes that occur at regular intervals after adding the enzyme.

Indicate the darkness with the same system of +'s used in the previous exercise. Record your observations in the spaces below.

Chart 5-4 Results of substrate concentration experiment.

Test tube	Color change and intensity after time intervals (min)							
	1	3	5	7	9	11	13	15
1.	+	+	+	+	+	+	+	+
2.	++	++	++	++	++	+++	+++	+++
3.	++●	++	+++	+++	+++	+++	+++	+++
4.	+++●	+++	+++	+++	+++	+++	+++	+++
5.	+++●●	+++	+++	+++	+++	+++	+++	+++

QUESTION

What are your conclusions regarding the effect of substrate concentration on reaction rate? State your conclusions in a few concise sentences.

the higher the concentration of substrate - the more immediate the reaction until the ES complex has formed completely and cannot react any longer.

EXERCISE 5-4 EFFECTS OF EXTREME pH AND HEAT

Objective To demonstrate the effects of extreme pH and heat on protein structure and function.

As Figure 5-1 showed, the structure of an enzyme is crucial to its proper functioning. Enzymes, like all proteins, have a specific three-dimensional shape; this shape is maintained through the maintenance of optimal or near-optimal conditions in an intact cell. Marked alterations in physical conditions distort the shape of an enzyme and rob it of its ability to act as a catalyst. Two factors that can change the shape of proteins—**denature** them—are heat and pH. You are no doubt familiar with the effect of heat on the protein in egg white, which when heated is rendered physiologically useless to the egg, albeit edible to humans. Very acidic conditions can also denature enzymes.

Your instructor will provide you with an appropriate acidic solution and also with a means of heating an enzyme solution. You should be able to design two experiments to test the effect of extreme pH and temperature on catecholase activity. Use experimental procedures similar to those shown for the previous exercises (catecholase activity in test tubes).

Each experiment should include the following parts:

Hypothesis A statement proposing how extreme pH or temperature will affect enzyme activity.

Methods A brief description of how the experiment will be conducted. Each experiment should use one test tube and a minimal amount of enzyme, substrate, and buffer solution.

Results A description of what happened in the experiment. Compare the results to those of the previous exercises.

Conclusions A summary, stating whether the results confirmed or disproved the hypothesis, and how the experiment could be improved.

Limit your experiment write-up to the spaces provided.

Experiment on Extreme pH

Hypothesis

Extreme pH will denature the enzyme and slow down the reactions.

Methods

Contents of test tubes

test tube	Drops catechol	Drops potato	Drops acid
1	10	10	1
2	10	10	5
3	10	10	10
4	10	10	15
5	10	10	25

Results

Color change + intensity (min.)

test tube		1 min	3	5	7	9	11	13	15
1.	++++	++++	++++	+++++	+++++	++++++	+++++	+++++	+++++
2.	+++	++++	++++	+++++	++++	++++++	+++++	+++++	+++++
3.	+++	+++	+++	+++	++++	++++	+++++	+++++	++++++
4.	++	++	++	++	+++	+++	++++	+++++	+++++
5	+	+	+	+	++	++	+++	+++	+++

Conclusions

The test tube w/ the most acid in it was the slowest to react as compared w/ the others

Experiment on Extreme Heat

Hypothesis

Extreme heat denature s enzyme completely and stops the enzyme

Methods

test tube	Drops buffer	Drops catechol	Drops potato	temp
1	10	10	10	boiling
2	10	10	10	room temp
3	10	10	10	ice

Results

test tube	1 min	3 min	5 min	7 min	9 min	11 min	13	15
1 no reaction	+	+	+	+	+	+	+	+
2	+++	+++	+++	+++	++++	++++	++++	++++
3	++	++	++	++	++	++	+++	+++

Conclusions

Extreme heat stops reaction completely + immediately whereas coldness will slow down the reaction but it still is reacting

The material in this chapter corresponds to Chapter 5 in your text.

6
OSMOSIS AND DIFFUSION

def osmosis + simple diffusion

Neither single cells nor large organisms are autonomous, sealed compartments. Both interact with their environments in myriad ways. To maintain an internal milieu favorable to the existence of their cells, multicellular animals and plants must expend large amounts of energy. In the process, materials pass between the organism and its environment as well as between cells inside the organism. Even unicellular organisms exchange materials with the surrounding water, air, or soil. In a real sense, the survival of an organism is dependent on the ability of its cells to regulate the flow of materials across cell membranes and walls.

Regulation of the movement of material into, out of, and between cells may be either passive or active. **Active transport** of various ions and organic compounds requires energy in the form of **ATP** (adenosine triphosphate), the "energy currency" of cells. In contrast, **simple diffusion** and **carrier-facilitated diffusion** are termed "passive" because they take place without any energy expenditure on the part of the cell. It is important to remember, however, that labeling these transfer mechanisms "passive" belies the complicated structure of the plasma membrane that makes them possible.

The exercises in this chapter demonstrate the passive and active processes involved in moving materials into and out of cells. The passive processes of diffusion and osmosis will be demonstrated both in models of cells and in living plant and animal cells.

EXERCISE 6-1 SIMPLE DIFFUSION

Objective To demonstrate the principle of diffusion in two nonliving mediums, a gas and a liquid, and to understand the passive nature of the process.

Diffusion is the tendency of a substance to move from a place of high concentration to one of lower concentration. The process is passive and occurs because of the random motion of molecules of the diffusing substance. Because we cannot see molecules, it is helpful to think of an example on a larger scale. For instance, think of a cookie sheet with a handful of chocolate chips clustered in one corner. The chips are in an area of high concentration. By shaking the cookie sheet we make the chips move randomly over its surface and simulate the passive, random motion of molecules in a liquid or gas. The chips gradually disperse across the cookie sheet, diffusing out from the original corner of high concentration. Although the diffusion is passive, the **rate** of diffusion is affected by the free energy in the system. In our cookie sheet model, we would simulate an increase in free energy by shaking the cookie sheet more vigorously. The amount of free energy in a liquid or gas is reflected by its temperature: The higher the temperature of the medium, the faster the random motion of molecules and the higher the rate of diffusion in the medium.

A. Measuring Diffusion Rate in a Gas

- Your instructor or a student will stand at the front of the class with a Petri dish and a closed container of a volatile substance (such as ammonia or ether). A student with a stopwatch will act as timer. Students should arrange themselves at their desks or stand in rows (3–4 students per row) parallel to the front of the room. Each student should have a pencil and a slip of paper. The layout of the laboratory should look something like Figure 6-1, which your instructor will also draw on the chalkboard. The class should measure the distance between desks and calibrate the scale bar.
- Everyone but the instructor and timer should remain quiet until the end of the exercise. The instructor will pour a small amount of the volatile liquid into the Petri dish as the timer starts the stopwatch. As the liquid evaporates, the odor will diffuse out from the Petri dish (area of high concentration) through the room (area of low concentration). The timer should call out the time at 5-second intervals. Each student will detect the odor of the volatile liquid as it

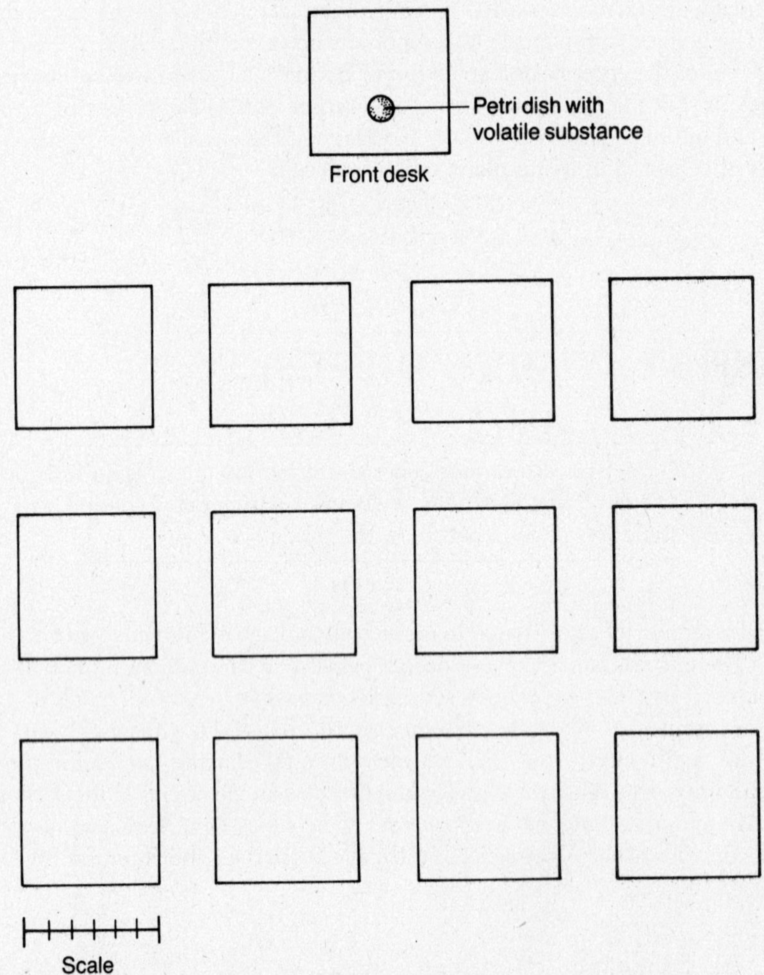

Figure 6-1 Suggested arrangement of laboratory for Exercise 6-1.

diffuses through the room. When the odor is detected, the student should mentally count off the seconds until the timer calls out the next time interval. By subtracting the number of seconds counted off, the student should calculate the time that the odor reached his or her position. The student should write down the time on the slip of paper and sit quietly until the end of the experiment. Each student should trust his or her own nose and not record a time simply because the adjacent person does so. (To forestall peer pressure, you can close your eyes if you like.) After a few minutes, the instructor will ask if everyone has recorded a detection time. After everyone has done so, the volatile liquid should be disposed of in a waste bottle or sink. If possible, air out the room so the next laboratory can start the exercise with fresh air.

- The instructor will ask each student to record his or her detection time and write the number of seconds on the chalkboard at the appropriate position. Refer to the chalkboard to fill in Figure 6-1.

nearest 198 cm 15 sec farthest 718 cm 40 sec

QUESTIONS

671 cm - 40 sec 365 cm - 15 sec

Compare the time it took for the odor to reach the closest student and the farthest student. Calculate the diffusion rate by dividing the distance to each of the two students (in centimeters) by their respective detection times. Record the values below.

Diffusion rate to nearest student 24 cm/sec

Diffusion rate to farthest student 17 cm/sec

Did the odor diffuse at a uniform rate throughout the laboratory? no

Describe how air movement in your laboratory might cause nonuniform diffusion of the odor.

There may have been air movement from the heating system to where it pushed the odor faster or vice versa. When students moved, it could cause the same effect

Describe how differences between classmates' sensory capabilities might have affected the results of this experiment.

Some classmates could have had colds on that particular day, so they wouldn't be able to smell as well! Or even some are not as sensitive as others, so when it reached them it wasn't noticed right away, so that would cause the results to be off.

B. Measuring Diffusion of a Solid Dissolved in a Liquid

- Divide into small groups for this exercise. Each group should take the bottom half of a Petri dish and place it on a blank sheet of paper on a level desktop. Trace a circle around the Petri dish and set the dish aside. Draw two lines across the circle and label them in centimeters as shown.

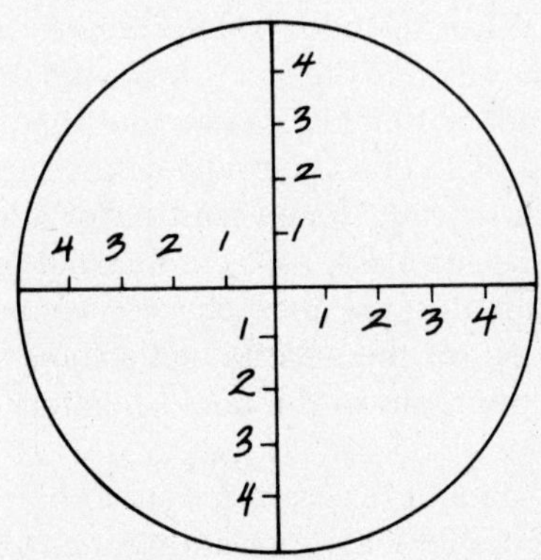

Place the Petri dish back on the circle.

- Obtain three equal-sized crystals of potassium permanganate ($KMnO_4$) from your instructor and place them on a dry sheet of paper. Be careful not to get them wet.
- Fill the Petri dish two-thirds full with water from a beaker kept at 70–80°C in a warm water bath. Measure the actual temperature of water in the beaker. Hot water temperature = 76 °C.
- One student in the group should act as timer by using a stopwatch or a watch with a second indicator. Using forceps, place one of the crystals of $KMnO_4$ in the dish at the point of intersection of the lines, and start timing. As the purple color diffuses, record the time that the circle of color reaches the numbers on the lines. The circle may not enlarge at an equal rate in all directions; if you find that is the case, pick the most rapidly moving edge on one of the lines and record the time at which it reaches each number. Write the time in the appropriate space in Chart 6-1. (You may write the time in minutes and seconds and convert to seconds later.)
- Rinse the Petri dish, dry it with a paper towel, and place it over the numbered lines. Repeat the experiment, this time using water from a beaker that has been sitting at room temperature. Measure the temperature of water in the beaker. Room temperature water = 23 °C.

  Record the times when the circle edge reaches each number on the lines and write the times in the appropriate spaces in Chart 6-1.
- Rinse the Petri dish and dry it with a paper towel. Now, repeat the experiment a third time using water from a beaker kept in an ice bath. Measure the temperature of water in the beaker.

  Temperature of cold water = 1 °C.

  Record the times when the circle edge reaches each number on the lines and write the times in the appropriate spaces in Chart 6-1.

Chart 6-1 Rate of diffusion of potassium permanganate in water.

		Time (seconds) to reach distance			
		1 cm	2 cm	3 cm	4 cm
Hot water temp. 76	°C	30	95	135	190
Room temp. 23	°C	90	185	400	705
Cold water temp. 1	°C	165	475	590	760

- Graph the data from the chart on Figure 6-2. The y-axis represents the radius of the spreading circle of color (numbers on the grid lines under the Petri dish). The x-axis is the *time* taken to

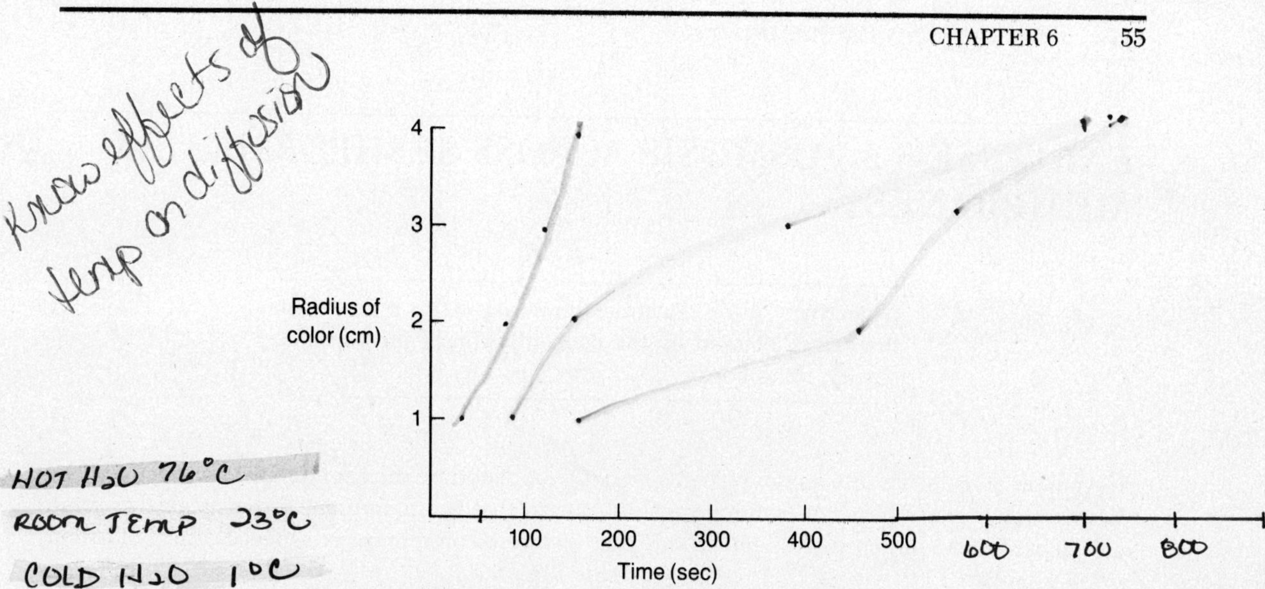

Figure 6-2 Diffusion of $KMnO_4$ in water at three temperatures.

reach the numbers. Plot the four time values for the experiment with hot water and connect the points with a line. Label the line "Hot Water ___76___°C." Plot the time values for the other two temperatures and label the lines appropriately. The completed graph will have three lines on it.

QUESTIONS

What do you conclude about the effect of temperature on diffusion of a solid dissolving in water?

The effect that temperature has on diffusion is a very obvious one. When heat is applied, diffusion occurs more rapidly because the movement of particles is increased and vice versa w/ cooling the temp.

Compare the diffusion rates of the volatile liquid in room air and the $KMnO_4$ crystals in water at room temperature.

The diffusion rate of the liquid in room air is faster than that of the crystals in water.

Speculate on how this difference in diffusion rates might be important to organisms living in water compared to organisms living on land.

EXERCISE 6-2 OSMOSIS ACROSS SEMIPERMEABLE MEMBRANES

Objective To demonstrate how osmosis in a model of the cell is affected by the concentration of the solution outside the model.

Movement of materials into and out of cells is partly mediated by the **semipermeable** nature of the plasma membrane. The term "semipermeable" means that the membrane is permeable to some substances but not others. Movement of water across the cell membrane is a special case of diffusion called **osmosis.**

As in other diffusion processes, water moves from an area of high concentration to an area of lower concentration. However, the concentration of water is high in dilute solutions; this is converse to our usual way of thinking about concentration, in which we focus on the concentration of a *substance* dissolved in water rather than the concentration of the water itself.

Thus, when water moves across a cell membrane, it moves from a dilute solution (high concentration of water molecules) to a less dilute one (with high concentration of a substance dissolved in water). That is why cells in dilute solutions experience an inflow of water and swell up. The internal pressure exerted by this swelling is called **osmotic pressure.** The surrounding dilute medium is said to be **hypotonic** to the cytoplasm inside the cell. If osmotic pressure builds up high enough, the cell may burst or **lyse.** Conversely, cells in concentrated solutions lose water and may shrivel up; in this case the surrounding medium is said to be **hypertonic** to the cell. When the concentrations of water on both sides of a semipermeable membrane are equal, the cell and its surrounding medium are said to be **isotonic.**

The movement of water across a membrane does not require energy—it is a passive process. However, a cell may actively pump water into its dilute surroundings to avoid bursting. Also, cells can actively transport some substances across the membrane (a process requiring ATP) or manufacture others to change the concentration gradient across the cell membrane and thereby affect the direction or rate of movement of water across the cell membrane.

This exercise uses a model of the cell to demonstrate osmotic processes. The cell model is made of **dialysis tubing,** which is a semipermeable membrane with submicroscopic pores that allow the passage of water and small molecules but not large molecules. Selective diffusion of substances through a semipermeable membrane is called **dialysis** and is the process involved in cleansing the blood of patients with kidney disease.

- Work in small groups.
- Dialysis tubing comes in one long piece on a roll. Cut off three segments of equal length (about 8–10 cm). Moisten each segment with water to make it pliable, then fold one end back on itself and tie it tightly shut with a piece of string. Leave about 5 cm of string free, and attach a label to the end of it. On the label write a tube number (1–3) and identifying initials for your laboratory group.
- Open the free end of Tube 1 by moistening and rubbing it between your fingers. Fill it about ⅓ full with full-strength Karo syrup or another concentrated sugar solution. Fold over the free end and tie it snugly with another piece of string. Do not squeeze the tube or it will leak at the ends. Rinse any syrup off the outside, blot the tube dry on a paper towel, and weigh it on a scale. Record its weight (actually its mass) in Chart 6-2 under the column labeled "Pre-test weight."
- Fill Tube 2 about ½ full with a solution of 50% Karo syrup or make your own half-strength solution by adding equal measures of full-strength syrup and distilled water. Tie off the free end as before, rinse, blot dry, and weigh the tube. Record the weight in Chart 6-2.

- Fill Tube 3 as full as possible with distilled water. Tie it shut, blot dry, and weigh the tube. Record the weight in Chart 6-2.
- Prepare three beakers large enough to hold the tubes with the following solutions:
  Beaker 1: distilled water
  Beaker 2: 50% Karo solution
  Beaker 3: 50% Karo solution
- Place Tube 1 in Beaker 1, Tube 2 in Beaker 2, and Tube 3 in Beaker 3 (Figure 6-3). Note the time when each tube is placed in the beaker.

  Tube #1, time immersed: 11:48

  Tube #2, time immersed: 11:50

  Tube #3, time immersed: 11:50

- Allow the tubes to sit in the beakers for 45–60 minutes. Then remove the tubes, if necessary rinse any sugar solution off, gently blot them dry, and weigh them. Record the weights in the column "post-test weight."

Chart 6-2 Weight of solutions in dialysis tubing.

Tube	Tube contents	Pre-test weight (g)	Post-test weight (g)
1	100% syrup	7.34	7.93 g
2	50% syrup	10.27	10.59 g
3	dist. water	12.94	13.34 g

- Calculate the percentage weight gained or lost by each tube and record the values in Chart 6-3.

Chart 6-3 Weight change of solutions in dialysis tubing.

Tube	Weight change (g)	% original weight
1	.45g	
2	1.18g	
3	32.28	

understand what was expected

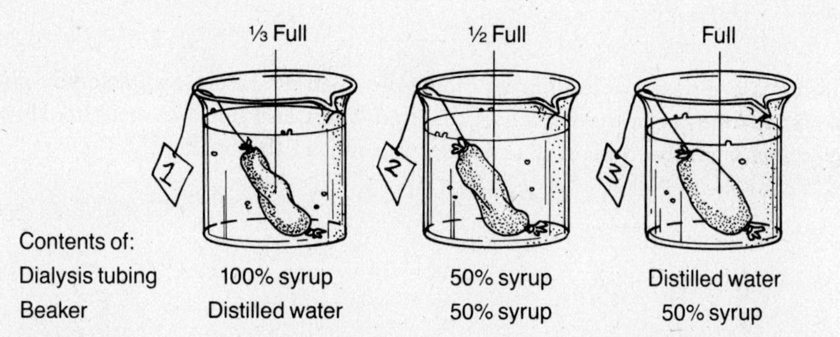

Figure 6-3 Experimental set-up for observing osmosis across dialysis tubing membrane.

QUESTIONS

Use the terms hypotonic, hypertonic, and isotonic to describe the concentration of the three tubes relative to the solutions in the beakers.

The beaker with Tube 1 inside of it is hypotonic to the tube.
The beaker w/ Tube 2 in it is isotonic to the tube
the beaker w/ Tube 3 in it is hypertonic to the tube.

Describe the changes in osmotic pressure (if any) that took place in each tube, and relate it to osmosis across the model cell membrane.

A change in osmotic pressure occured in tube 1 - the pressure increased because water moved into the cell and caused it to expand. the vice versa occured for tube 3.

Explain how the changes in mass (if any) of the tubes correspond to changes in osmotic pressure in the tubes.

The change in mass of tube 1 increased so the tube expanded which caused an increase in the osmotic pressure. Vice versa w/ tube 3.

Dialysis tubing is permeable to sugar, although sugar molecules diffuse across the tubing membrane more slowly than water molecules. What do you think would have happened to the tubes if you had left them in the beakers overnight? Why?

Tube 1 would have gotten even fatter and tube 3 would have gotten even littler because sugar molecules aren't moving at same rate as H_2O so there will never be equilibrium

Dialysis tubing is not permeable to large molecules such as starch. Suppose you placed a tube filled with starch solution in the beaker of distilled water and left it overnight. How would its appearance differ from the tube of glucose after a night in the beaker?

It would be fatter because H_2O would have moved in but no starch moved out. The glucose would have moved out at same rate as H_2O after equilibrium was reached

EXERCISE 6-3 OSMOSIS IN LIVING CELLS

what happens place
in dist H_2O as to
salt?

Objective To develop and test a hypothesis about the response of a living plant cell to a concentrated salt solution.

Based on the experiments so far, you should be able to develop a hypothesis about the responses of a living cell to a concentrated salt solution. Your instructor will provide you with a sprig of living *Elodea* (sometimes called *Anacharis*). This plant normally lives in freshwater ponds and lakes.

- Based on the experiments on diffusion and osmosis, formulate a hypothesis predicting what will happen to cells in *Elodea* leaves placed in a concentrated salt solution. State your hypothesis in a single sentence:

  The cells in the Elodea leaves will shrink.

- Now, use the following solutions to make two wet mount slides of leaves of the plant:

  Slide 1: aquarium water
  Slide 2: 10% sodium chloride (salt) solution

- Observe the leaves under the compound microscope. Make a drawing of a typical cell on each slide in the spaces below.

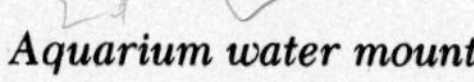

Aquarium water mount

10% salt solution mount

QUESTIONS

In this experiment, what was the control?

The aquarium water mount.

Did this experiment fit the prediction in your hypothesis?

Yes. Because the cells did appear to shrink when they were placed in a salt solution

Did this experiment adequately test your hypothesis? yes

If not, suggest a further experiment that would provide a better test of the hypothesis.

The material in this chapter corresponds to Chapter 6 in your text.

7

CELL STRUCTURE AND ORGANELLES

Cells are basic to life. In a sense, they partly define life because every virtually living thing is made of one or more cells. Even noncellular viruses require cells to propagate themselves. The literal borderline between life and nonlife is the cell boundary (the plasma membrane in animal cells or the cell wall in plants and most bacteria). Inside it, the complex chemical reactions unique to living things take place.

Cells come in diverse sizes and shapes. There are two basic cell types: **prokaryotic** and **eukaryotic.** Prokaryotic cells are considered primitive in the sense that they resemble the earliest cell types theorized to have arisen on Earth. They lack the more complex internal structures of eukaryotic cells such as nuclei, chromosomes, chloroplasts, and so forth. Because cells are generally very small, they must be observed with either light or electron microscopes. In the following exercises you will be making observations of living and preserved cells with the compound light microscope; you will also interpret images produced by electron microscopy.

EXERCISE 7-1 CELL TYPES OF MAJOR GROUPS OF ORGANISMS

Objective To use light microscope observations to distinguish between the cell types of the major groups of organisms: bacteria, protists, animals, and plants; and to identify internal structures of these cells visible with the light microscope.

- Your instructor will provide prepared slides and/or live cultures of the major groups of organisms. If live cultures are provided, prepare wet mount slides of specimens from liquid cultures. Make labeled drawings of all specimens in the spaces provided on the following pages and include a scale for each drawing. In your drawings, include the structures named in boldface in the following descriptions.

Prokaryotes

Bacteria

Bacteria are prokaryotic and thus lack a nucleus or other internal cell structures (aspects of their structure that you will study in more detail in Exercise 7-2). Bacteria are generally very small, even by microscopic standards—often so small that observing the absence of internal stuctures with the light microscope is impossible. The prepared slide you will observe consists of one or more types of bacteria stained with a dye to make them more visible.

- Observe the slide under various magnifications to get a feel for the size of the bacteria. Draw the bacterial types on the slide; label the **cell wall** and describe the shape of the cells (**rods, spheres,** and **spirals**).

Eukaryotes

The rest of the cell types you will observe in this exercise are eukaryotic. Eukaryotes possess a nucleus and other discrete internal structures called **organelles,** which are storage sites or compartments where chemical synthesis and metabolism occur. At least some of these organelles are believed to have originated billions of years ago when one prokaryotic cell engulfed another and incorporated it as a permanent internal fixture.

Amoeba

- Observe the prepared slides of *Amoeba* or prepare a wet mount slide of the culture provided. (Suction fluid from near the bottom of the culture vessel or from near any large food particles in the culture medium—*Amoeba* congregate near them.)

Unlike many microscopic unicellular organisms, an *Amoeba* lacks a rigid outer **cell wall.** The **nucleus** is roughly in the center of the amorphous cell. **Pseudopods** (false feet) are the temporary protrusions formed by streaming of the **cytoplasm.** The pseudopods extend and pull the cell forward in a characteristic **amoeboid movement.** Pseudopods also engulf food particles, which are digested inside **food vacuoles.**

- Draw *Amoeba* and label its structures.

- Make a diagram showing amoeboid movement.

Euglena

Euglena is a single-celled photosynthetic eukaryote containing green **chloroplasts.** The cell swims by means of a single **flagellum** at one end. A red **eye spot** is located near the site where the flagellum extends out of the cell, although the eye spot may be difficult to see with the light microscope. In *Euglena,* the cell membrane is reinforced internally with semirigid helical strips of protein that wrap around the cell. These strips form the **pellicle** and give the *Euglena* cell a stiffer structure than *Amoeba*.

- Draw *Euglena* and label its structures.

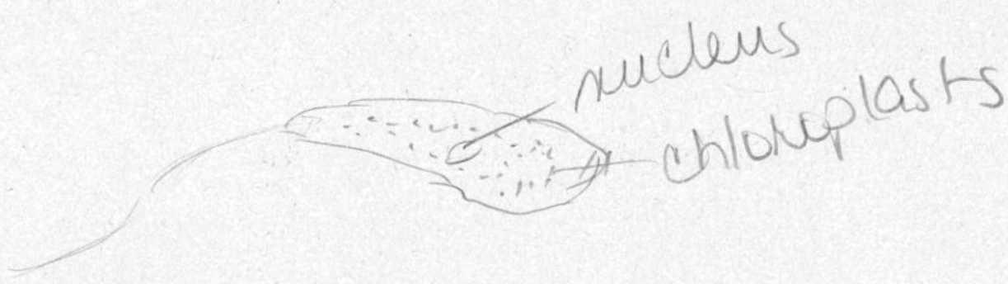

- Diagram the **euglenoid movement** of the cells and describe how the structural difference in the cell covering of *Euglena* affects its swimming motion compared to that of *Amoeba*.

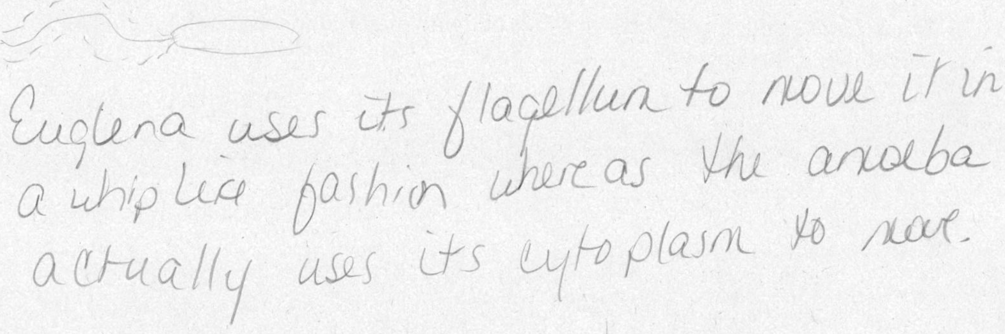

Euglena uses its flagellum to move it in
a whip like fashion whereas the amoeba
actually uses its cytoplasm to move.

Diatoms

Your instructor will provide you with a culture of one or more diatoms. Diatoms may be **single cells, filaments,** or **colonies.** The transparent **cell wall** consists of two overlapping **valves** made of silica (the compound used to manufacture glass). Notice the many grooves and pits in the valves and the variety of cell shapes. Diatoms are also photosynthetic, but their **chloroplasts** are golden instead of green because they contain a brown pigment that masks the green chlorophyll. Diatoms lack flagella but many are capable of moving by exuding a substance through a fine groove in the valve.

- Prepare a wet mount slide of the diatom culture. Draw a diatom and use arrows to indicate the direction of movement of any motile diatoms you observe.

Ulothrix

Ulothrix is an unbranched **filamentous** green alga. This alga contains a single **chloroplast** in each cell. The chloroplast is cylindrical and may be incomplete on one side like a bracelet. Starch from photosynthesis is stored in small round structures in the chloroplasts called **pyrenoids.**

- Draw *Ulothrix* and label its structures.

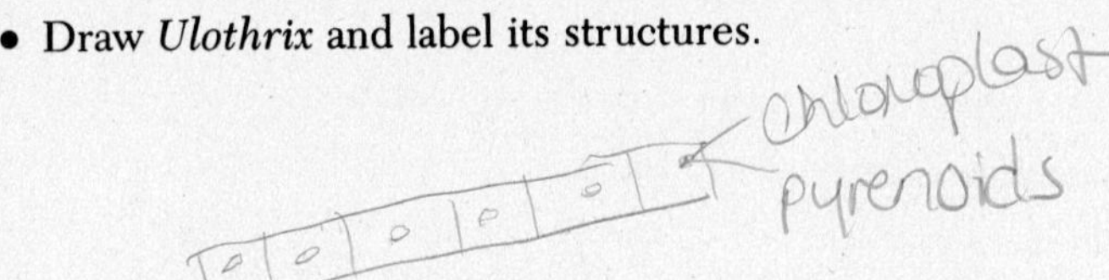

Elodea

Elodea is the same aquatic plant you used in the experiment on osmosis in the previous chapter. Under the light microscope the **cell wall, central vacuole,** and **chloroplasts** are easily visible.

- Draw *Elodea* and, if you observe slides of living material, describe the motion of the cytoplasm surrounding the vacuole.

Onion Epidermal Cells

Onions are the subterranean bulbs of onion plants. Prepare and stain red-onion epidermal cells for microscopic examination as follows:

- Cut a small piece of tissue from the outermost layer of the onion bulb provided by your instructor.
- The inner surface of the tissue is covered by a thin, almost transparent layer of epidermal cells. Using forceps, peel off a piece of this thin layer.
- Prepare a wet mount slide of the piece of epidermal tissue and observe under a compound light microscope.
- Draw several of the onion cells and label the **cell wall, nucleus, oil droplets, cytoplasm,** and **central vacuole.**

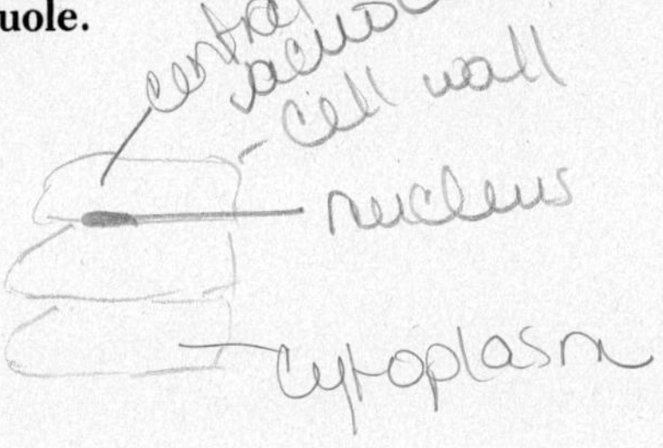

What shape are the cells?

Kind of oblong

Why are no chloroplasts visible?

Onions do not need the chloroplasts to use for photosynthesis or do they not need them for the green color.

- Place a drop of acetocarmine stain on one edge of the cover slip. Touch a piece of paper towel to the opposite edge to draw the stain under the cover slip. Acetocarmine stains the cell nucleus red. Focus up and down to get a three-dimensional impression of the tissue. Where is the nucleus of each cell relative to the cell wall?

The nucleus is up against the cell wall.

Human Squamous Epithelial Cells

The cells lining the mucous membranes of your mouth are easily sloughed off. They are called squamous ("scalelike") epithelial cells. Obtain a sample from yourself or one of your laboratory partners and observe it under the light microscope as follows:

- With a toothpick, gently scrape a small mass of cells from the inside lining of your cheek. Mix the mass of cells into a drop of water on a slide and add a small drop of methylene blue. Cover the stained mixture with a cover slip and observe under the compound light microscope.
  Note Because these slides contain saliva, be careful when handling them, and wash your hands afterwards. Dispose of them in the alcohol bath provided.
- Draw several cells and label the **nucleus, cell membrane,** and **cytoplasm.**

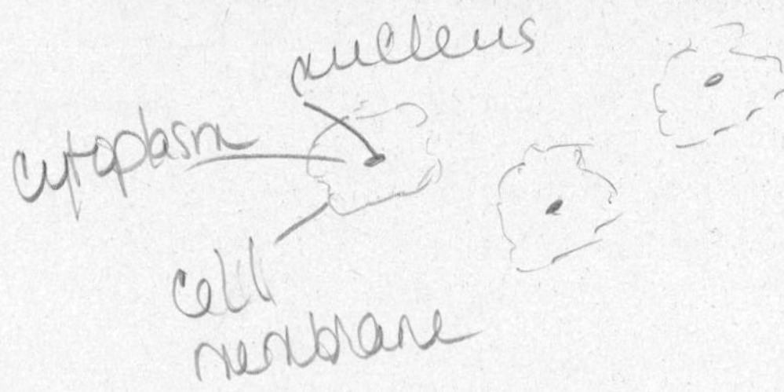

- Draw a cluster of cells that have not been separated from each other.

What structures are lacking or different from those you observed in a plant cell?

Plant cellshave a central vacuole and also they have chloroplasts

Based on the drawing you made of a cell cluster, describe the spatial orientation of cells in the intact lining of your mouth.

They are layered so as to provide protection to the inner mouth

EXERCISE 7-2 ELECTRON MICROGRAPHS OF CELL ORGANELLES

Objective To identify organelles and structures in electron micrographs of cells, and to describe the differences between prokaryotic and eukaryotic cells.

The internal structures of prokaryotic and eukaryotic cells are best observed with an electron microscope. Unfortunately, electron microscopes are quite expensive and too difficult to use in an introductory course. However, the electron photomicrographs in Figures 7-1 to 7-3 show the major internal features of a prokaryote, an animal cell, and a plant cell. You should be able to identify these structures in other electron photomicrographs.

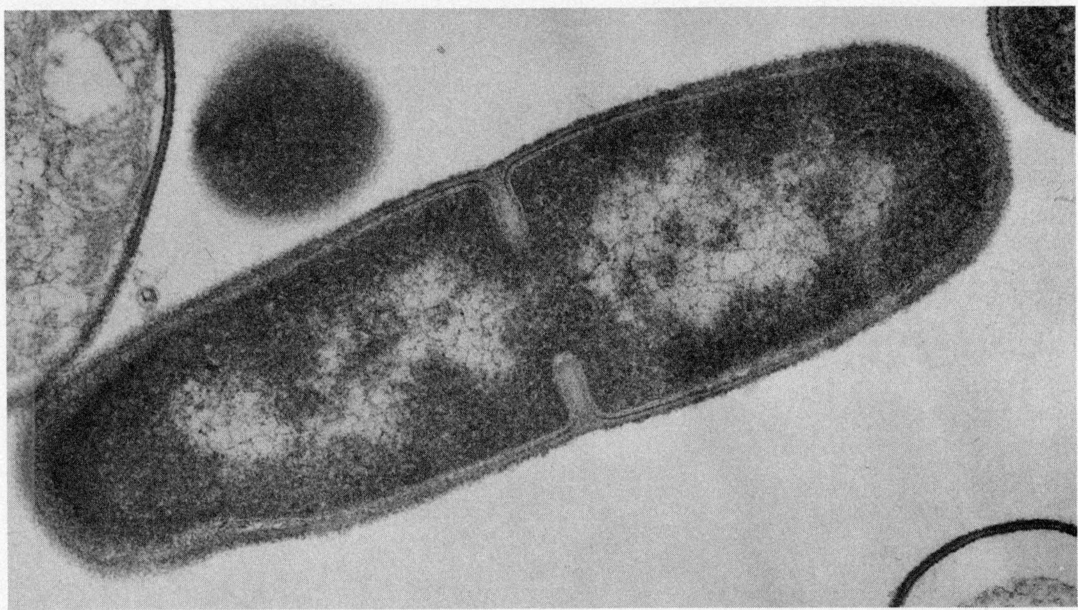

Figure 7-1 Prokaryotic cell. This bacterium is beginning binary fission, as evidenced by the septum that is starting to form.

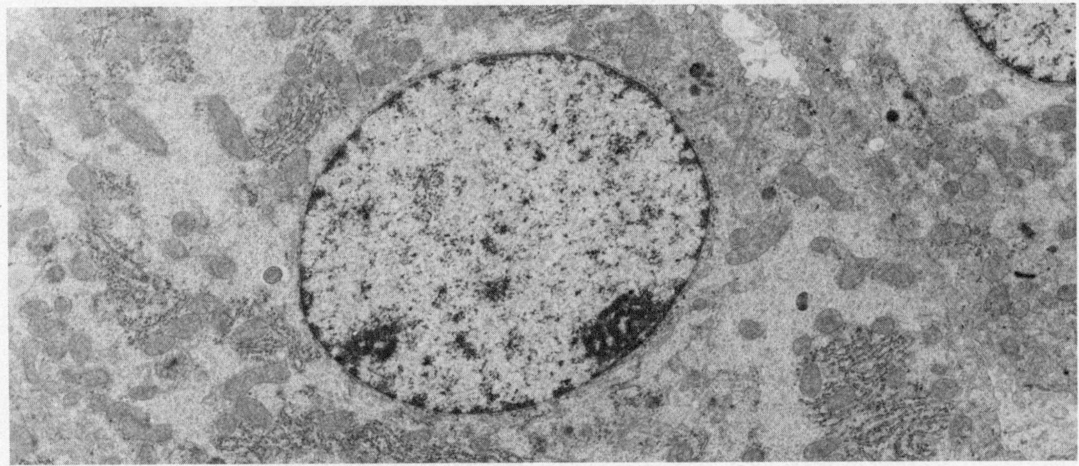

Figure 7-2 Eukaryotic animal cell.

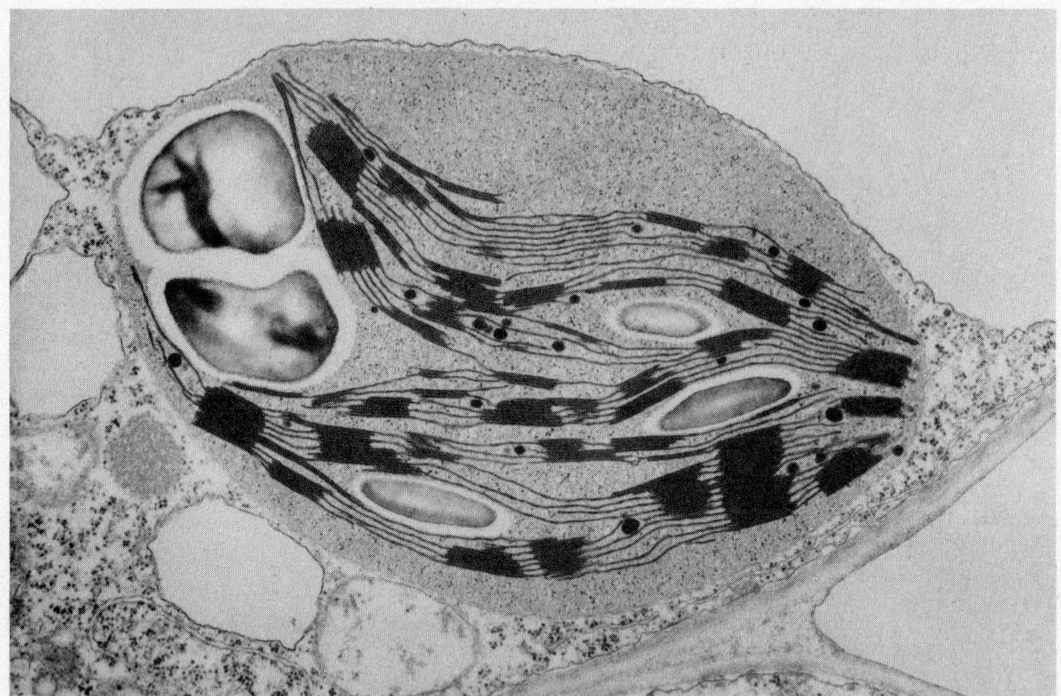

Figure 7-3 Eukaryotic plant cell.

- Briefly describe in Chart 7-1 the function of each structure.

Chart 7-1 Functions of internal features of cells.

Figure	Structure	Function of structure
7-1 (Prokaryotic cell)	Cell wall	protection, support
	Nuclear zone	contains DNA
	Ribosome	protein synthesis
7-2 (Animal cell)	Cell membrane	maintains wholeness, controls passage materials into-out of cell
	Cytoplasm	holds organelles, nutrients
	Nucleus, nuclear envelope with pores, and nucleolus	contains DNA controls passage materials to cytoplasm
	Ribosome	protein synthesis
	Endoplasmic reticulum	transports materials w/i cell
	Golgi complex	export materials packaging
	Lysosome	digestion & waste disposal system
	Mitochondrion	"powerhouse" of cell, energy-forming

(continued)

Chart 7-1 (continued) Functions of internal features of cells.

Figure	Structure	Function of structure
7-3 (Plant cell)	Cytoplasm	holds organelles, nutrients
	Ribosomes and endoplasmic reticulum	protein synthesis, modification, transportation
	Vacuole	food + fluid storage + processing
	Chloroplast	nutrient molecules built here
	Cell wall and plasma membrane	protection, support
	Thylakoid membranes	houses contains chlorophyll, enzymes, cofactors participate in photosynthesis
	Grana	houses contain enzymes required for photosynthesis
	Stroma	gas diffusion
	Starch granule	support
	Plasma membrane	regulation of flow of molecules into and out of cell

The material in this chapter corresponds to Chapter 5 in your text.

8
FERMENTATION AND CELLULAR RESPIRATION

Only through an intricate series of chemical reactions can cells extract energy from nutrient molecules. The "bottom line" in the conversion of nutrients into energy is the production of the cellular "currency" of **adenosine triphosphate,** or **ATP.** The energy-rich phosphate bonds of this molecule are used in the chemical reactions of the cell, from the construction of cell membranes and organelles to the synthesis of enzymes that control metabolism.

The energy contained in the bonds of nutrient molecules is transferred to high-energy phosphate bonds in ATP through a series of reactions called **oxidation-reduction reactions.** Universal to all cells is the series of these reactions called **glycolysis.** Glycolysis generates a small amount of ATP, but more importantly, it produces **pyruvate** molecules that are metabolized in either of two succeeding series of reactions. These series of reactions are called **fermentation** and **cellular respiration.** The following exercises demonstrate fermentation and cellular respiration in living yeast cells and in germinating bean seeds. You will detect the end products given off by fermentation and measure the uptake of oxygen used in cellular respiration.

EXERCISE 8-1 LOCALIZATION OF METABOLIC REACTIONS IN THE CELL

Objective To identify the regions of the eukaryotic cell where important processes of glycolysis, fermentation, and respiration occur.

The metabolic phases of glycolysis, fermentation, and cellular respiration occur in particular regions of the cell.

- Based on your reading in Chapter 7 of your textbook, indicate in Figure 8-1 where the following processes occur: glycolysis, fermentation, Krebs cycle, and electron transport chain.

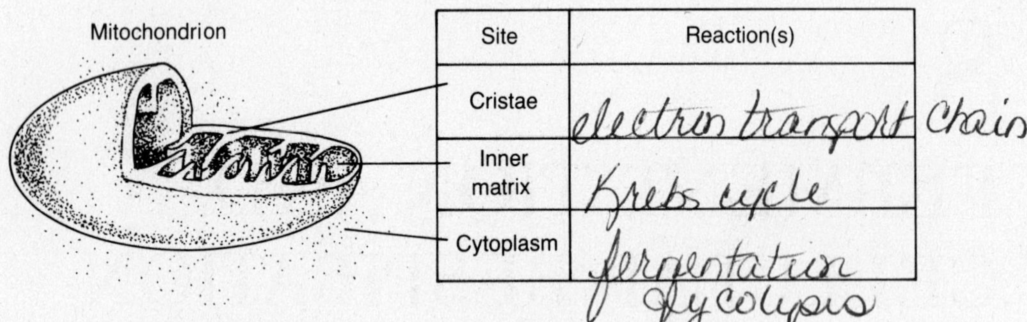

Mitochondrion
Site
Reaction(s)
Cristae
electron transport chain
Inner matrix
Krebs cycle
Cytoplasm
fermentation
glycolysis

Figure 8-1 Cellular sites of metabolic reactions in respiration.

EXERCISE 8-2 FERMENTATION

Objective To detect the end products of fermentation of sugar by living yeast cells.

Glycolysis produces ATP and pyruvate molecules through the breakdown of glucose. Fermentation uses this pyruvate to regenerate NAD^+, the essential cofactor for glycolysis. Fermentation thus produces no ATP directly, but if it did not regenerate NAD^+, the ATP-producing reactions of glycolysis would grind to a halt.

The end products of fermentation are NAD^+ and various kinds of organic compounds. Two familiar examples of fermentation occur in yeast and human muscle cells. In yeast, which is used to brew beer, pyruvate accepts electrons from NADH and is modified to ethanol and carbon dioxide:

$$\underset{\text{pyruvate}}{H_3C{-}\overset{\overset{\displaystyle O}{\|}}{C}{-}\overset{\overset{\displaystyle O}{\|}}{C}{-}OH} + NADH \rightarrow \underset{\text{ethanol}}{H_3C{-}CH_2{-}OH} + NAD^+ + CO_2$$

In hard-working muscle cells, a different end product, **lactic acid,** or **lactate,** is produced:

$$\text{pyruvate} + NADH \rightarrow \underset{\text{lactate}}{H_3C{-}\overset{\overset{\displaystyle OH}{|}}{C}H{-}\overset{\overset{\displaystyle O}{\|}}{C}{-}OH} + NAD^+$$

This reaction is a rapid means of metabolizing pyruvate and occurs in, for example, a sprinter's leg muscles, when not enough oxygen is available to utilize aerobic respiration to supply the short-term energy needs of the muscle.

The following exercise demonstrates anaerobic fermentation in yeast. Yeast cells are **facultatively aerobic;** they can use oxygen if it is present to metabolize sugars to carbon dioxide and water. If, however, no oxygen is available, yeast cells metabolize pyruvate to ethanol and carbon dioxide as shown in the equation above. You will place part of a yeast solution in anaerobic environments with various sugars and starch and observe the end products of yeast metabolism. Work in groups.

- Put 50 ml of the following solutions in five appropriately sized test tubes or graduated cylinders:

Tube	Contents
1	distilled water
2	10% glucose solution
3	10% sucrose solution
4	10% galactose solution
5	10% starch

- Place the test tubes in a rack (or line up the graduated cylinders) and add 5 drops of phenol red to each tube. Phenol red is a pH indicator that turns yellow in basic solutions and red in acidic solutions.
- Mix 10 ml of yeast solution into each tube.
- Carefully fill each of four small vials with the solution from each tube. Invert the vials and quickly slide them into the test tubes so that little if any air is trapped inside them. Record the length of any air space (in millimeters) trapped in the vial. Return the tubes to the rack. Record the color of the solution at time "0 min." for each tube in Chart 8-1.
- Observe the tubes and vials at 15-minute intervals. Record in Chart 8-1 any sign that gas has accumulated in the vials by estimating the length of the air space in the closed end of the vial. Subtract the length of any air space present at the start of the experiment and record the net increase of air space in Chart 8-1. Also record any color change in the yeast-sugar solutions.

Chart 8-1 Fermentation in yeast cultures.

Start 11:00	Length of air space at start	Net increase in air space (mm)	Color change
Tube 1			
0 min.	4 mm		milky yellow
15 min.	8 mm	+4	none
30 min.	8 mm	+4	none
45 min.	8mm	+4	none
60 min.	9mm	+5	none
Tube 2			
0 min.	5 mm		milky yellow
15 min.	7mm	+2	none
30 min.	7mm	+2	none
45 min.	9mm	+4	none
60 min.	9mm	+4	none

(continued)

Chart 8-1 (continued) Fermentation in yeast cultures.

	Length of air space at start	Net increase in air space (mm)	Color change
Tube 3			
0 min.	5 mm		milky yellow
15 min.	12 mm	+7	none
30 min.	12 mm	+7	none
45 min.	12 mm	+7	none
60 min.	13 mm	+8	none
Tube 4			
0 min.	4 mm		milky yellow
15 min.	4 mm	+0	none
30 min.	6 mm	+2	none
45 min.	8 mm	+4	none
60 min.	9 mm	+5	none

QUESTIONS

What gas accumulated in the tubes?

CO_2

Why does the evolution of this gas cause a color change in the solution in the tubes?

The CO_2 forms a carbonate which is an HCO_3 group then an H^+ comes off and goes into the solution so therefore the pH will drop.

In the space below, draw a bar graph showing the amount of gas accumulated in each tube. Indicate with vertical bars the net lengths of the air spaces that accumulated in each tube after 60 minutes. This type of bar graph is called a "histogram."

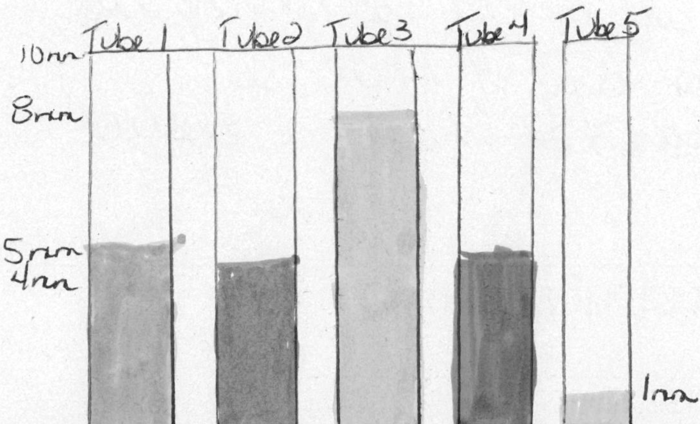

Assuming the volume of carbon dioxide produced is proportional to glycolytic activity, which sugar(s) were most completely metabolized by the yeast?

The 10% glucose solution was most completely metabolized by the yeast followed by the 10% galactose solution.

Was the yeast effective at breaking down starch? no On what do you base this conclusion?

Because the air bubble in the tube of starch didn't hardly grow at all.

Do the fermenting tubes give off an odor that you can identify? If so, what is it?

Yes. It smells like bread baking.

Beer brewers use germinating barley seeds ("malted" barley) in which starch stored in the seeds is converted to sugar in enzymatic reactions. Based on a comparison of the results in the tubes containing sugars compared to the results in the tube with starch, explain why using only malted barley is crucial to making beer.

If one used pure starch, it would take such an enormous amount and alot of sugar would be wasted because sugars are not completely metabolized by yeast.

Your observations involved the production of a gas and changes in pH in some of the tubes. In one or two sentences, state your assumptions regarding the end products that guided your interpretation of these results.

In our results we ended up having no color change on any of them, so therefore we cannot have a correct assumption

EXERCISE 8-3 CELLULAR RESPIRATION

Objective To demonstrate the uptake of oxygen by germinating bean seeds during cellular respiration.

Cellular respiration is far more efficient than fermentation in harvesting energy from nutrient molecules. Respiration uses oxygen as a final electron acceptor and oxidizes organic nutrients to carbon dioxide and water. The more complete oxidation of carbon atoms to carbon dioxide (rather than to lactate or ethanol as in fermentation) releases more of the energy in the molecules and results in a far higher yield of ATP.

Germinating bean seeds metabolize the nutrients stored in the seed. Oxygen is consumed in the process, and stored nutrients are oxidized to carbon dioxide and water. Thus, to measure the rate of metabolism in a germinating seed, we could measure the amount of oxygen taken up or the amount of carbon dioxide given off. Such measurements are made using a **respirometer.** You will be using a simple respirometer similar to the one shown in Figure 8-2. Your instructor will provide you with directions for its construction and use. The class will probably divide into small groups for this experiment.

As noted earlier, germinating seeds consume oxygen and produce carbon dioxide. Therefore, simply measuring the overall gas volume change in a flask of germinating seeds would only reveal *net* volume change, the difference between carbon dioxide given off and oxygen taken up. But one would not know the actual amounts of carbon dioxide produced and oxygen consumed. We solve this problem by putting a carbon dioxide trap in the respirometer. This trap consists of a layer of potassium hydroxide (KOH) pellets that absorb carbon dioxide from the air. Because the trap absorbs carbon dioxide produced by the seeds, any change in gas volume in the flask is due to a decrease in oxygen.

In this exercise, you will measure the amount of oxygen consumed by germinating bean seeds over a set period of time and calculate the volume of oxygen consumed per unit weight of seeds. To assess the effect of temperature on respiration, you will do 3–5 replicates at room temperature and 3–5 replicates at a warmer temperature. If time permits, you will also do replicates without a carbon dioxide trap to determine the amount of carbon dioxide given off by the seeds relative to the amount of oxygen consumed. The ratio of carbon dioxide produced to oxygen consumed is called the "respiratory quotient" (R.Q.).

- Take 10–15 germinating bean seeds and determine their mass. Record this information in Chart 8-2. Take an approximately equal mass of freshly boiled dead seeds or pebbles and record their mass in Chart 8-2.
- Take the tubes for the respirometer and place the live seeds in one and the boiled seeds or pebbles in the other. Insert a layer of cotton in each tube, then add 1–2 cm of KOH on top of the cotton.

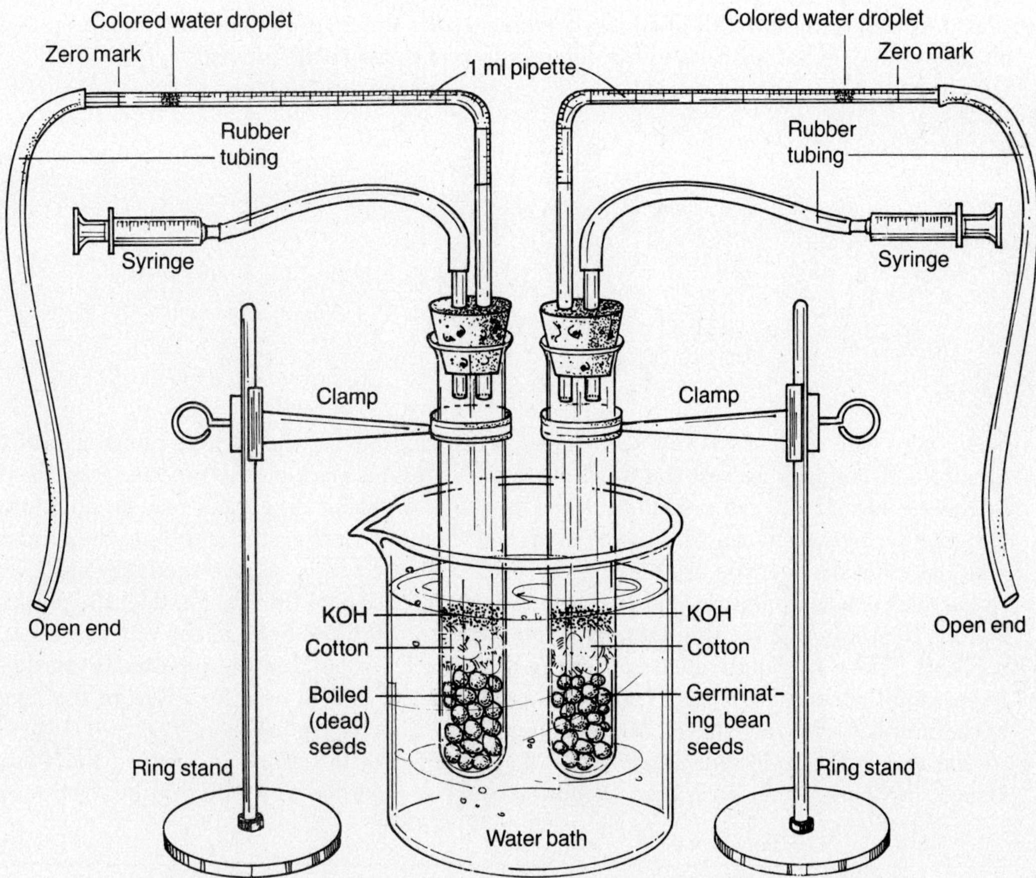

Figure 8-2 Respirometer to measure oxygen uptake of germinating seeds.

- Insert a two-holed rubber stopper in each tube. Take a 1-ml pipette and, holding it over the very low flame of a Bunsen burner, make a 90° bend about 4 m from the tapered end (at approximately the 0.8 ml mark). Allow the bent pipette to cool for several minutes. DO NOT USE WATER TO COOL THE PIPETTE—this will shatter it. Then rub a small amount of glycerin around the tapered end, being careful not to obstruct the opening. Holding the stopper in a paper towel (for protection) in one hand and the bent pipette in a paper towel in the other, insert the tapered end of the pipette into one of the holes in the wide end of the stopper by gently pushing and twisting. The end of the pipette should barely poke through the other side of the stopper. Now, again using glycerin as lubricant, insert a short, straight piece of glass tubing into the other hole in the plug. Insert the stopper into one of the two test tubes.
- Repeat these procedures to prepare a stopper for the other test tube.
- Clamp the tubes in place in the room-temperature water bath. The portion of each tube containing seeds or pebbles should be below the water line. Record the temperature of the water bath in Chart 8-2. Allow the tubes to sit in the water bath for 10 minutes to let the temperature in the tube equilibrate with that of the water.
- Next, attach a 10- to 15-cm piece of rubber tubing to the free end of the straight piece of glass tubing on one of the stoppers. Take a syringe without its needle and pull the plunger halfway out. Attach the syringe tip to the free end of the rubber tubing. Use a small pipette and bulb to transfer a drop of colored water from the stock solution to the free end of the bent pipette. Attach another 10- to 15-cm piece of rubber tubing to the free end of the bent pipette.
- Repeat these procedures for the other stopper.

- Both test tubes are now closed systems. Demonstrate this by slowly pulling out the plunger on the syringe. What happens to the colored drop of water in the pipette?

- Now, "zero" the drop of colored water in each tube by moving the syringe plunger until the meniscus of the drop nearest the test tube is at the 0.1 ml mark on the pipette. Practice this technique so that you can zero both drops at nearly the same time. (You may be able to use only one syringe if you can zero the drop on one tube, clamp the rubber tubing, then quickly zero the other drop. If you use only one syringe, zero the tube with live seeds second.)
- At the start of each replicate, zero the drop in each pipette, note the time, and let the replicate run for 10 minutes. If the droplet moves too quickly toward the bend in the pipette, stop the replicate before 10 minutes. Do not let the drop reach the bend in the pipette. If you do so, try to stop the run on a minute interval (for example, 6, 7, or 8 minutes). Record the length of the time interval and run the other replicates for this same interval.
- At the end of the replicate, measure the displacement of the drops and record the volume change in Chart 8-2 for each tube. Volume change is recorded as positive if the drop moves

Chart 8-2 Oxygen consumption in germinating bean seeds at room temperature.

Temperature of water bath = ______________ °C

Mass of germinating (live) bean seeds = ______________ g

Mass of boiled (dead) bean seeds or pebbles = ______________ g

Time interval = 10 minutes or ______________

	Volume change (ml)		
Replicate	Live seeds	Boiled seeds	Net volume change (live-dead)
1	______	______	______
2	______	______	______
3	______	______	______
4	______	______	______
5	______	______	______

Mean net volume change = ______________ ml

Mean net volume change per g = ______________ ml per g

Mean net volume change per g per minute = ______________ ml per g per minute away from the bend and negative if the drop moves toward the bend. Re-zero the drops and run two to four more replicates as time permits. Record the results in Chart 8-2. Calculate the net volume change (live-dead) in the right column.

- Replace the KOH in each tube and run another series of replicates using tubes immersed in a warm water bath (about 40°C). Allow the tubes to equilibrate at the warmer temperature for 10 minutes before running the first replicate. Record the temperature of the warm water bath and the results of the replicates in Chart 8-3. You may run these replicates for a shorter time interval than those at room temperature, but keep the interval constant for all replicates at a given temperature.
- To compare the volume changes for the room-temperature and the warm-water replicates, you must standardize the values by expressing them as average or mean ml volume change per gram of seeds or pebbles per minute. To standardize the values, perform the following calculations and record the values in the appropriate spaces in Charts 8-2 and 8-3. Calculate the mean net volume change for each set of replicates by adding the volume changes for all replicates at a given temperature and dividing the total by the number of replicates. Next, calculate the mean net volume change per gram of seeds or pebbles by dividing the mean net volume changes by the respective mass of seeds or pebbles. Finally, calculate the mean volume change per gram per minute by dividing the volume change per gram by the number of minutes in the respective time interval for each set of replicates.
- If time permits, run one or more replicates in the warm water bath, but this time remove the KOH from both tubes. Zero the drop at a starting mark near the center of the bent pipette and run the replicates for 5 minutes or less, depending on how quickly the drop moves. Record the results in Chart 8-4 and calculate the mean volume change per gram per minute. Remember, if the drop moves away from the bend, record the volume change as positive; if it moves toward the bend, record the volume change as negative.

Chart 8-3 Oxygen consumption in germinating bean seeds at warm temperature.

Temperature of water bath = ____________ °C

Mass of germinating (live) bean seeds = ____________ g

Mass of boiled (dead) bean seeds or pebbles = ____________ g

Time interval = 10 minutes or ____________

Replicate	Volume change (ml) Live seeds	Boiled seeds	Net volume change (live-dead)
1	____________	____________	____________
2	____________	____________	____________
3	____________	____________	____________
4	____________	____________	____________
5	____________	____________	____________

Mean net volume change = ____________ ml

Mean net volume change per g = ____________ ml per g

Mean net volume change per g per minute = ____________ ml per g per minute

Chart 8-4 Volume change in tubes of bean seeds without KOH carbon-dioxide trap.

Temperature of water bath = ____________ °C

Mass of germinating (live) bean seeds = ____________ g

Mass of boiled (dead) bean seeds or pebbles = ____________ g

Time interval = 10 minutes or ____________

	Volume change (ml)		
Replicate	Live seeds	Boiled seeds	Net volume change (live-dead)
1	________	________	________
2	________	________	________
3	________	________	________
4	________	________	________
5	________	________	________

Mean net volume change = ____________ ml

Mean net volume change per g = ____________ ml per g

Mean net volume change per g per minute = ____________ ml per g per minute

QUESTIONS

What was the control in this experiment? ____________

Explain how this provided a comparison to the experimental treatment.

Assuming that volume changes in the room-temperature and warm-water replicates (with KOH) were due to oxygen consumption, what do you conclude about the effect of temperature on respiration in these seeds?

Was there any variability between replicates at the same temperature? ____________ Can you suggest any reasons for this variability?

With KOH in the tube with live seeds, any volume change was caused by oxygen consumption by the seeds. Without KOH in the tube, carbon dioxide accumulated and the volume change was less. In fact, if a greater volume of carbon dioxide is produced than the volume of oxygen consumed, the drop will move the other way in the tube. The volume of carbon dioxide produced can be calculated using the measurements in Charts 8-3 and 8-4:

mean volume of CO_2 produced = mean net volume change per g per minute in tubes without KOH
− mean net volume change per g per minute in tubes without KOH

Calculate the R.Q. of the bean seeds:

$$\frac{\text{volume of carbon dioxide produced}}{\text{volume of oxygen consumed}} = \underline{\qquad\qquad}$$

R.Q. is often near 1 when carbohydrates are being oxidized completely. R.Q. is less than 1 when fats and oils are oxidized. Based on the R.Q. value you calculated, what do you conclude about the substances being oxidized by the seeds?

9 PHOTOSYNTHESIS

Photosynthesis is the basic means by which the living system of Earth captures energy from the sun. The process produces carbohydrates essential to plants as well as to the organisms that use plants as food, and it also yields oxygen needed for aerobic metabolism.

The net effect of photosynthesis, in which carbohydrates are synthesized, is essentially the chemical reverse of cellular respiration, in which carbohydrates are broken down to release energy. **Pigments** of various types absorb light photons; this process is the first event in a series of chemical reactions called the **light reactions. ATP** and **NADPH** generated during the light reactions are then used in the **dark reactions** to produce carbohydrates.

In the exercises in this chapter you will use **chromatography** to isolate individual pigments associated with photosynthesis. You will also measure the **absorption spectrum** of pigments extracted from a leaf. Finally, you will measure the production of oxygen by a living aquatic plant.

EXERCISE 9-1 CHROMATOGRAPHY OF PHOTOSYNTHETIC PIGMENTS

Objective To use chromatography to isolate pigments from a whole-leaf extract.

Imagine a group of people at the starting line of a race. According to the rules, some of them run, others walk, and others hop on one foot. The starting gun sounds and after a while you notice three distinct groups as the runners, walkers, and hoppers separate according to speed. Chromatography is analogous to such a footrace.

Chromatographic techniques separate the components of a mixture of chemical substances. A solvent carrying the mixture moves through a stationary phase—a special paper in this exercise—which has differential affinities for the components. Thus, as the solvent moves, some components are absorbed onto the stationary phase more readily than others and fall behind as the solvent front moves ahead. After a period of time the various components will have moved different distances through the stationary phase and appear as separate spots or bands.

In this exercise you will use chromatography to separate the pigments in an extract from a leaf.

- Use a razor blade to macerate the leaves provided by your instructor. Place the pieces in a blender with a small amount (20–30 ml) of acetone or ethanol. Run the blender at high speed to further macerate the pieces, then turn off the blender and allow it to sit for a few minutes while the bits of leaf settle. Pour the resulting green supernatant into a clean test tube. (Try not to pour any leaf bits into the test tube.) Cover the mouth of the tube with plastic wrap or paraffin film to prevent evaporation and set the tube aside in a rack.

- Next, obtain a sheet of chromatography paper from your instructor. This is the stationary phase you will use to separate the photosynthetic pigments. Carry the paper with forceps to avoid contaminating its surface with your fingers.

Your instructor may have you use thin-layer chromatography (TLC) instead of paper chromatography. In TLC, a glass surface such as a microscope slide is coated with a thin layer of a substance (silica gel is often used) that acts as the stationary phase. The slide is dipped almost completely into a slurry of silica gel and acetone and then set upright in a slide holder to dry. After the acetone evaporates, the silica gel is wiped off one side, and the thin layer on the other side is used as the stationary phase. Several slides may be made this way and used in lieu of a single sheet of chromatography paper. Avoid touching the silica gel to prevent contamination of the surface; also avoid breathing particles of the gel, which are essentially tiny pieces of glass. Consult your instructor for minor modifications in the following procedures if TLC is used.

- Lay the paper on a clean desktop and use a pencil to draw a straight **origin** line parallel to one side, 2–3 cm from the edge of the paper (Fig. 9-1a). Use the pencil to mark three or four tiny *x*'s, equally spaced along the line. Next, dip a capillary pipette in the tube of leaf extract. A small amount of fluid will flow into the pipette by capillary action. Lightly touch the pipette

(a)

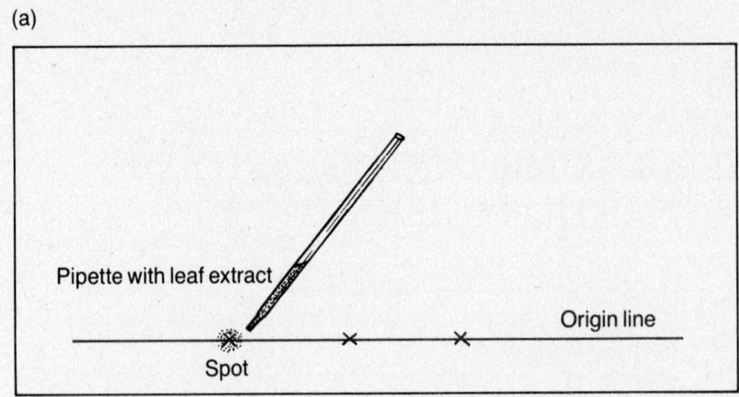

(b)

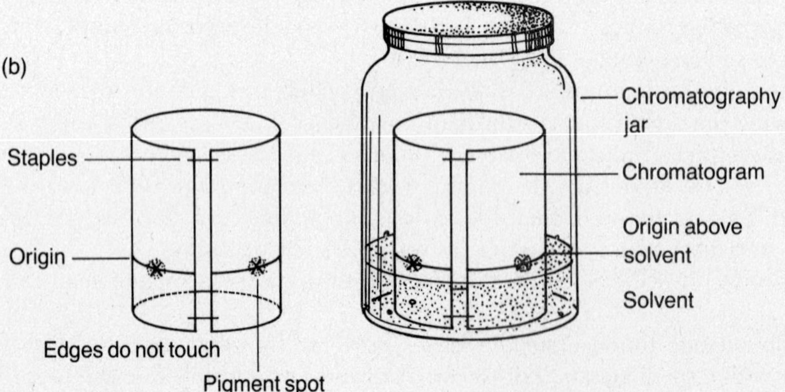

Figure 9-1 Preparation of paper chromatogram for separation of pigments in leaf extract. (a) Spotting the paper with leaf extract. (b) Placing chromatogram in solvent container.

tip to each x; do not touch the pipette to the paper for more than a moment. If your instructor has stock solutions of pigments prepared, spot the leaf extract on one x and the stock solution(s) on the others. Allow all the spots to dry. (A warm blow dryer will help.) Repeat the spotting procedure until you have accumulated a small, concentrated dark green spot of extract over each x. The paper and spots are called a **chromatogram.**

- Bend the chromatogram into an open cylinder, and staple or tape the edges so that it can stand on its own. Place the cylinder in the jar containing **solvent** (Fig. 9-1b). The paper should not touch the sides of the jar, and the solvent should not cover the origin line. Cover the container with a lid; the solvent, a 9:1 mixture of ether and acetone, is volatile and will quickly evaporate. The solvent is also flammable—DO NOT USE OPEN FLAMES NEAR THE SOLVENT.
- The chromatogram **develops** as the paper absorbs the solvent. Notice both the location of the **solvent front** as it moves upward on the paper, and the appearance of any spots behind the front. When the front is 2–3 cm from the top, take out the chromatogram and mark in pencil the location of the solvent front with an "f"; do this quickly because the front line disappears as the solvent evaporates from the paper. Outline the spots in pencil and number them in increasing order according to distance traveled from the origin. Fill in Chart 9-1 and calculate the R_f value for each spot using the equation:

$$R_f = \frac{\text{distance of spot from origin}}{\text{distance of solvent front from origin}}$$

R_f values can be used to identify compounds by spotting a chromatogram with several solutions and comparing R_f values for known substances with R_f values for unknowns. If you have spotted the chromatogram with stock pigment solutions as well as leaf extract, you can identify the components in the leaf extract directly by matching the locations of spots for the stock solutions to the location of spots for the leaf extract. Alternatively, your instructor may provide you with R_f values for known pigments. The colors of the spots also provide information on the identity of the pigments in them. For example, Chlorophyll *a* is grass green, Chlorophyll *b* is more-yellow green, and carotenes and xanthophylls are yellow to orange.

Chart 9-1 Data for developed chromatogram of leaf extract

Spot #	Color	Distance traveled from origin	Probable identity of compound
spinach	lgt green	45 mm	spinach
carotenoid	orange	74 mm	carotenoid
Chlorophyll	dk green	76 mm	Chlorophyll
Solvent front			

Spot #	R_f value
spinach	.55
carotenoid	.90
chlorophyll	.92

QUESTIONS

Is ether a polar or nonpolar solvent?

Ether is nonpolar.

What does this tell you about the relative polarity of the pigments and the distances they traveled relative to the solvent front?

Being that ether is nonpolar, the pigments than traveled with this substance.

When spotting the chromatogram, why weren't you asked to simply expel 1 ml of leaf extract onto each spot all at once?

The leaf extract would not be able to soak all of the way through and probably would not dry all the way through also.

EXERCISE 9-2 ABSORPTION SPECTRUM OF A WHOLE-LEAF EXTRACT

Objective To determine the ability of leaf pigments to absorb light of different wavelengths.

Actively photosynthesizing leaves are normally green because they reflect light in green wavelengths, whereas other wavelengths in the visible light spectrum are absorbed. We can measure the relative absorbance of light of different wavelengths by observing what happens as light passes through a solution of leaf extract.

The **spectrophotometer** is a device that exposes a sample solution in a glass tube or vial to a specific wavelength of light and measures the quantity of light that passes through the solution. The **transmittance** (T) of a sample is the ratio of radiant power transmitted by the sample to the radiant power of light entering the sample. The **absorbance** (A) of a sample is a measure of how much light entering a solution is absorbed by the chemical compounds (such as pigments) it contains.

Theoretically, photosynthetic pigments should absorb some wavelengths more effectively than others. Absorbance is related to transmittance by the formula:

$$A = \log 10 \, (1/T)$$

Absorbance is sometimes called **optical density.** Most spectrophotometers provide readouts of both A and T on the same meter, so you will not need to calculate one from the other.

Your instructor will provide you with specific directions for using the spectrophotometer in the laboratory. The following general instructions apply to a commonly used instrument, the Spectronic 20, often called the "Spec 20" for short (Fig. 9-2).

- Turn on the spectrophotometer and allow it to warm up.
- Special test tubes or vials are used in the spectrophotometer. Hold this kind of tube near the mouth to avoid smudging the sides; fingerprints interfere with readings of absorbance. Fill one tube to the level specified with clear supernatant from the leaf extract (sample) and one tube with clear acetone or ethanol solution (blank). Cover the mouths of both tubes with plastic wrap or paraffin film to prevent evaporation.
- Turn the wavelength control to 350 nm.
- Turn the zero control so that the meter needle points to "0" on the percent transmittance scale.
- Wipe off any dirt or fingerprints on the blank with a cleansing tissue. Insert the blank in the sample holder. Make sure the indicator line on the tube lines up with the corresponding line on the sample holder. Close the cover and adjust the light control until the meter reads 100 on the percent transmittance scale (zero on the optical density scale).
- Remove the blank and insert the sample and close the cover. Read absorbance (A) on the optical density scale (use the significant digits rule). Graph the value in Figure 9-3 and write the numerical value in the space below the graph.
- Remove the sample. Turn the light control down (counterclockwise) to protect the meter from burning out. Change the wavelength control to 375 nm. Insert the blank in the sample holder and close the cover. Turn up the light control so that the meter reads 100. Remove the blank, insert the sample and read absorbance at this new wavelength. Graph and record the value on Figure 9-3.

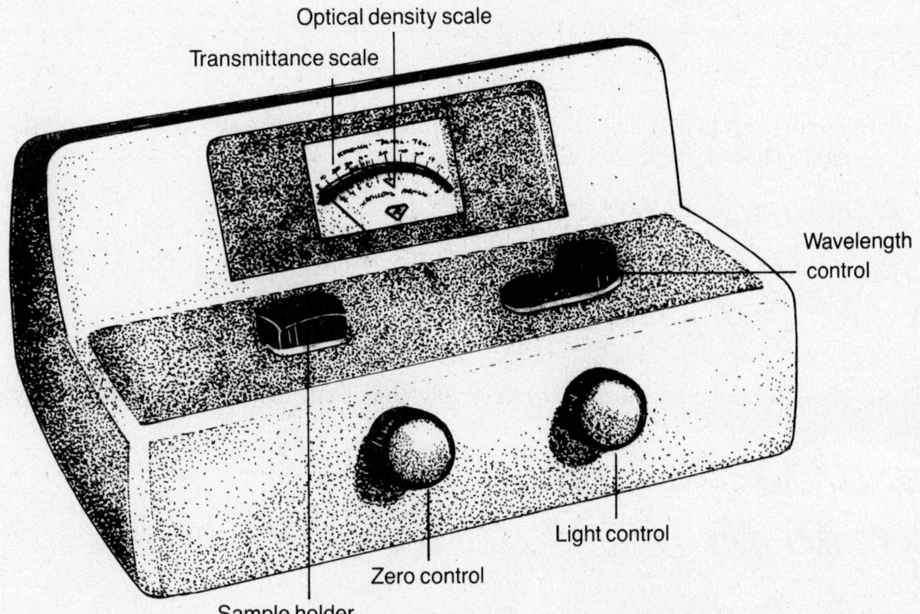

Figure 9-2 The Spectronic 20 spectrophotometer.

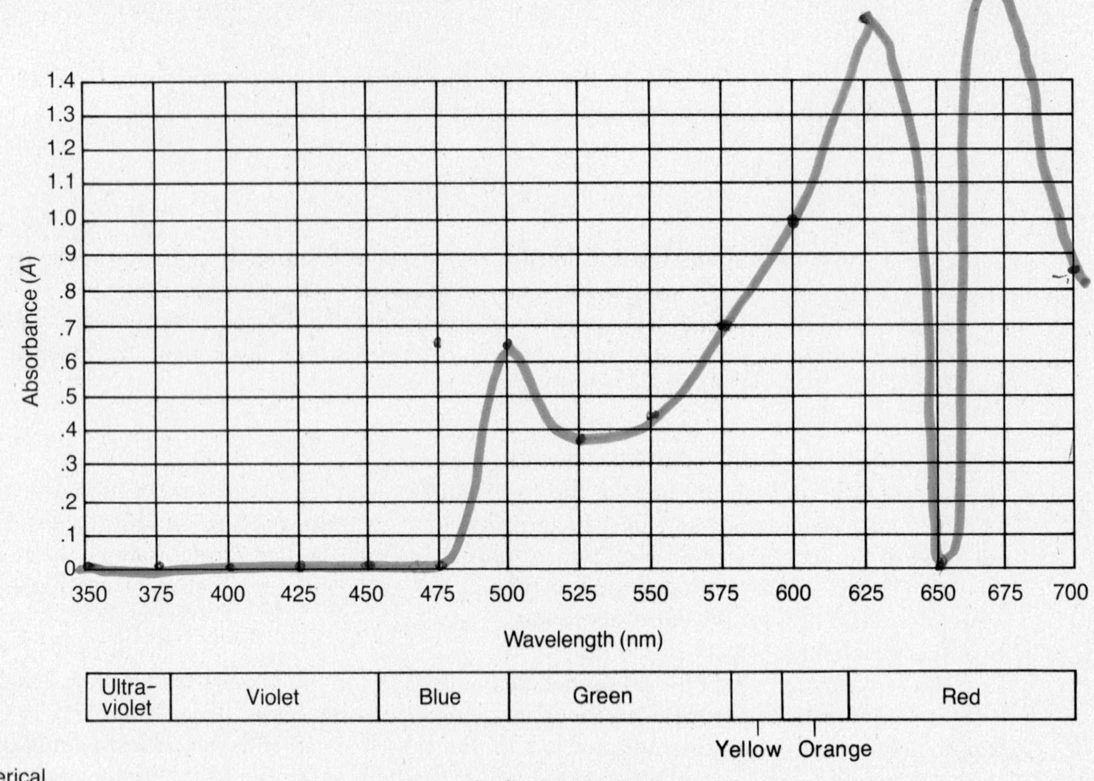

Numerical value of *A*: 0 0 0 0 0 0 .165 .37 .44 .7 1.0 1.6 0 1.7 .85

Figure 9-3 Absorption spectrum for leaf extract.

- Repeat at 25-nm intervals of wavelength up to 700 nm. Some models of the Spec 20 may require use of a different "red" phototube and filter for wavelengths above 625 nm. Consult your instructor for details.
- Connect the points in Figure 9-3 to draw a relatively smooth curve.

QUESTIONS

What wavelengths and hence "colors" of light are most effectively absorbed by the pigments in the leaf extract? (These are called **absorption maxima.**)

The orang and red colors of light are the most effectively absorbed by the pigments in the leaf extract

Which wavelengths and colors are least effectively absorbed? (These are called **absorption minima.**)

The ultra-violet, violet, and blue colors of light are the least effectively absorbed by the pigments.

What inferences can you make regarding the effect on photosynthesis of light of the wavelengths tested?

There are certain wavelengths that the characteristics ~~are not~~ of absorption minima are not met, ∴ no absorbance is created and likewise for the absorption maxima.

The absorption spectrum you have made is for whole-leaf extract. Suggest an experiment that tests differences in absorption spectra from chlorophylls compared to other carotenoid and xanthophyll pigments.

~~Just use all of the different carotenoids and xanthophyll pigments to instead of the chlorophylls and~~

Separate your chlorophylls from the carotenoids and the xanthophylls and then test ~~of~~ the absorbances of each and compare.

EXERCISE 9-3 OXYGEN EVOLUTION IN A LIVING PLANT

Objective To observe the effect of varying light intensity on photosynthesis in *Elodea*, an aquatic plant, by measuring oxygen production.

A simple way to measure photosynthetic rate in a plant is to observe net oxygen production by an aquatic plant, *Elodea* (also called *Anacharis* by fish hobbyists). You will vary light intensity in this experiment by placing the plant at different distances from a constant light source.

You can use the respirometer set-up from Chapter 8 to measure volume changes due to oxygen production. The *Elodea* produce oxygen via photosynthesis, but they also produce carbon dioxide and consume oxygen in respiration. Therefore, the several processes affect the volume change in a closed system like the respirometer. You can measure net oxygen production via photosynthesis by comparing the volume change in a tube with one *Elodea* sprig kept in the light and one in the dark. In the dark, volume changes are the difference between carbon dioxide produced and oxygen consumed:

$$\text{volume change in dark} = \text{ml carbon dioxide produced} - \text{ml oxygen consumed}$$

These same processes occur in a tube in the light, but oxygen is also produced via photosynthesis:

$$\text{volume change in light} = \text{volume change in dark} + \text{ml oxygen produced in photosynthesis}$$

So the net amount of oxygen produced via photosynthesis can be calculated as:

$$\text{net ml oxygen produced in photosynthesis} = \text{volume change in light} - \text{volume change in dark}$$

Notice that the volume change in the dark may be negative (more oxygen is consumed than carbon dioxide is produced); if so, the amount of oxygen produced in photosynthesis is greater than the net volume change in light. Also notice that you cannot measure total oxygen produced by photosynthesis because this technique does not measure the amount of oxygen consumed in the dark.

- Take two equal-sized sprigs of *Elodea*, blot them dry, and determine their masses. Clip off the bottom portions of the stems to make them equal in weight to within 0.1 g.
- Place each sprig, cut end up, in a large test tube to be used in the respirometer set-up. Fill the tubes two-thirds full with tap water. Wrap one tube up to the mouth in aluminum foil. Clamp the tubes to the ring stands and partially submerge them in the water bath. Prepare the stoppers as described in Chapter 8 and insert them in the tubes. Place the light source (a 300 W photoflood lamp or similar device) about 25 cm from the water bath. In between the lamp and the water bath, place a 1-L beaker of cool tap water to insulate the water bath from heat produced by the lamp. Turn on the lamp and allow the tubes to equilibrate with the syringes removed from the rubber tubing (so that each is open to room air).
- Replace the syringe in each piece of rubber tubing. In the dark tube, zero the colored water drop near the middle of the pipette. In the light tube zero the drop nearer the bend in the pipette. Explain why the drop should be located in these positions at the beginning of each replicate.

- Run three replicates for 5 minutes each. Record the data in Chart 9-2. Calculate the mean ml of oxygen produced and record the value in Chart 9-2. You may need to run the replicates for a longer or shorter amount of time depending on how fast the drop moves in the pipette, but keep the time period constant for all replicates.
- Another way of measuring oxygen production is to count the number of bubbles produced by the cut end of the *Elodea* sprig during a set period of time. Count the number of bubbles produced in a one-minute period during each of the three replicates. Record the data in the margin next to Chart 9-2. How do the counts compare to actual volume measurements?

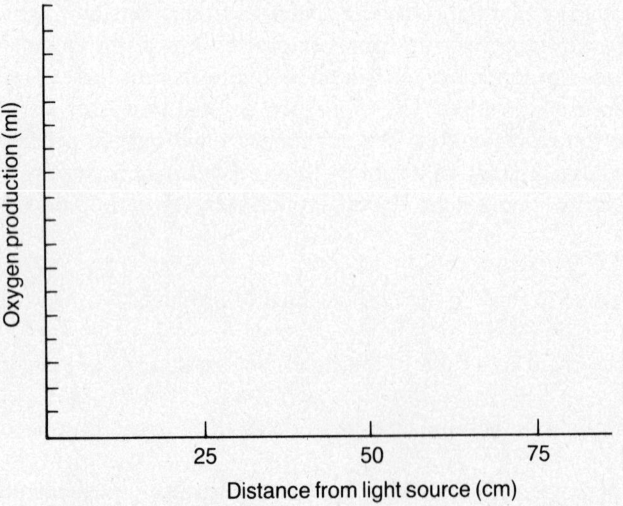

Figure 9-4 Oxygen production by *Elodea* at three distances from light source.

- After completing three replicates at 25 cm, move the lamp to 50 cm away and run three replicates. Then move the lamp to 75 cm away and run three replicates. Record the data in Chart 9-2, and calculate the mean ml oxygen produced at each distance. If the water in the 1-L insulating beaker becomes warm, replace it with cool tap water. If a light meter is available, measure the light intensity in foot-candles at each distance and record the values in Chart 9-2.

Chart 9-2 Oxygen production by *Elodea*.

25 cm from lamp

Replicate	Volume change (ml) in Light tube	Volume change (ml) in Dark tube	Net oxygen produced (ml) (light-dark)
1	________	________	________
2	________	________	________
3	________	________	________

Mean net ml oxygen produced = ________ ml

Light intensity = ________ foot-candles

50 cm from lamp

Replicate	Volume change (ml) in Light tube	Volume change (ml) in Dark tube	Net oxygen produced (ml) (light-dark)
1	________	________	________
2	________	________	________
3	________	________	________

Mean net ml oxygen produced = ________ ml

Light intensity = ________ foot-candles

75 cm from lamp

Replicate	Volume change (ml)in Light tube	Volume change (ml)in Dark tube	Net Oxygen produced (ml) (light-dark)
1	________	________	________
2	________	________	________
3	________	________	________

Mean net ml oxygen produced = ________ ml

Light intensity = ________ foot-candles

- Draw a bar graph (histogram) in Figure 9-4 of net oxygen produced at the three distances. The height of each bar should represent mean ml of oxygen produced for the three replicates at that distance. Use the data from Chart 9-2.

QUESTIONS

What effect does light intensity have on mean net volume of oxygen produced (photosynthetic rate)?

What is the relationship of light intensity to distance from the light source?

Which set of reactions (light or dark) are directly involved in oxygen evolution?

Why did you insulate the tubes from the heat of the light source?

EXERCISE 9-4 MICROSCOPIC STRUCTURE OF C_3 AND C_4 PLANTS

Objective To understand how leaf anatomy differs in C_3 and C_4 plants and how this anatomy affects photosynthesis under different environmental conditions.

On display are microscope slides of leaf cross-sections from C_3 and C_4 plants. Make a drawing of both types and label the following structures:

bundle sheath cells
cuticle
mesophyll
stoma
vein

C_3 plant **C_4 plant**

QUESTIONS

Where do the reactions of the Calvin-Benson cycle take place in C_3 plants? ____________ In C_4 plants? ____________

What enzyme occurs in this region of the C_4 leaf and not elsewhere? ____________

What gas is "pumped" to this region of the C_4 leaf? ____________

The anatomical specializations of C_4 plants are considered adaptations to a dry, arid environment. Explain the reasoning behind this conclusion.

The material in this chapter corresponds to Chapter 9 in your text.

10
MITOSIS AND MEIOSIS

The division of cells, like the Earth's turning, is so orderly and constant that we often take it for granted. The regular replication of genetic material (chromosomes) and the production of new cells are the bases of organismal growth and asexual and sexual reproduction. However, unlike the Earth's rotation, cell division occasionally goes awry. Sometimes the result is trivial—a few easily sloughed abnormal cells. Other times the results are more serious—rapidly dividing cancer cells or a sex cell with one too many chromosomes, which leads to serious malformation.

In order to understand such exceptions, the rule must be studied; that is, the rule of normal, orderly cell division and the apportioning of chromosomes and cytoplasm that it entails. In the following exercises you will study the processes of cell division—mitosis and meiosis—through which new cells with a normal complement of chromosomes arise.

The cell cycle

Individual cells grow, prepare for division, and divide in an orderly progression of events called the **cell cycle.** Distinct phases occur in the cell cycle (Fig. 10-1). The $\mathbf{G_1}$ (gap 1) phase is cellular "business as usual." The various components of normal cellular metabolism are synthesized and used. During the **S** phase, these regular processes also occur, but in addition the DNA in the nucleus is replicated (doubles in amount). **Histones** and other proteins synthesized in the cytoplasm move into the nucleus and combine with the DNA to form the **chromatin** that makes up **chromo-**

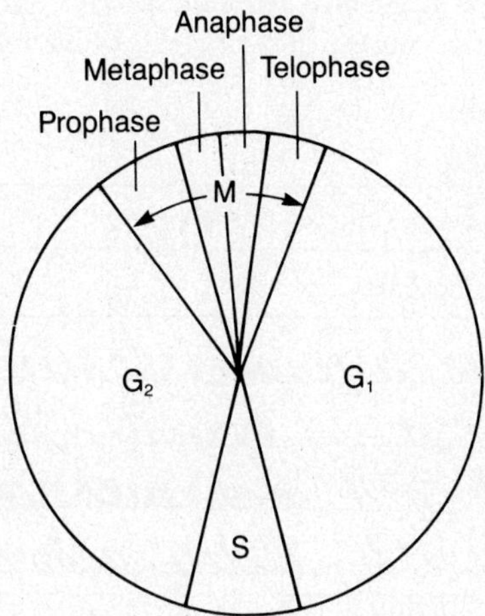

Figure 10-1 The cell cycle.

(a)

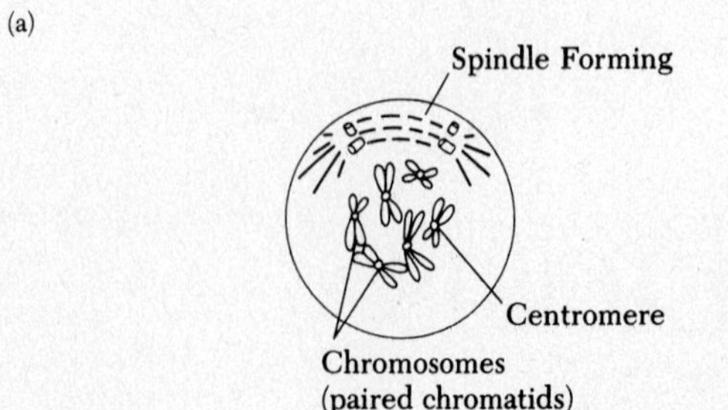

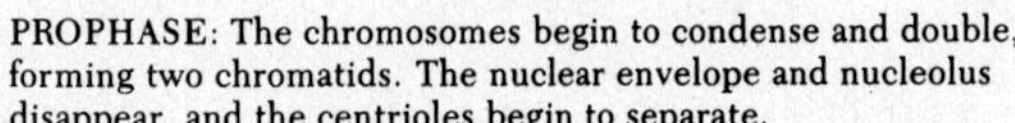
PROPHASE: The chromosomes begin to condense and double, forming two chromatids. The nuclear envelope and nucleolus disappear, and the centrioles begin to separate.

(b)

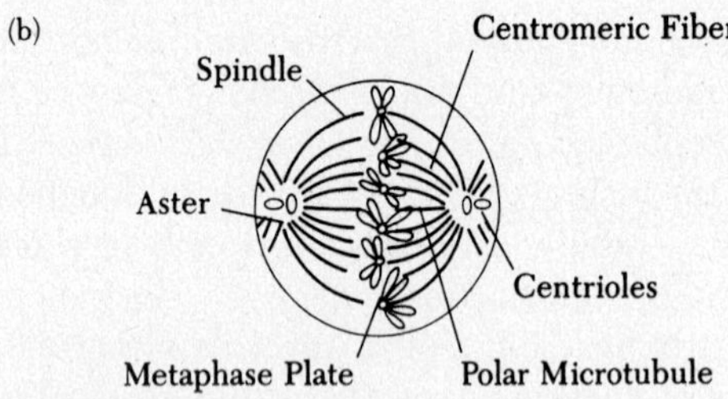

METAPHASE: The centrioles have organized the spindle microtubles, which cause chromosomes to align on the metaphase plate.

(c)

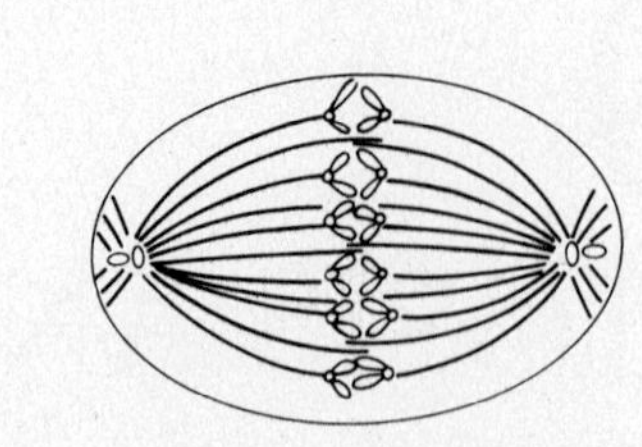

ANAPHASE: The centromeres separate, and each pulls along a single attached chromatid toward a spindle pole.

(d)

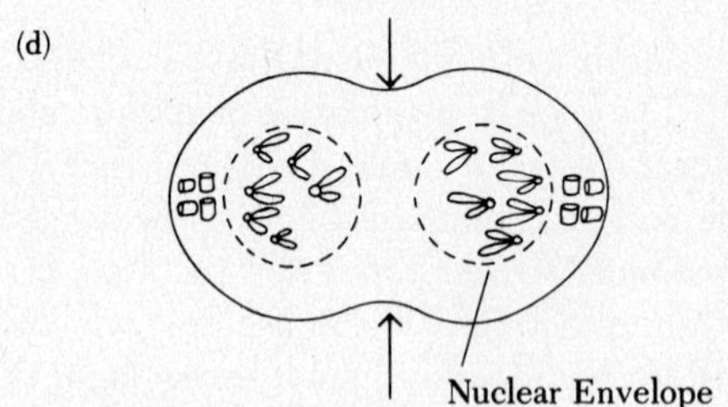

TELOPHASE: The chromatids reach the poles, and two nuclei form. The division of the cytoplasm begins.

Figure 10-2 The phases of mitosis (M phase).

somes. Each chromosome now consists of two identical sister **chromatids.** The G_2 phase follows S and is similar to G_1 in that normal cell metabolism occurs. Throughout G_1, S, and G_2 (collectively called **interphase**), the cell may increase in size.

These larger cells with a doubled DNA content are now ready for **mitosis**—the **M** phase, or actual division phase. The chromosomes condense into rods of tightly compacted DNA and histones. The chromosomes come together at the center of the cell, then separate so that each **daughter cell** contains a complete set of chromosomes. Each chromosome, in contrast to its condition before mitosis, now consists of only a single chromatid. As you saw in Figure 10-1, the M phase often takes up only a small proportion of the cell cycle.

The M phase is subdivided in turn into the four phases shown schematically in Figure 10-2. Based on your reading and lecture notes, describe the behavior of the chromosomes during each phase in Chart 10-1.

Chart 10-1 Behavior of chromosomes during the M phase.

Phase	Behavior of chromosomes
Prophase	Chromatin condenses, chromosomes become visible
Metaphase	Chrom. assoc w/ spindle & line up in center of cell
Anaphase	Chromatids split and each moves toward diff poles
Telophase	Chrom. uncoil & become attached to nuclear lamina

Following mitosis, the second step of cell division occurs. The cytoplasm and its other cell contents divide in the process of **cytokinesis.** In animals, the parental cell is pinched off in the middle to yield two equal-sized daughter cells. Cytokinesis in plant cells involves the building up of a **cell plate** between the newly divided nuclei. The cell plate eventually forms the new cell membranes and cell wall. Cytokinesis does not always follow mitosis (nuclear division), however. Some animal tissues are normally multinucleate; for example, human liver cells. Many algae and fungi are coenocytic and contain numerous nuclei in a continuous mass of cytoplasm. In many plants (and a few animals) **polyploid** forms occur that have double (or higher multiples of) the normal number of chromosomes per cell. Polyploids often form through an altered form of meiosis in which diploid (2n) gametes are formed instead of the normal haploid (n) types.

EXERCISE 10-1 MITOSIS IN PLANT CELLS

Objective To observe and describe the phases of mitosis in onion root tip cells.

Although mitosis may occur millions of times each day in a plant body, cells divide more frequently in certain parts of the plant than others. These growing regions or **meristems** are usually localized in root and shoot tips and in certain areas of the stem. (Meristems will be discussed in detail when we consider plant anatomy in Chapter 22.) Microscope slides of thin sections of these meristematic regions contain a high proportion of dividing cells.

You will use such slides of onion root-tip cells to observe the phases of mitosis in meristematic tissue. Onion root-tip cells are chosen not only for their high frequency of mitosis, but also because they contain large, well-defined chromosomes.

- Your instructor will provide you with prepared slides of onion root tips. Prepared slides contain thin sections of root tips stained with a dye that reveals chromosomes as dark rods.
- Scan the root tip under low power and draw it below. Note the **root cap,** a pyramid of loosely organized cells at the very tip of the root. The root cap covers the blunt end of the root, which itself surrounds regions of cells of increasing length.

Onion root tip

- Switch to high power and look for the region of the root tip with the most dividing cells. You will recognize these cells by the distinct rodlike chromosomes within them. Label this meristematic region on your drawing of the root tip.
- Cells do not divide synchronously, and different cells will be in different phases of mitosis. Pick out and draw a cell that best displays each of the four phases you saw in Figure 10-2 (prophase, metaphase, anaphase, and telophase*). Draw the cells in the following spaces and show the correct number of chromosomes for onion cells. Include a scale bar, and label the structures listed for each phase.

*A handy mnemonic device to remember the order of phases in mitosis—including interphase—is: "The *inter*national *pro* *met* *Ana* (or *Ana*tole) on the *telo*phone."

Remember that mitosis is a more or less continuous process; cells do not progress jerkily from one phase to the next like stops on a subway. The named phases are guideposts for our own understanding of the process.

Interphase

nucleus

nucleolus

Prophase

nucleus

condensing chromatin

Metaphase

chromosomes

chromatids

metaphase plate

spindle

spindle poles

Anaphase

chromosomes (single chromatids)

centromeres

spindle

spindle poles

Telophase

nuclear envelope

daughter cells

chromatin

- Scan the root tip from left to right and score 100 cells according to the phase of mitosis they appear to be in. Some cells may appear to be intermediate between two phases; put them in the category in which they fit best or score one-half a count each of the phases. Tally your scores in Chart 10-2.

Chart 10-2 Number of cells in phases of mitosis in onion root tip.

Interphase	Prophase	Metaphase	Anaphase	Telophase
49	31	7	8	5

Make a pie chart showing the proportion of cells in each phase of mitosis.

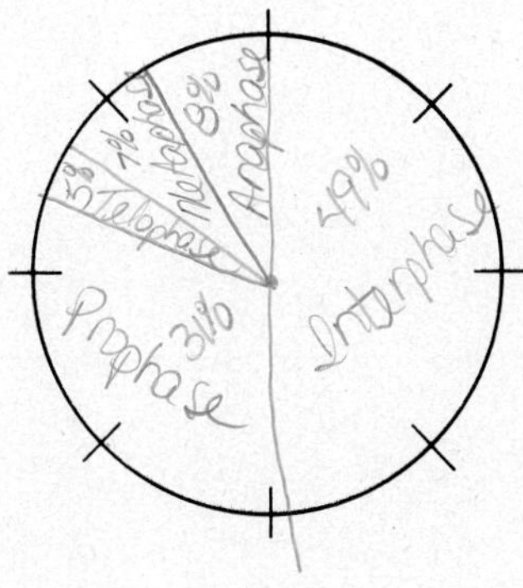

QUESTIONS

What material is likely to be the darkly stained portion of the chromosomes?

It is the protein located in the chromosome.

What is your best estimate of the number of chromosomes in a diploid onion cell?

Our best estimate was 4 chromosomes in a diploid onion cell.

Which phase of mitosis is best for counting chromosomes? Why?

Anaphase. Because as the chromosomes were pulling apart, we were able to count the single chromatids much more clearly than the other phases.

Describe the orientation of the spindles. Are they the same relative to one another (do they point in the same direction)? ___Yes___ What effect is this likely to have on growth of the root?

The growth would only go in one direction, So the root would go down into the ground.

Refer to your drawings and write a sentence describing each of the phases of mitosis in onion root tip cells.

Interphase

The nucleus and nucleolus are apparent and the chromatin has bunched together in one area.

Prophase

The nuclear envelope is starting to disappear, the nucleus is appearing fainter and chromatin is beginning to condense.

Metaphase

The chromosomes are beginning to line up along the metaphase plate in the center and spindle is now apparant

Anaphase

The single chromatids begin to move to either side of the cell, spindle is apparant.

Telophase

The nuclear envelope begins to reappear, cell wall plate of cell is apparent, and chromatin is again recondensed.

Refer to the pie chart you drew. What do you conclude about the timing of the various phases of mitosis in root tip cells?

A cell spends most of its time in interphase followed by prophase and only a little time in the rest of the three phases.

EXERCISE 10-2 MITOSIS IN ANIMAL CELLS

Objective To observe and show stages of mitosis in whitefish embryos and to compare the process to mitosis in plant cells.

Animals lack the well defined meristematic regions found in plants, but certain cell types are useful for observing mitosis. Blastulae (singular: blastula) are early-stage embryos that contain many actively dividing cells. They are hollow balls of cells.

- Your instructor will provide you with prepared slides of whitefish blastulae. Observe them under the compound microscope.
- Scan the slide under low power and sketch the blastulae as they appear on the slide.

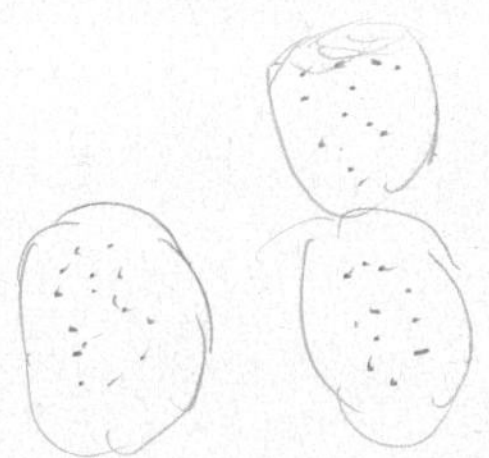

Find representative cells in each of the phases of mitosis and draw them in the spaces provided. Label the structures listed next to each phase.

Interphase
cell membrane

Prophase
nucleus
chromatin

Metaphase
chromosomes
metaphase plate
spindle
spindle fibers

Anaphase
chromosomes
spindle
spindle fibers

Telophase

chromosomes

daughter cells

As you did with the onion root tip, score 100 cells of the whitefish blastulae according to the phase of mitosis they appear to be in. Tally the results in Chart 10-3.

Chart 10-3 Number of cells in phases of mitosis in whitefish blastulae.

Interphase	Prophase	Metaphase	Anaphase	Telophase
44	31	15	6	4

Again, make a pie chart showing the proportion of cells in each phase of mitosis.

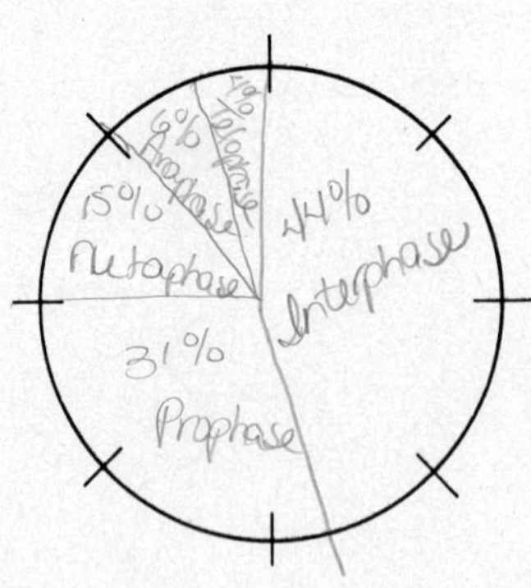

QUESTIONS

Is the nucleus visible in cells of a blastula?

Yes it is in the prophase state.

Compare the orientation of spindles in whitefish cells with the orientation of spindles in onion cells. What does this suggest about growth patterns in the two organisms?

the spindles in the whitefish cells go into different directions. the whitefish would appear to grow at into different ways in order to keep the shape of the organism.

Estimate the diploid number of chromosomes in whitefish blastulae. 6 Why is this estimation more difficult than in onion root tip cells?

the chromosomes appear to be smaller and more closely condensed

Refer to the two pie charts you completed earlier. Describe any differences in the timing of the phases of mitosis in whitefish compared to the timing of mitotic phases in onion root tips.

Interphase and prophase are still the two longest phases although metaphase appears to be longer in the whitefish cells and anaphase and telophase are almost the same.

List in Chart 10-4 at least four differences between mitosis in whitefish blastulae and mitosis in onion root tip cells. These differences may involve the presence or absence of structures.

Chart 10-4 Differences between mitosis in whitefish blastulae and onion root tips.

	Whitefish blastulae	Onion root tips
1.	furrowing occurs	cell wall plate forms
2.	forms centrioles	doesn't form centrioles
3.	forms asters	doesn't form asters
4.		

EXERCISE 10-3 THE CHOREOGRAPHY OF MEIOSIS

Objective To simulate the general process of meiosis and understand the differences between this process and mitotic cell division.

So far, you have been observing **diploid** cells (with $2n$ chromosomes) dividing asexually to produce more identical diploid cells. However, another type of cell division is needed to produce **haploid** sex cells (with n chromosomes). **Meiosis** accomplishes the **reduction division** in cells.

To demonstrate the choreography of chromosomes in meiosis, you will simulate meiosis by literally walking through it.

Activities

- Divide the class into even-numbered groups of at least six people. Alternatively, the entire class may choose to play a diploid cell of $n = 20$ or more chromosomes. Two people in each group play the roles of the centrioles, or "studentrioles." Each studentriole obtains a ball of yarn and scissors or razor blade from the instructor.
- Each student other than the studentrioles picks an identification badge from a box and attaches it to his or her arm. The badges come in pairs; each student is now one of a pair of homologous chromosomes or "studentsomes." One student is a maternal studentsome, the other a paternal studentsome. Each maternal studentsome obtains four blue marbles, representing four genes; each paternal studentsome obtains four red marbles, representing the same four genes, but colored differently to show that they come from the paternal chromosome.
- The instructor or a designated unpaired studentsome calls out the phases of meiosis. Proceed according to the following directions. As with square dancing, this exercise may need to be done more than once to go smoothly. Fill in the blanks as you proceed or afterward by referring to your text.
- **Interphase I** Chromosomes are dispersed throughout the room (or section of the room if more than one group or cell is involved). Chromatin is not condensed at this stage, but this is not possible to represent with a nonstretchable studentsome. During late Interphase I, the ______________ phase of the cell cycle, DNA replication occurs. Just prior to entering Prophase I, each studentsome consists of two ______________ joined at the ______________. (Since humans cannot divide asexually, assume each studentsome has successfully completed this process.)
- **Prophase I** Homologous studentsomes find each other. This activity represents ________ of homologous studentsomes. Corresponding regions of studentsomes associate in the ______________ ______________, which later dissolves in late Prophase I. **Crossing over** takes place at Prophase I. This is represented by the exchange of one or more colored marbles between homologous studentsomes. Homologous studentsomes dissociate, and in late Prophase I pairs begin to migrate to the center of the room.
- **Metaphase I** Pairs of studentsomes are now arranged in a line at the center of the room or room section at the ______________ ______________. Each of the two studentrioles attaches a spindle fiber (piece of yarn) to the waist of one studentsome from each homologous pair. This point of attachment represents the ______________. Whether a particular studentriole attaches a spindle fiber to a maternal or paternal studentsome is determined by a coin flip or other random process. The studentrioles now take positions at the ______________ ______________ at opposite sides of the room or room section, drawing out their spindle fibers with them. (In a more accurate portrayal of meiosis the studentrioles would not have moved from these positions to attach the spindle fibers to studentsomes.)
- **Anaphase I** Studentrioles shorten the spindle fibers, separating homologous studentsomes.
- **Telophase I** Half the studentsomes are now gathered at each pole, and each pole should have only one representative from each pair of homologous studentsomes.
- **Cytokinesis I** A piece of yarn should be used to demarcate the new cell boundary.

- **Interphase II** Studentsomes again disperse but only within the confines of each daughter cell.
- **Prophase II** Studentsomes recondense and begin to approach the center of the cell.
- **Metaphase II** Studentsomes line up at the ______________ ______________, which is perpendicular to the new cell boundary and also perpendicular to the orientation of this same structure in Metaphase I. Remember, each studentsome actually consists of a pair of ______________. Pursuing the analogy used in your textbook, we will represent this pair of chromatids with the pair of shoes on each student. Remove your shoes and line them up on the ______________ ______________. (Because of spilled chemicals or bits of broken glass on the floor, your instructor may choose to represent chromatids with sticks or some other item.) Each daughter cell from the earlier meiotic division has one studentriole, who plays the role of the two studentrioles of Metaphase II and acts as a spindle. Each studentriole attaches one end of a spindle fiber (piece of yarn) to each shoe or other chromatid equivalent in the cell and the other end to one of the spindle poles.
- **Anaphase II** The studentriole in each cell shortens the spindle fibers and separates the chromatids, moving half to each pole.
- **Telophase II** Each pole now has a haploid number of chromatids, one half the original diploid number of studentsomes. Also, each pole has one shoe-chromatid from each pair.
- **Cytokinesis II** A second cell boundary (piece of yarn) forms in each of the two daughter cells produced in Meiosis I. The room or room section should now be divided into four daughter cells, each with a haploid number of shoe-chromatids.

QUESTIONS

How many studentsomes at the spindle pole in Telophase I were paternal homologs? __________

How many were maternal homologs? ______________ If you started over, how likely is it that the same groups of studentsomes would end up at the same poles? ______________ Are the chances of this affected by the number of studentsomes? Explain.

Explain how the apportioning of maternal and paternal studentsomes in meiosis resulted in chromosome complements in the gametes that were different from the original maternal and paternal chromosome complements.

Independent segregation of chromosomes contributes to genetic diversity between gametes by mixing up maternal and paternal chromosomes. Crossing over, the exchange of segments between nonsister chromatids at Prophase I, also contributes to genetic diversity. Explain how this was demonstrated by the exchange of colored marbles between homologous studentsomes.

If you had choreographed mitosis instead of meiosis, how would the arrangement of homologous studentsomes at Metaphase I have differed from the arrangement in this exercise?

In which meiotic division (Cytokinesis I or II) is the chromosome number reduced to the haploid level?

List at least three differences between the behavior of chromosomes in mitosis and meiosis.

1.

2.

3.

EXERCISE 10-4 MEIOSIS IN ANIMAL CELLS

Objective To observe prepared slides of the stages of meiosis in animal cells.

The process of mieosis is readily observed in the parasitic roundworm *Ascaris*. The sperm of *Ascaris* form through a process of **spermatogenesis** that is basically similar to the process choreographed in Exercise 10-3. A single **primary spermatocyte** divides in meiosis I to produce two **secondary spermatocytes,** each of which produces a pair of haploid **spermatids** (Fig. 10-3a). Each spermatid matures into a **sperm.**

In contrast to the process in males, meiosis in a **primary oocyte** produces only one egg through the process of **oogenesis** (Fig. 10-3b). A primary oocyte undergoes meiosis I to produce a haploid **secondary oocyte** and a small **polar body.** The secondary oocyte undergoes meiosis II to produce an **ovum** and another polar body. (In some organisms, the first polar body also undergoes a second meiotic division and yields two polar bodies. In any case the one to three polar bodies do not function as eggs.) In *Ascaris* and many other organisms, meiosis is arrested at some stage until a sperm penetrates the oocyte. After fertilization, meiosis proceeds to completion and the sperm fuses with the ovum.

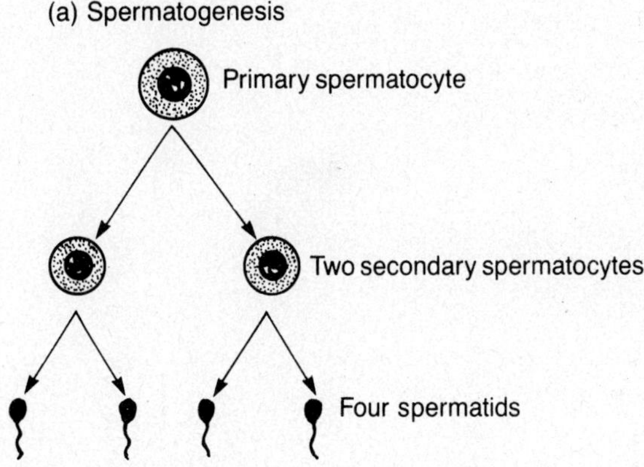

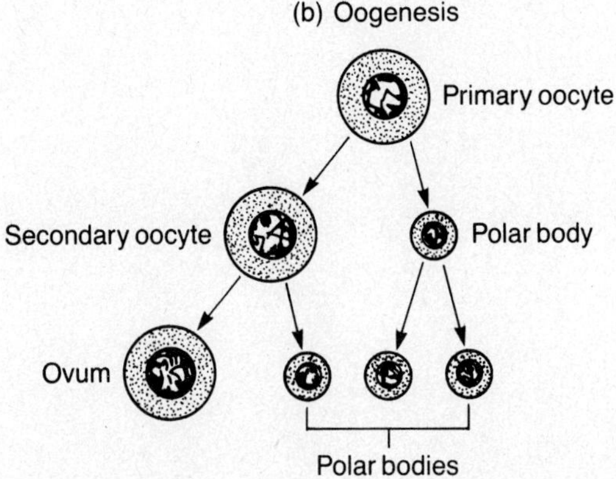

Figure 10-3 Meiosis in spermatogenesis and oogenesis.

- Your instructor will have slides of the stages in meiosis in *Ascaris* ovaries available for you to observe under the compound microscope. Sketch the stages below. *Ascaris* cells contain a diploid complement of $2n = 4$ chromosomes. Label each stage n or $2n$ according to the number of chromosomes it contains. Sketch polar bodies if visible.

Primary oocyte

Secondary oocyte

Ovum

The material in this chapter corresponds to Chapter 10 in your text.

11 GENETICS I. MONO- AND DIHYBRID CROSSES

Biologists, like other scientists, construct conceptual **models** to explain biological processes. These models are basically similar to the **theories** described in Chapter 1 of this manual. A model involves a number of assumptions; a scientist uses the assumptions to predict the logical outcome of a proposed experiment or set of experiments. Models may be stated in words or mathematical equations. Some very complex models are contained in computer programs, hence the term **computer models.**

The assumptions in a model may be well founded ("Corn kernel color is assumed to be determined by the action of a series of alleles at a single gene locus"). Other assumptions may be true in certain cases but not others ("Mating between corn plants is assumed to be completely random"). Some assumptions are intended to simplify a complex situation so that straightforward predictions can be made (for example, "Mutations affecting corn kernel color are so rare that it is assumed they will not interfere with the results of a short-term experiment"). If the outcome of an experiment does not match the predictions, then the assumptions are wrong or too simplified to be useful.

The exercises in this chapter use mathematical models of monohybrid and dihybrid crosses to predict the outcome of corn-breeding experiments. These models are tested using a nonbiological system (bean-bag genetics) and a biological one (kernels on natural corn cobs).

EXERCISE 11-1 THE LAW OF SEGREGATION: THE MONOHYBRID CROSS

Objectives To demonstrate the segregation of alleles at a single gene locus using bean-bag genetic models and to test the predictions of a model of a monohybrid cross by observing and counting corn kernel phenotypes.

A monohybrid cross involves breeding two individuals (or populations of individuals) to investigate different alleles at a single locus. In the monohybrid cross that you will study, one parent is homozygous recessive and one is homozygous dominant for a single trait. ("Mono" refers to the single trait; "hybrid" refers to the combination of nonidentical alleles resulting from the cross between the two parental types.) The homozygous recessive individual is symbolized by two lower case letters, such as *aa*, while the homozygous dominant individual is symbolized by two upper case letters, *AA*. The model of a monohybrid cross involves the following assumptions:

1. Kernel color is determined by the action of two alleles, one dominant (*P*) for purple color and one recessive (*p*) for yellow color. This is known from previous studies.
2. The F_1 generation is produced by matings of *PP* individuals with *pp* individuals; the F_2 generation is produced by random matings between individuals in the F_1 generation. This is accomplished by controlled breeding between plants.
3. All offspring are equally likely to survive regardless of genotype. This is true under controlled growth conditions.

We can use these assumptions of the model to predict the genotypes and phenotypes of offspring that should result in F_1 and F_2 generations and to see if the observed breeding results match those expected.

A. Bean-Bag Genetics

- First, calculate the frequencies of the expected genotypes and phenotypes of F_1 and F_2 generations. Your text provides examples similar to this cross. In the cross of purple (*PP*) with yellow (*pp*) corn,

$$PP \times pp$$

the genotype of all the progeny will be ______ and the phenotype will be ______.

- The F_2 generation is produced by mating between members of the F_1 generation. When two individuals of the F_1 generation cross,

______ × ______

the possible gamete types are ______ or ______ from one parent, and ______ or ______ from the other parent. Three possible genotypes occur in the F_2 offspring, ______, ______, and ______; whose proportions in the F_2 offspring are ______, ______, and ______; and whose phenotypes are ______ and ______; with proportions of ______ and ______.

- **Bean-bag genetics** is the name affectionately given to models that use beans (real or conceptual) as stand-ins for alleles. You will use real beans of various colors to represent alleles in the monohybrid-cross model. (Your instructor may provide you with marbles or beads, and the colors may differ from those listed here, but the principles are the same.) Each bean is one allele; a pair of alleles represents the genotype of a plant. The bag of purple beans represents the **gene pool** of the *PP* plants. The bag of yellow beans represents the gene pool of the *pp* plants. An F_1 offspring is produced when you take one *P* allele from the purple-bean bag and one *p* allele from the yellow-bean bag.
- What is the genotype of all the F_1 offspring? ______ What is the phenotype of all the F_1 offspring? ______
- Put equal numbers (more than 100) of purple and yellow beans in one bag. This mixed bag represents the gene pool of all the F_1 offspring. Without looking, take two beans from the mixed bag. This is the first F_2 offspring. The possible genotypes are ______, ______, and ______. Enter these possible genotypes in the first column

of the chart below. Replace the beans in the bag and mix them. Sample at least 100 F_2 offspring and tally their genotypes in Chart 11-1. Add the totals for each genotype and calculate their proportions in the F_2 generation.

Chart 11-1 F_2 offspring of a monohybrid bean-bag cross.

Genotype of bean pair	Tally	Total	Proportion
BB	29 ⅢⅢⅢⅢⅢ	29	29/100
Bb	ⅢⅢⅢⅢⅢⅢⅢⅢⅢⅢ	54	54/100
bb	ⅢⅢⅢ 11	17	17/100

- What phenotypes were represented in the F_2? 1. blue 2. brown. What are the proportions for these genotypes? 1. 83/100 2. 17/100.

How well did the observed results match the expected results?

they matched almost exactly to the expected results.

Later, you will use a statistical test to evaluate these data.

B. Monohybrid Cross in Corn

The monohybrid-cross model can be used to predict the genotypes and phenotypes of corn kernels. Your instructor will provide you with corn cobs from the parental (P_1), F_1, and F_2 generations in a monohybrid cross. A corn cob resulting from a **test cross** of the F_1 with the homozygous recessive P_1 will also be provided. As the model states, the allele for purple (*P*) is dominant over the recessive allele for yellow (*p*).

- **Parental (P_1) cobs:** What color are the kernels on the P_1 cobs? purple and yellow. What are their respective genotypes? PP or Pp and pp.

- **F_1 cobs and the test cross:** What color are the kernels on the F_1 cob? purple. What genotypes are present in the kernels? PP or Pp. Explain how a test cross will reveal the genotypes present in the F_1.

The F1 generation gets an allele from each parent and if both are homozygous or one homozygous and one heterozygous, they will produce a total purple cob.

- Diagram the test cross by showing the genotypes of the F_1 and the homozygous P_1 and the genotypes of their offspring.

Genotypes of F_1 and P_1 ~~Pp~~ Pp × ~~Pp~~ pp

Genotypes of offspring ~~Pp~~ Pp × ~~pp~~ Pp

What colors are present on the cob produced by a test cross? purple and yellow.

What is the expected ratio of these two colors? 40 : 60.

- Score several rows of kernels on this cob for color (sample at least 100 kernels). Tally your results in Chart 11-2 and indicate the genotypes for kernels of each color.

Chart 11-2 Kernel colors of F_1 cob.

Kernel color	Tally	Total	Genotype
Purple	[tally marks]	100	~~purple~~ PP or Pp

- How can you be sure of the genotypes of kernels in the cob from the test cross?

Because 100% of the kernels are purple and purple is dominant, so it has to be homozygous dominant or heterozygous dominant.

- **F_2 cob:** What colors are the kernels on the F_2 cob?

The kernels on the F_2 cob are yellow and purple

- Score several rows of kernels on the F_2 cob for color (sample at least 100 kernels). Tally your results in Chart 11-3 and indicate the genotype or possible genotypes for kernels of each color.

Chart 11-3 Kernel colors of F_2 cob.

Kernel color	Tally	Total	Genotype
Purple	[tally marks]	72	PP or Pp
Yellow	[tally marks]	28	pp

- How do these results compare with the model and with the bean-bag experiment?

These results are very close to what we obtained from the model and the bean-bag experiment.

Again, these data will be tested statistically in a later section.

EXERCISE 11-2 THE LAW OF INDEPENDENT ASSORTMENT: THE DIHYBRID CROSS

Objectives To demonstrate the independent assortment of alleles at two loci using bean-bag genetic models and to test the predictions of a model of a dihybrid cross by observing and counting corn kernel phenotypes.

The **law of independent assortment** deals with the inheritance of more than one character or trait. The law states that genes for different characters are inherited independently of one another. For example, the color of a kernel is determined by the combination of alleles present at one gene locus, while the shape of a kernel is determined by a different pair of alleles at another locus. These alleles are passed on independently; in other words, a purple kernel has the same chance of having a particular shape as a yellow kernel. You will demonstrate this principle by observing the results of a **dihybrid cross.** The term refers to a hybrid cross between individuals or populations of individuals that differ in homozygosity at two gene loci. One parental type is homozygous dominant at two loci (*AABB*), whereas the other parental type is homozygous recessive at these same loci (*aabb*). The same assumptions apply as in the monohybrid cross, and there is an added assumption that the two traits in question are not linked; that is, they are not on the same chromosome and are thus assorted independently at meiosis.

This exercise demonstrates the law of independent assortment in a dihybrid cross. As in Exercise 11-1, you will work first with bean-bag genetics and then with ears of corn.

A. Bean-Bag Genetics

- You will be provided with four colors of beans. One pair of colors (purple/yellow) represents the alleles at one gene locus. (This gene could be for any trait; color here is simply used to distinguish alleles.) Purple (*P*) is dominant, and yellow (*p*) is recessive. The other pair of colors (red/blue) represents the other pair of alleles. Red (*R*) is dominant, and blue (*r*) is recessive. In this bean-bag system, a single phenotype is represented by a combination of colors, and four combinations are possible: purple-red, yellow-red, purple-blue, and yellow-blue.
- In a dihybrid cross, one parental type is homozygous dominant at both loci; its genotype at these two loci is ________. The other parental type is homozygous recessive; its genotype is ________. Explain in a sentence why all F_1 offspring will be heterozygous at both loci.

Write the formula for the F_1 genotype:

Red R
White r
Blue B
Brown b

- To represent the gene pool of the F_1 generation and the independence of assortment at the two loci, mix one bag of equal numbers of purple and yellow beans and in a separate (independent) bag mix equal numbers of red and blue beans.
- What is the ratio of purple:yellow beans in the first bag? 1 : 1

  What is the ratio of red:blue beans in the second bag? 1 : 1
- Figure 11-1 shows a **Punnett square** depicting the gamete genotypes from a cross of members of the F_1 generation. The squares represent all possible combinations of gametes from the F_1

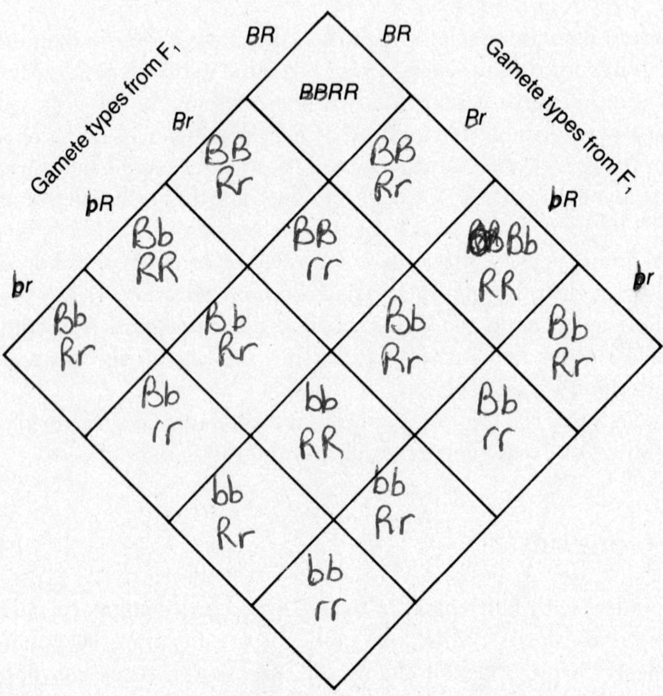

Figure 11-1 Punnett square for a dihybrid cross of two pairs of alleles (*Pp*, *Rr*).

Chart 11-4 Genotypes and phenotypes from Figure 11-1.

Genotype	Number of times occurring	Phenotype
BBRR	7	Blue, Red
BBRr	15	Blue, Red
BbRR	12	Blue, Red
BbRr	28	Blue, Red
Bbrr	12	Blue, white
bbRr	11	Brown, Red
bbrr	5	Brown, white
BBrr	5	Blue, white
bbRR	5	Brown, Red

generation, that is, the array of offspring genotypes in the F_2 generation. (Punnett squares are discussed in detail in the text.) The uppermost box is filled in to show the genotype resulting from a pairing of the two gamete types *PR* and *PR*. Fill in the remaining boxes to show the other genotypes in the F_2 generation.

- Some of the 16 boxes in the Punnett square share the same genotype. List in Chart 11-4 the genotypes represented in the Punnett square and how many times each occurs. Also indicate the phenotype (purple/yellow or red/blue) of each genotype.
- Notice that different genotypes sometimes result in the same phenotype. Combine the counts for genotypes that yield the same phenotype and fill in Chart 11-5.

Chart 11-5 Phenotypes from Figure 11-1.

Phenotype	Number of times occurring
Blue, Red	52
Blue, White	17
Brown, Red	16
Brown, White	5

Blue - Bb or BB Red RR or Rr
White rr brown - bb

The number of times the phenotypes occur in the Punnett square represent the proportions of these phenotypes expected in the F_2 offspring.

B. Dihybrid Cross in Corn

- The trait of corn-kernel color assorts independently from the trait of kernel shape. Kernel shape may be either plump or shrunken. The four possible phenotypes are shown in Figure 11-2. Instead of learning beforehand which allele is dominant and which is recessive for kernel shape, score the four kernel phenotypes first and compare the proportions of the phenotypes with those predicted by the model (see the results from the Punnett square).
- Score several rows of kernels on the F_2 cob for kernel shape and color (sample at least 100 kernels—more is better). Record your results in Chart 11-6. Also indicate the relative proportions of each phenotype. (Divide the smallest number into each of the larger ones.)

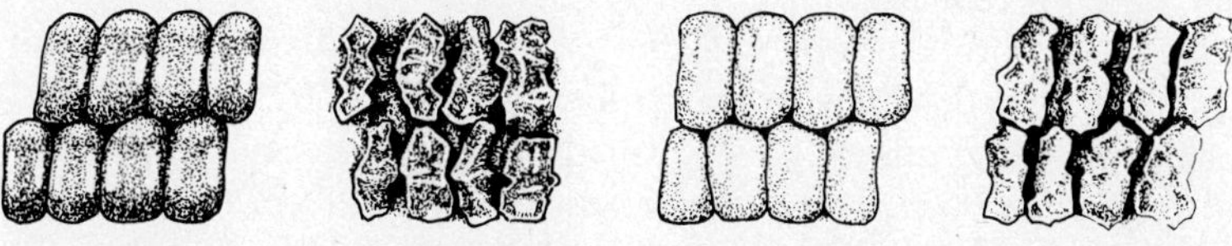

(a) Purple, plump (b) Purple, shrunken (c) Yellow, plump (d) Yellow, shrunken

Figure 11-2 Kernel color and kernel shape combined phenotypes.

Chart 11-6 Kernel shape and color on F_2 cob.

Kernel shape/color	Total	Proportion
Purple plump	54	54/100
Purple shrunken	19	19/100
Yellow plump	24	24/100
Yellow shrunken	3	3/100

- Compare the relative proportions of each of the four phenotypes with those you calculated from the Punnett square. Which alleles are dominant and which are recessive, and what are their effects on the phenotype? (Use an upper-case or lower-case "s" for the shape allele.)

Dominant alleles: SS + Ss Phenotypic effects: Purple, plump

Recessive alleles: ss Phenotypic effects: Shrunken, yellow

EXERCISE 11-3 THE CHI-SQUARE TEST

Objective To apply the chi-square test to the data from the bean-bag and corn-cob experiments as a means of testing the applicability of the mono- and dihybrid cross models to corn-kernel phenotype.

The monohybrid model in Exercise 11-1 predicted a 3:1 ratio for F_2 progeny for a particular trait. If you sampled 100 beans and found that 75 were purple and 25 were yellow, you would probably conclude that the results supported the model. But what if the counts were 79 purple and 21 yellow? Or 65 purple and 35 yellow? We could say that such differences from our predicted 75:25 counts were due to chance. But how could we be more certain that chance was really the reason instead of another factor that affected kernel color?

Statistical tests have been devised to give us that assurance. Such tests cannot tell you if another factor is involved. What they can do is take a result such as a 65:35 count and tell you how often you would get that count *due to chance effects of sampling*. Even though the model you are testing may be correct, there is a chance, however small, that an "oddball" count can occur because of sampling effects. For example, you might reach into a bag of purple and yellow beans and pull out 50 purple beans in a row, or you could flip a coin and have it come up heads 50 times in a row. The chances are small, but the statistical test tells you exactly *how small*. Given the results, the statistical test calculates the **probability** that you would obtain those results by chance alone, even though the model you were testing is correct. This probability is expressed as a number between 0 and 1; it can also be expressed as a ratio or a percentage. For example, a probability of 0.05 is the same as 1 chance in 20, or a 5% chance.

Once the statistical test provides you with the probability that your results were due to chance sampling effects, you have to decide what that probability means. If the probability that your results were due to chance sampling effects is very small, it is not reasonable to conclude that chance sampling caused the result. Instead, the model is probably incorrect. This is not necessarily a bad result—it is part of the prediction-hypothesis testing theory modification described in Chapter 1. Scientists have established a rule-of-thumb to evaluate statistical probabilities:

> If the probability calculated in a statistical test is less than or equal to 0.05, the model or hypothesis being tested is assumed to be incorrect.

You will perform a chi-square test on the bean-bag and corn-kernel data and compute the probability that your results fit the model; that is, the probability that your observed counts would be obtained by chance, even though they do not exactly match the expected counts.

Probability and statistics is an entire field of mathematics, and a large one at that, so do not expect to understand the mathematical details of the chi-square test immediately. You should, however, understand how to interpret the test.

Calculation of Chi-Square

In each bean-bag and corn-cob data set, we have a group of observed counts. The expected counts are calculated from the ratios predicted in the model. For example, if we expect a 3:1 ratio of purple:yellow kernels, in a sample of 100 kernels, 75 would be the expected purple count, and 25 would be the expected yellow count. (For other sample sizes multiply the total sample size by $\frac{3}{4}$ and $\frac{1}{4}$ to get the respective values.) "Chi-square" refers to the Greek symbol (χ^2), which is the value computed in the formula:

$$\chi^2 = \sum \frac{(\text{observed count} - \text{expected count})^2}{\text{expected count}}$$

where Σ is the symbol for summation.

To calculate the quotients summed in the χ^2 equation, take each observed count, subtract the respective expected count, square that value, and divide by the expected count. Then add all these values together (as indicated by the Σ symbol). The following example will demonstrate how to apply the formula.

Example Assume that you counted 72 purple and 28 yellow kernels when the model predicted a 3:1 ratio. The data can be entered in Chart 11-7.

Chart 11-7 Calculations of sample chi-square data.

Kernel color	Observed counts	Expected count	Obs − exp	(Obs − exp)^2
purple	72	75	−3	9
yellow	28	25	3	9

$$\begin{aligned}\chi^2 &= \frac{9}{75} + \frac{9}{25}\\ &= .12 + .36\\ &= .48\end{aligned}$$

The next step is to look up this value for chi-square in the statistical table reproduced in Table 11-1. This table indicates the probabilities associated with chi-square values. You will also need to know one other number to find the probability for a chi-square value. This number is the **degrees of freedom,** or **d.f.**, for your data set. The degrees of freedom for these data sets is one less than the number of phenotypes you counted. For two kernel colors (or phenotypes), the d.f. = 2 − 1 = 1; for four phenotypes the d.f. = 4 − 1 = 3. In the example above, d.f. = 1. The top row of values in Table 11-1 is for data sets with d.f. = 1. The calculated value of .48 is between 0.45 and 0.71 in the table—closer to 0.45. The probability associated with a chi-square value of 0.48 is close to 0.5 (50%). In other words, the probability of getting these counts instead of the expected 75:25 is about 50%, much higher than 0.05 (5%) cutoff value for a result to be called significantly different from chance sampling. In other words, these results are not "oddball" results at all, and we conclude that the difference between observed and expected counts *was* due to chance. The

Table 11-1 Values of chi-square for various degrees of freedom.

Degrees of freedom	Probability levels						
	0.99	0.95	0.90	0.80	0.70	0.60	0.50
1	0.00	0.00	0.02	0.06	0.15	0.27	0.45
2	0.02	0.10	0.21	0.45	0.71	1.02	1.39
3	0.11	0.35	0.58	1.01	0.42	1.87	2.37
4	0.30	0.71	1.06	1.65	2.19	2.75	3.36
5	0.55	1.15	1.61	2.34	3.00	3.66	4.35
6	0.87	1.64	2.20	3.07	3.83	4.57	5.35
7	1.24	2.17	2.83	3.82	4.67	5.49	6.35
8	1.65	2.73	3.49	4.59	5.53	6.42	7.34
9	2.09	3.33	4.17	5.38	6.39	7.36	8.34
10	2.56	3.94	4.87	6.18	7.27	8.30	9.34
11	3.05	4.57	5.58	6.99	8.15	9.24	10.34
12	3.57	5.23	6.30	7.81	9.03	10.18	11.34
13	4.11	5.89	7.04	8.63	9.93	11.13	12.34
14	4.66	6.57	7.79	9.47	10.82	12.08	13.34
15	5.23	7.26	8.55	10.31	11.72	13.03	14.34
16	5.81	7.96	9.31	11.15	12.62	13.98	15.34
17	6.41	8.67	10.09	12.00	13.53	14.94	16.34
18	7.01	9.39	10.86	12.86	14.44	15.89	17.34
19	7.63	10.12	11.65	13.72	15.35	16.85	18.34
20	8.26	10.85	12.44	14.58	16.27	17.81	19.34
21	8.90	11.59	13.24	15.44	17.18	18.77	20.34
22	9.54	12.34	14.04	16.31	18.10	19.73	21.34
23	10.20	13.09	14.85	17.19	19.02	20.69	22.34
24	10.86	13.85	15.66	18.06	19.94	21.65	23.34
25	11.52	14.61	16.47	18.94	20.87	22.62	24.34
26	12.20	15.38	17.29	19.82	21.79	23.58	25.34
27	12.88	16.15	18.11	20.70	22.72	24.54	26.34
28	13.56	16.93	18.94	21.59	23.65	25.51	27.34
29	14.26	17.71	19.77	22.48	24.58	26.48	28.34
30	14.95	18.49	20.60	23.36	25.51	27.44	29.34
50	29.71	34.76	37.69	41.45	44.31	46.86	49.33
100	70.06	77.93	82.36	87.95	92.13	95.81	99.33

Degrees of freedom	0.40	0.30	0.20	0.10	0.05	0.01	0.001
1	0.71	1.07	1.64	2.71	3.84	6.63	10.83
2	1.83	2.41	3.22	4.61	5.99	9.21	13.82
3	2.95	3.66	4.64	6.25	7.81	11.34	16.27
4	4.04	4.88	5.99	7.78	9.49	13.28	18.47
5	5.13	6.06	7.29	9.24	11.07	15.09	20.52
6	6.21	7.23	8.56	10.64	12.59	16.81	22.46
7	7.28	8.38	9.80	12.02	14.07	18.48	24.32
8	8.35	9.52	11.03	13.36	15.51	20.09	26.12
9	9.41	10.66	12.24	14.68	16.92	21.67	27.88
10	10.47	11.78	13.44	15.99	18.31	23.21	29.59
11	11.53	12.90	14.63	17.28	19.68	24.72	31.26
12	12.58	14.01	15.81	18.55	21.03	26.22	32.91
13	13.64	15.12	16.98	19.81	22.36	27.69	34.53
14	14.69	16.22	18.15	21.06	23.68	29.14	36.12
15	15.73	17.32	19.31	22.31	25.00	30.58	37.70

Table 11-1 (continued) Values of chi-square for various degrees of freedom.

Degrees of freedom	Probability levels						
	0.40	0.30	0.20	0.10	0.05	0.01	0.001
16	16.78	18.42	20.47	23.54	26.30	32.00	39.25
17	17.82	19.51	21.61	24.77	27.59	33.41	40.79
18	18.87	20.60	22.76	25.99	28.87	34.81	42.31
19	19.91	21.69	23.90	27.20	30.14	36.19	43.82
20	20.95	22.77	25.04	28.41	31.41	37.57	45.31
21	21.99	23.86	26.17	29.62	32.67	38.93	46.80
22	23.03	24.94	27.30	30.81	33.92	40.29	48.27
23	24.07	26.02	28.43	32.01	35.17	41.64	49.73
24	25.11	27.10	29.55	33.20	36.42	42.98	51.18
25	26.14	28.17	30.68	34.38	37.65	44.31	52.62
26	27.18	29.25	31.79	35.56	38.89	45.64	54.05
27	28.21	30.32	32.91	36.74	40.11	46.96	55.48
28	29.25	31.39	34.03	37.92	41.34	48.28	56.89
29	30.28	32.46	35.14	39.09	42.56	49.59	58.30
30	31.32	33.53	36.25	40.26	43.77	50.89	59.70
50	51.89	54.72	58.16	63.17	67.50	76.15	86.66
100	102.9	106.9	111.7	118.5	124.3	135.8	149.4

model is confirmed. If we had obtained counts markedly different from 75 and 25, we might have calculated a chi-square of 3.84 or higher (see Table 11-1), in which case we would have concluded that chance sampling was not the cause of the counts; instead the model would be judged incorrect.

- Calculate the chi-square values for the bean-bag data and kernel counts in Exercises 11-1 and 11-2. Base your expected values on the monohybrid and dihybrid models. Use the following charts to help in your calculations.

A. Monohybrid Model

Chart 11-8 Bean-bag data for F_2 offspring.

Phenotype	Observed count	Expected count	Obs − exp	$(\text{Obs} - \text{exp})^2$
purple (*PP* or *Pp*)	83	75	8	64
yellow (*pp*)	17	25	-8	64

$\chi^2 = \sum \frac{(\text{obs} - \text{exp})^2}{\text{exp}} = \frac{64}{75} + \frac{64}{25}$

.85 + 2.56 = 3.41

Probability from Table 11-1 = .05 (5%)

Interpretation:

Model is assumed to be incorrect. It is significantly different from chance sampling.

Chart 11-9 Kernel color on cobs from the test cross.

Phenotype	Observed count	Expected count	Obs − exp	(Obs − exp)^2
purple (*PP* or *Pp*)	100	100	0	0
yellow (*pp*)				

$\chi^2 = \sum \frac{(obs - exp)^2}{exp} = \frac{0}{100} = 0$

Probability from Table 11-1 = .99 (99%)

Interpretation:

The results were not oddball results, the difference was all due to chance.

Chart 11-10 Kernel color on F_2 cobs.

Phenotype	Observed count	Expected count	Obs − exp	(Obs − exp)^2
purple (*PP* or *Pp*)	72	75	−3	9
yellow (*pp*)	28	25	3	9

$\chi^2 = \sum \frac{(obs - exp)^2}{exp} = \frac{9}{75} + \frac{9}{25}$

Probability from Table 11-1 = .50 (50%)

Interpretation:

The results were not oddball results, the difference was all due to chance.

B. Dihybrid Model

Chart 11-11 Bean-bag data—F_2 offspring.

Phenotype	Observed count	Expected count	Obs − exp	(Obs − exp)^2
purple, red (*PP* or *Pp*, *RR* or *Rr*)	52	54	−2	4
purple, blue (*PP* or *Pp*, *rr*)	17	27	10	100

Chart 11-11 (continued) Bean-bag data—F_2 offspring.

Phenotype	Observed count	Expected count	Obs − exp	(Obs − exp)^2
yellow, red (*pp*, *RR* or *Rr*)	16	27	-11	121
yellow, blue (*pp*, *rr*)	5	9	-4	16

$\chi^2 = \sum \frac{(\text{obs} - \text{exp})^2}{\text{exp}} = \frac{4}{54} + \frac{100}{27} + \frac{121}{27} + \frac{16}{9}$

.07 + 3.7 + 4.48 + 1.78 = 10.03

Probability from Table 11-1 = .01 (1%)

Interpretation:

~~The results were not oddball results, difference was due to chance.~~

Model is assumed to be incorrect, significantly different from chance sampling.

Chart 11-12 Kernel color on F_2 cobs.

Phenotype	Observed count	Expected count	Obs − exp	(Obs − exp)^2
purple, plump (*PP* or *Pp*, *SS* or *Ss*)	54	54	0	0
purple, shrunken (*PP* or *Pp*, *ss*)	19	27	-8	64
yellow, plump (*pp*, *SS* or *Ss*)	24	27	-3	9
yellow, shrunken (*pp*, *ss*)	3	9	-6	36

$\chi^2 = \sum \frac{(\text{obs} - \text{exp})^2}{\text{exp}} = \frac{0}{54} + \frac{64}{27} + \frac{9}{27} + \frac{36}{9}$

2.37 + .33 + 4 = 6.7

Probability from Table 11-1 = .10 (10%)

Interpretation:

Results were not odd ball results, difference due to chance.

QUESTIONS

Were any of your probability values smaller than 0.05? yes
Check the probability values of other members of the class. Are any values smaller than 0.05?

?

If so, what is your interpretation? (Is the model wrong or are some "oddball" results expected in a large number of tests?)

I cannot answer this because we did not look at the values of the other people in our class.

The material in this chapter corresponds to Chapter 15 in your text.

12

GENETICS II. HUMAN GENETICS

"Every person is unique," the truism goes. But every individual is also more or less similar to other people. In a variety of ways we are especially similar to our parents and siblings. Some of that similarity can be attributed to the cultural sharing between family members who live together for two decades or more. But biologically close relatives also share large numbers of genes. Thus, of the millions of genes in your cells—the assemblage of which makes you unique—half are exact copies of half your mother's genes and half are exact copies of half your father's genes. As you know from your reading, the processes of genetic control of growth and development are extremely complicated. Although molecular biologists know a great deal about the translation of the genetic code from DNA to proteins, the details of how immense numbers of genes coordinate to produce an integrated organism are still the subject of exciting research.

The exercises in this chapter deal with the action of human genes on discrete, easily observable traits. You will make observations of these traits in yourself and your classmates to gain an understanding of how particular genes are expressed in the human organism.

EXERCISE 12-1 SURVEY OF HUMAN GENETIC TRAITS

Objectives To observe the expression of a series of genes in your own phenotype, and to understand the mode of inheritance in these genes.

Medical geneticists naturally focus on genes that are expressed as unusual physical, behavioral, or biochemical traits. However, in the process, they have discovered a number of traits that are mildly unusual or, because such a large proportion of the population shares them, are simply another version of normal.

In this exercise, you will inventory yourself for the series of genetic traits listed in Table 12-1, some of which are illustrated in Figure 12-1. These are known to be single-gene traits, expressions of two alleles at one gene locus. The textbook mentions the drawbacks to studying human genetics (small samples, the "missing F_2," and the "marriage gamble" or lack of controlled mating), and you will notice the lack of statistical rigor in this exercise compared to the corn genetics studies of the previous chapter. Nevertheless, it is interesting to take a limited genetic inventory of oneself.

- Divide into groups of four students. Go through the traits in Table 12-1; score your own phenotype for each trait in Chart 12-1. Write the symbols for your possible genotypes in the

Table 12-1 Single-gene human genetic traits and their alleles.

Trait (alleles)	Expression
Bent pinky (*B*, *b*)	Dominant allele causes distal segment of fifth finger to bend distinctly inward toward fourth (ring) finger (Fig. 12-1a).
Pattern baldness (*P*, *p*)	Dominant allele causes premature loss of hair on top and front of head in heterozygous or homozygous dominant males and in homozygous dominant females.
PTC tasters (*T*, *t*)	Phenylthiocarbamide (PTC) tastes bitter to heterozygous or homozygous dominant individuals, but is tasteless to homozygous recessives.
Blue eyes (*E*, *e*)	Blue-eyed persons are homozygous recessive and lack pigment in iris; heterozygous or homozygous dominant individuals have iris pigment, the color of which is determined by other genes.
Red-green color blindness (*C*, *c*)	Recessive allele on X chromosome causes the inability to distinguish between red and green in males and in homozygous recessive females; heterozygous females are carriers but have normal vision. Your instructor might have a chart you can use to test yourself if you do not know whether you are color blind.
Tongue rolling (*R*, *r*)	Persons with dominant allele in heterozygous or homozygous condition can roll their tongues into tubelike shape (Fig. 12-1b); homozygous recessives are nonrollers.
Widow's peak (*W*, *w*)	Dominant allele in heterozygous and homozygous individuals results in V-shaped front hairline (Fig. 12-1c); homozygous recessives have straight hairlines.
Thumb crossing (*C*, *c*)	In relaxed interlocking of fingers, left thumb over right indicates dominant allele present in either heterozygous or homozygous individuals; homozygous recessives naturally place right thumb over left.
Attached ear lobe (*A*, *a*)	Homozygous recessives have attached ear lobes (Fig. 12-1d); heterozygous or homozygous dominant individuals have detached ear lobes.
Hitchhikers' thumb (*H*, *h*)	Homozygous recessives can bend distal joint of thumb backward to nearly 90° angle; heterozygous or homozygous dominant condition yields thumb that cannot bend backward more than approximately 30°.

space provided (use the symbols given in Table 12-1). If you know your parents' phenotypes, include them in the space provided. Your instructor will tally the phenotypes and genotypes for the entire class on the chalkboard.

QUESTIONS

At how many gene loci do you carry at least one dominant allele?

I carry the dominant allele on all of the gene loci mentioned above except the bent pinky and pattern baldness, and PTC test

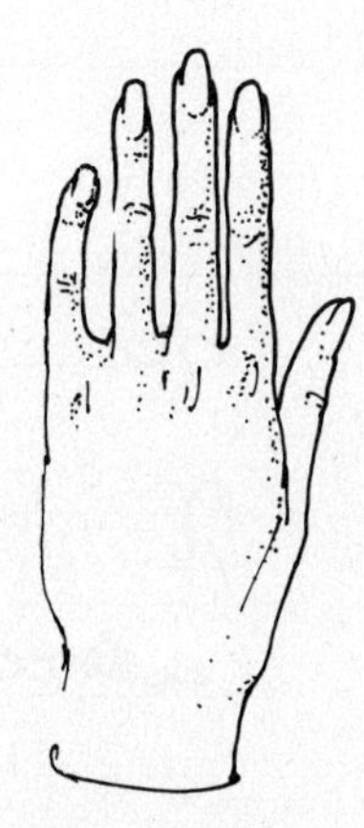

(a) Bent little finger

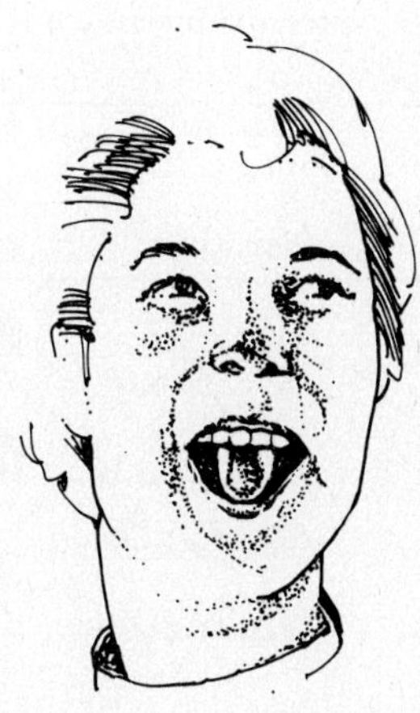

(b) Ability to roll tongue

(c) Widow's peak

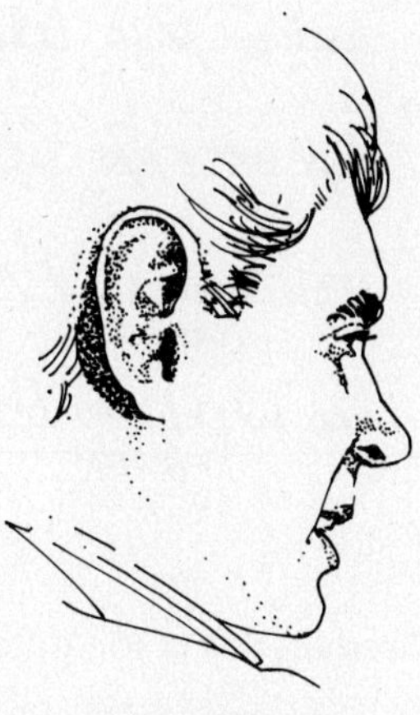

(d) Attached ear lobe

Figure 12-1 Some human single-gene traits.

At how many gene loci are you homozygous recessive?

At three of the gene loci are I homozygous recessive - the bent pinky and the pattern baldness, and the PTC test

Do all four members of your group share one or more phenotypes? yes Which ones?

PTC, tongue rolling, thumb crossing

Chart 12-1 Personal inventory of phenotypes and possible genotypes for single-gene traits described in Table 12-1.

Trait	Your phenotype	Your possible genotypes	Parents' phenotypes if known	Phenotypes of potential progeny	Frequency of phenotype in class
Bent pinky	straight pinky	bb		bb	15
Pattern baldness	no baldness	pp		pp	16
PTC taster	no taste	tt		tt	7
Blue eyes	brown eyes	EE or Ee		EE or ee	14
Red-green color blindness	no color blindness	CC or Cc		CC or cc	18
Tongue rolling	tongue rolling	RR or Rr		RR or rr	17
Widow's peak	widows peak	WW or Ww		WW or ww	6
Thumb crossing	left over right	CC or Cc		CC or cc	12
Attached ear lobes	unattached lobes	AA or Aa		AA or aa	14
Hitchhiker's thumb	no hitchhikers thumb	HH or Hh		HH or hh	8

Compare the frequencies of the different phenotypes in the class. Are phenotypes for some traits clearly more abundant than their alternate phenotypes for these traits? yes Which traits?

red-green color blindness, tongue rolling, pattern baldness

Compare the frequency of dominant and recessive alleles for several traits. Is one type of allele consistently more abundant than the other? yes What do you conclude about the frequency of an allele relative to its dominant or recessive nature?

An allele that is dominant will be more abundant than a recessive one.

Write your genotype for the characters in Table 12-1 in the space below. If you are unsure about any alleles, use a dash (that is, if your genotype might be *Aa* or *AA*, write A–).

bb, PP, tt, E–, C–, R–, W–, C–,

A–, H-

Compare your genotype to that of each of the members of your group. For each group member, count the number of alleles that are the same for both of you (disregard dashes), divide by the total number of alleles (20 minus the number of dashes), and multiply by 100. This is the percent similarity between you and the group member. Enter the data in Chart 12-2.

Chart 12-2 Comparison of percent similarity of alleles for genotypes. 13

Group member	Number of alleles shared with you	Total number of alleles	Percent similarity
Heather	卌卌 I	11	85%
Kim	卌 III	8	62%
Amy	卌 I	6	46%

Does the percent similarity vary greatly in the various comparisons? yes
Do any of the people in your group have identical phenotypes for all the traits listed in Table 12-1? no What is the largest number of phenotypes shared by any two members of your group? 8
What do these comparisons of genotypic and phenotypic similarity tell you about the genetic uniqueness of individuals in general?

this is a great diversity between everyone because everyone is unique. Not everyone inherits the same alleles.

How many traits could you trace to one or both of your parents? ? Suppose a long-lost sibling (not an identical twin) showed up in class. Could you predict for certain if he or she would show a particular phenotype for any of the traits listed in Table 12-1? Explain which traits, if any, and the reasoning leading to your conclusion. (Hint: You would need to know the phenotypes of both your parents, and even then only certain phenotypes would be predictable.)

I am not able to get the phenotypes of my parents - as one doesn't live in close range.

To fill in the next to last column in Chart 12-1, assume that you married a person with the same phenotype as your own for all the traits listed. This does not mean you share identical genotypes for these traits. Assume that all the alleles assort independently. Are there any of these phenotypes that you can predict with certainty in your children? yes If so, write the phenotypes in the last column and explain below why this trait is predictable. (Hint: Refer to your genotype and determine the possible gamete types and F_1 genotypes for each pair of alleles.)

Bent pinky, pattern baldness and PTC will be all homozygous recessive because if I am and I marry one - that is the only possible combo.

Are there any traits in Table 12-1 that will occur for certain in your progeny regardless of whom you marry? Which ones and why?

No. I don't find that there are any traits such as this

EXERCISE 12-2 BARR BODIES IN EPITHELIAL CELLS

Objectives To observe the presence or absence of Barr bodies in cells of human females and males, and to understand why they occur only in cells of one sex.

Only one X chromosome in a human cell is activated. Normal male cells have a single X chromosome, which is activated in all nonsex cells. Normal female cells have two X chromosomes, one activated and one inactivated. The inactivated X chromosome consists of condensed chromatin. **Barr bodies,** named for their discoverer and not their shape, are the condensed X-chromosome material visible in stained interphase nuclei of human cells.

- Your instructor will have prepared several slides of epithelial cells (scraped from inside the cheek) stained with the DNA-specific Giemsa stain. If time permits, prepare these slides from your own cheek cells according to the directions of your instructor. Each slide contains cells from a single individual. The prepared slides will not be labeled male or female. A Barr body shows up as a darkly stained mass adjacent to the nuclear membrane. Observe the prepared slides under the compound microscope and determine which cells are female and which are male. Make a sketch of a female and a male nucleus in the spaces below. Indicate the location of the Barr body (if present), and include a scale bar for each diagram.

Female nucleus **Male nucleus**

- Barr-body staining can be used to detect abnormal numbers of sex chromosomes in human cells. Such abnormal counts of sex chromosomes are associated with some physical and behavioral traits. Chart 12-3 lists syndromes associated with abnormal numbers of sex chromosomes. Indicate how many Barr bodies would be revealed by Giemsa staining of cells from these individuals.
- The last column in Chart 12-3 refers to a different test for sex chromosomes. A fluorescent dye called quinacrine mustard stains the distal section of the long arm of the Y chromosome. The fluorescent spot that results is called the **F body** or **Y body.** Fill in the last column with the numbers of F bodies that would appear in nuclei of cells of each genotype.

Which genotypes would be definitively identified by Giemsa staining alone?

Chart 12-3 Results of Giemsa staining and quinacrine-mustard staining of cells with abnormal numbers of sex chromosomes.

Sex chromosomes	Syndrome	Number of Barr bodies	Number of F bodies
Females			
XO, monosomic	Turner's		
XXX, trisomic	Metafemale		
XXXX, tetrasomic			
XXXXX, pentasomic			
Males			
XYY, trisomic	Normal		
XXY, trisomic	Klinefelter's*		
XXYY, tetrasomic			
XXXY, tetrasomic			
XXXXY, pentasomic			
XXXXXY, hexasomic			

*XXY is the common genotype in Klinefelter's syndrome; the other genotypes for this syndrome listed in the table are rare.

Explain how you could use the quinacrine-mustard stain to decipher the abnormal genotypes in Chart 12-3 that were not detected by Giemsa staining alone.

With the quinacrine-mustard stain, you can figure out how many Y chromosomes there are - to see if the abnormality results from this.

EXERCISE 12-3 KARYOTYPES AND CHROMOSOMAL REARRANGEMENTS

Objectives To observe the normal human karyotype and assemble a karyotype from a photograph of human metaphase chromosomes; to observe abnormal karyotypes involving translocation of chromosomal material.

A. Karyotype

Metaphase chromosomes can be arranged in a standard form called a **karyotype.** Human chromosomes are identified by standard conventions according to size and structure. The largest pair is number 1, the smallest pair is number 22, and the sex chromosomes are called XY chromosomes. However, size alone is insufficient to distinguish chromosome pairs. Pairs also differ in the location (or presence) of the centromere and the lengths of chromosome arms (Fig. 12-2).

To make a karyotype, one needs a photograph of chromosomes at metaphase of mitosis. The

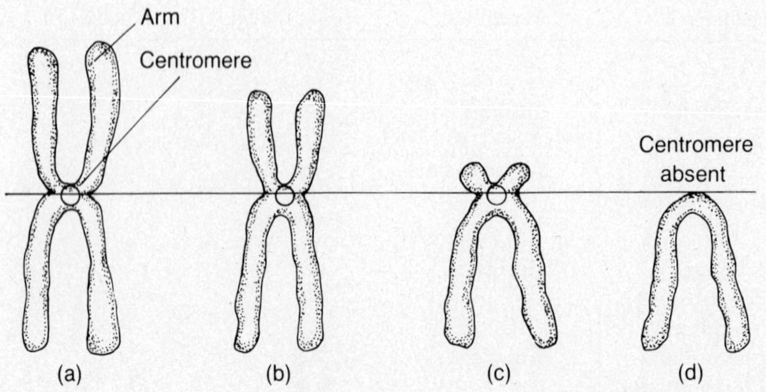

Figure 12-2 Chromosome morphology: Variation in length of arms and location of centromere.

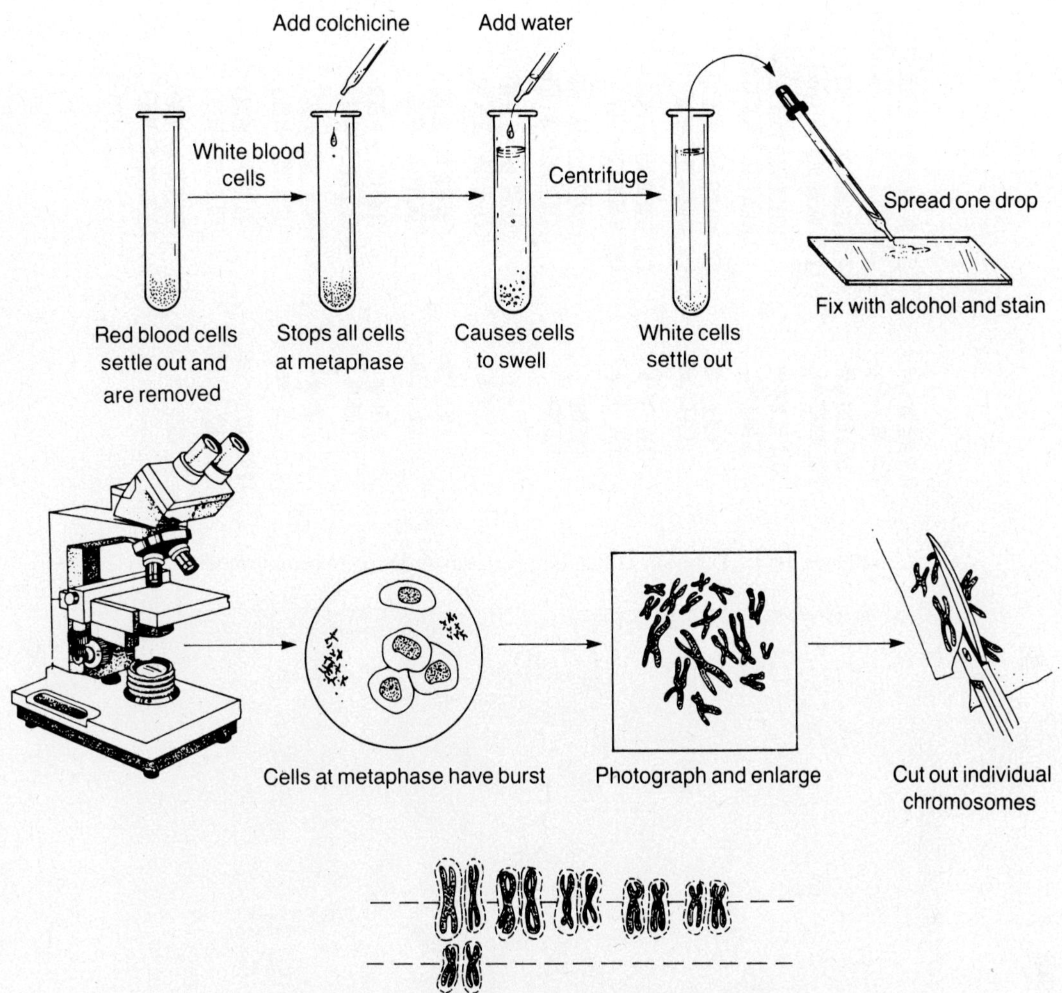

Figure 12-3 How a human karyotype is made.

technique for making a karyotype is shown in Figure 12-3. Human cells in tissue culture or blood cells are treated with the chemical colchicine to arrest cell division at metaphase, when chromosomes are readily stainable and visible. Special stains reveal the banding patterns of the randomly arranged chromosomes.

In the late 1960s, techniques were developed that stained adjacent sections on chromosome arms in a distinctive banding pattern (Fig. 12-4). The bands represent different types of chromatin and are used to match pairs in a karyotype. Figure 12-5 displays a typical metaphase spread of human chromosomes stained to show banding patterns. Each chromosome consists of two chromatids attached to a centromere.

- Cut out the individual chromosomes and arrange them on Figure 12-6 in pairs of similar size, centromere location, and banding patterns. Arrange the chromosomes so that the centromeres lie on the horizontal lines in the figure and so that chromatid arms are perpendicular to the lines (see Figures 12-2 and 12-4). Is this karyotype of a male or female individual? ________________

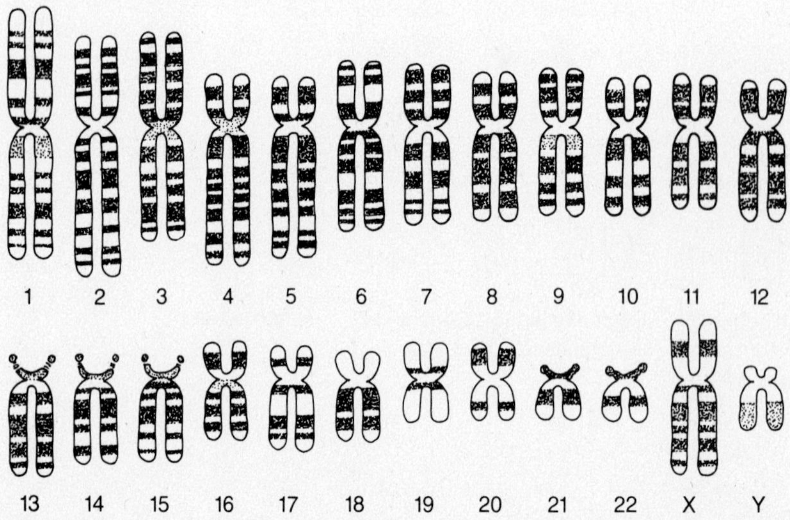

Figure 12-4 Diagram of banding patterns in human chromosomes.

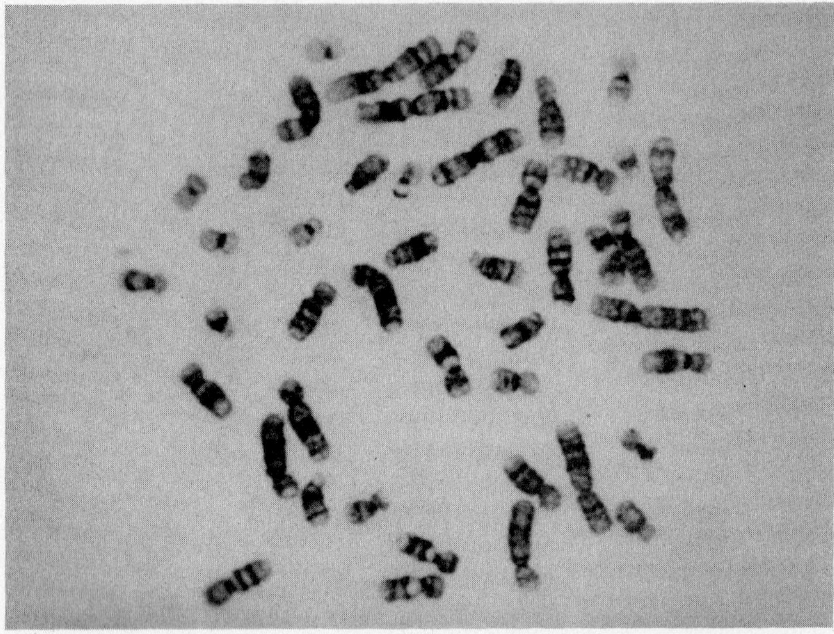

Figure 12-5 Metaphase spread of banded human chromosomes.

B. Translocation of Chromosomal Material

Homologous chromosomes exchange genetic material at meiosis in the process called **crossing over.** Occasionally, nonhomologous chromosomes may exchange material at meiosis, a process called **translocation.** Figure 12-7 shows human chromosome pairs 6 to 12 and two X chromosomes. Part of the arms of one of the pairs has been translocated to another pair.

- Compare the chromosome pairs in Figure 12-7 to those in Figure 12-4. Which two chromosome pairs are involved in the transaction? ______________ and ______________ .

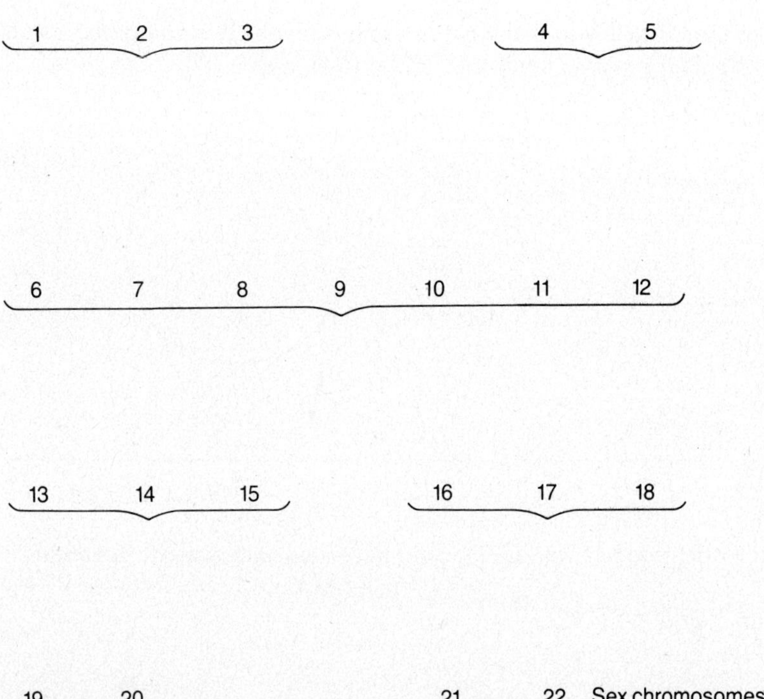

Figure 12-6 Human karyotype of chromosomes cut in Figure 12-4.

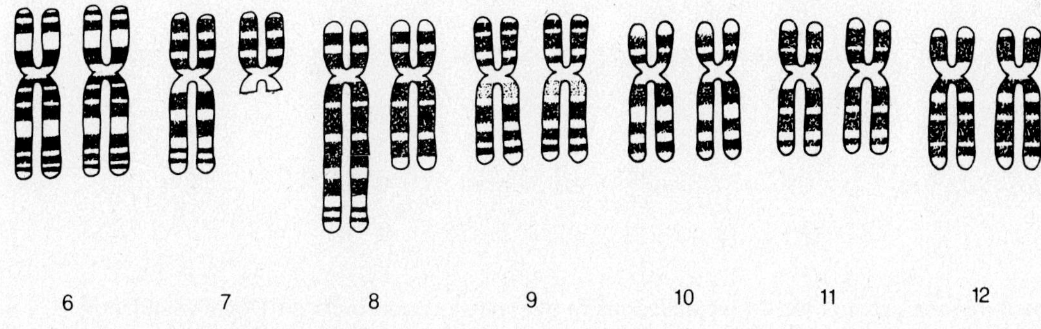

Figure 12-7 Translocation of chromosomes showing human chromosome pairs 6 to 12.

Is a cell with this karyotype viable? ____________ Why or why not?

- Show in the circles below how the chromosomes involved in the translocation would be distributed in the four possible meiotic products from such a cell.

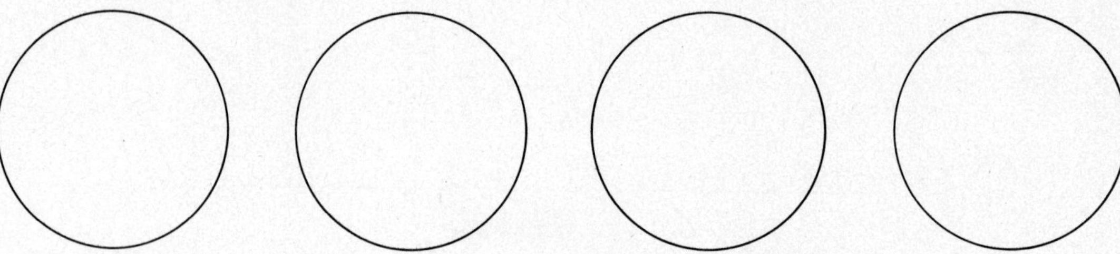

QUESTIONS

Which of the meiotic products you drew would have a normal gametic genotype?

Which meiotic products would have an abnormal gametic genotype?

Would you expect these abnormal genotypes to survive? Why or why not?

Which meiotic product would be analogous to the translocation-induced Down's syndrome described in your textbook?

The material in this chapter corresponds to Chapters 16–18 in your text.

13
ANIMAL REPRODUCTION AND DEVELOPMENT

The processes of cell division and inheritance presented in preceding chapters lay the groundwork for the topics considered here: **sexual reproduction** and **development.** Cell division is the basis of asexual reproduction, which is the predominant form of reproduction in bacteria and many types of protists and plants. Sexual reproduction, on the other hand, involves the union of two gametes—each containing one-half of the genome—to form the zygote. The unique genetic blueprint represented in the zygote is expressed during growth and differentiation into an adult organism.

Sexual reproduction in flowering plants is covered in Chapter 23 of this manual. The exercises in this chapter deal with the production of gametes and development of the embryo in animals. Because in many species the developing organism must be protected if it is to survive, the remarkable events of early development are often hidden inside the body of the parent. You will observe various developmental stages in living or preserved specimens of an invertebrate animal (a sea urchin or sea star) and a vertebrate organism (a chick). By studying these "landmark" stages, you will gain an appreciation of the close integration of the major reproductive events and early processes of development. Adult vertebrate anatomy, the end result of these processes, will be covered in Chapter 26.

EXERCISE 13-1 SPERMATOGENESIS AND OOGENESIS

Objectives To observe gamete production in mammalian sex organs; to describe how meiosis gives rise to haploid gametes; and to name the intermediate cell types involved in the production of sperm and ova.

The principal features of meiosis were covered in Chapter 10 of this manual, which included schematic diagrams of spermatogenesis and oogenesis (Fig. 10-3). You may wish to refer to these diagrams before examining the microscope slides of stained testis and ovarian tissue. **Gamete** is a general term for any haploid sex cell. Gametes are single cells, although in many plants and animals they are associated with other cells in reproductive tissues. These associated cells may help nourish the gametes during their formation. In later chapters you will observe gametes of a variety of organisms. Probably the most familiar gametes are **sperm** and **eggs** or **ova** (singular **ovum**). The steps in their production can be observed in microscope slides of thin sections of reproductive organs.

- Use the compound microscope to observe the microscope slide of a thin section through the testis of a rat or other mammal. The testes are the male organs that produce sperm. Spermatogenesis occurs in cells lining the wall of the **seminiferous tubules** of each testis. These tubules are highly coiled such that a section through the testis cuts through many at once. Locate the types of cells on the microscope slide by referring to the illustration in Figure 13-1. The **spermatogonial cells** lie directly next to the wall of the seminiferous tubules. These cells undergo mitosis throughout the reproductive life of the organism. Are any of the spermatogonial cells on the slide in the process of cell division? Yes How can you tell?

  Because you can start to see some of the characteristics of the different phases

Spermatogonial cells give rise to **primary spermatocytes,** in which the chromatids duplicate. Primary spermatocytes are located in the layer of cells just internal to the spermatogonial cells. Upon division, a primary spermatocyte produces two **secondary spermatocytes** (difficult to distinguish from the primary spermatocytes), each with a haploid number of chromosomes. Each chromosome consists of two sister chromatids. Each secondary spermatocyte divides to yield a pair of **spermatids,** which mature into sperm. Large helper cells called **Sertoli cells** help nourish the developing sperm.

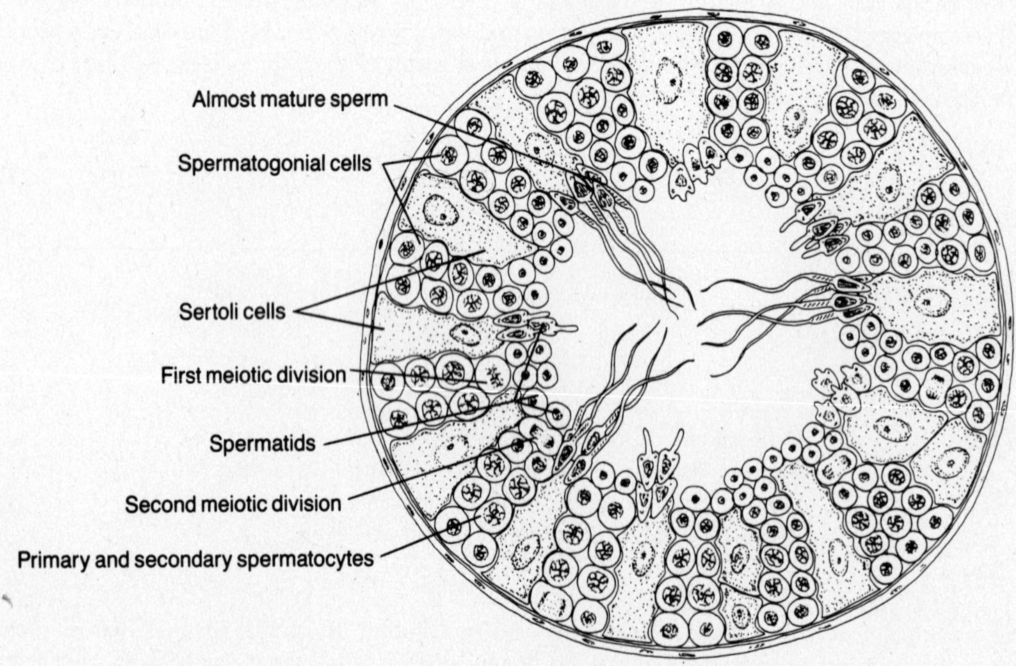

Figure 13-1 Spermatogenesis in the mammalian testis. Cross section of seminiferous tubule in a mammal.

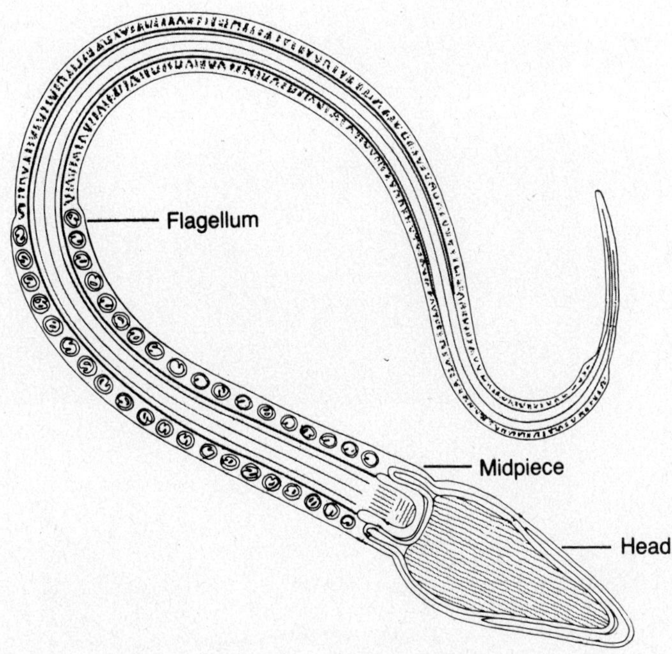

Figure 13-2 Mature sperm.

A mature sperm consists of a **head, middle piece,** and **tail** or **flagellum** (Fig. 13-2). The head contains the chromosomes and bears a cap of enzymes called the **acrosome.** The middle piece is rich in mitochondria that supply the energy used in swimming. The flagellum propels the sperm through body fluids to the egg. Sperm flagella are easily visible in the interstitial spaces between cells and protruding into the central lumen or space of the seminiferous tubule. Mature sperm are released into this space.

- Your instructor may have on display a smear of a rat or bull sperm. If so, observe the slide under the compound microscope, and locate the head and tail portions of the mature sperm.
- Now observe the microscope slides of thin sections through the ovary of a cat or other mammal. By scanning a number of sections you should be able to locate the structures of the mature follicle shown in Figure 13-3a. Unlike the spermatogonial cells of the testes, the **oogonia** in ovaries of female mammals do not complete their meiotic divisions before birth. At birth, the ovaries contain **primary oocytes** arrested at an early stage (prophase) of meiosis. The oocytes present at birth represent the total number of ova that the female is capable of producing during her lifetime.

An oocyte grows to a large size (relative to sperm) and contains nutrients to support early development. Oocytes arise in the outer layer (**cortex**) of the ovary (Fig. 13-3b). Each oocyte is surrounded by a layer of helper cells called **follicle cells,** which are believed to secrete substances that are incorporated into the oocyte. The oocyte, together with its layer of follicle cells, is called the **primary** or **growing follicle.** As the oocyte matures, follicle cells increase in number and surround a fluid-filled cavity with the oocyte on one side. The primary follicle becomes the **secondary** or **maturing follicle,** which in turn develops into the mature **Graafian follicle.** You should be able to locate large primary oocytes and Graafian follicles in the ovary section. The final stages of meiosis in mammalian oocytes are completed after ovulation and fertilization have occurred. After the ovum is released, the remnants of the follicle collapse to form the **corpus luteum** ("yellow body").

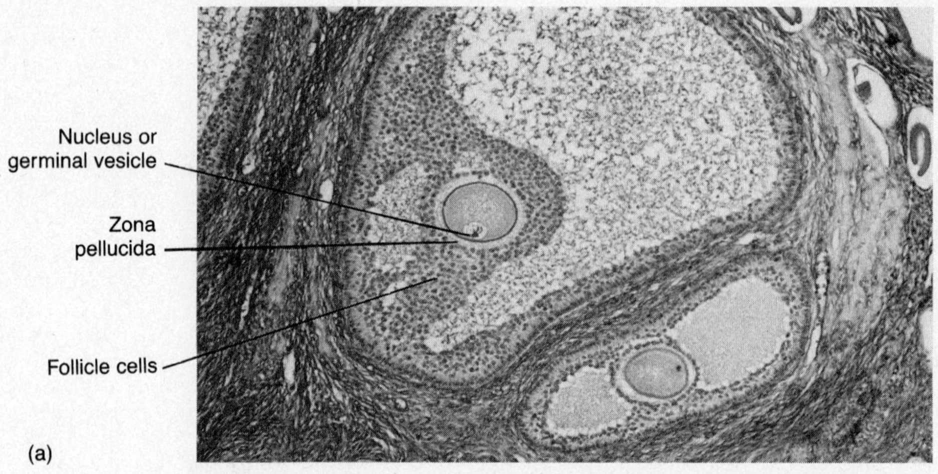

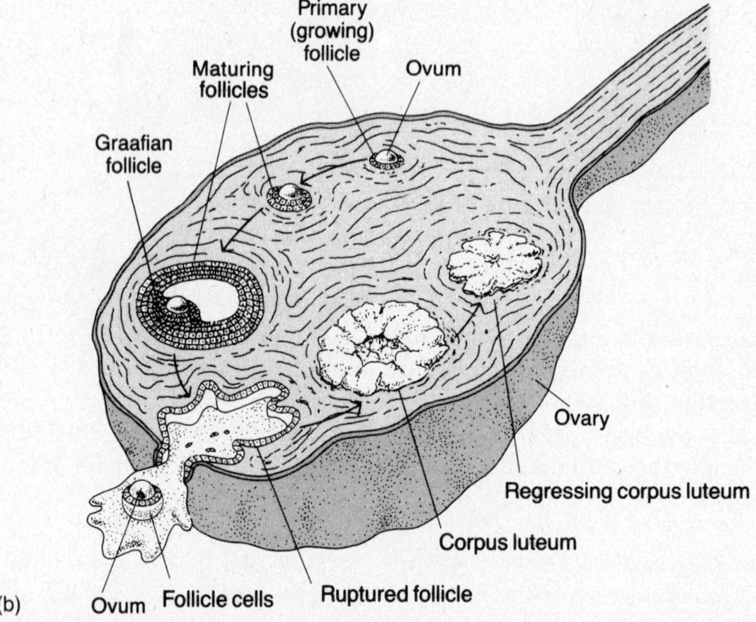

Figure 13-3 Oogenesis in a mammal. (a) Thin section through the ovary of a cat showing Graafian follicle. (b) Follicle growth in ovary.

- Complete Chart 13-1 contrasting the formation of sperm and eggs.

Chart 13-1 Comparison of spermatogenesis and oogenesis.

Feature	In sperm	In egg
Occurrence of mitotic divisions in gonial cells	produces spermatocytes repetitive throughout life	before birth (once)
Relative size of mature gamete		

Distribution of cytoplasm in meiotic divisions	evenly between 4 spermatids	uneven - more to one oocyte + less to the first polar body
Maturation stage at time of fertilization	fully mature	froze at beginning stages of meisos
Helper cells	Sertoli cells	follicle cells

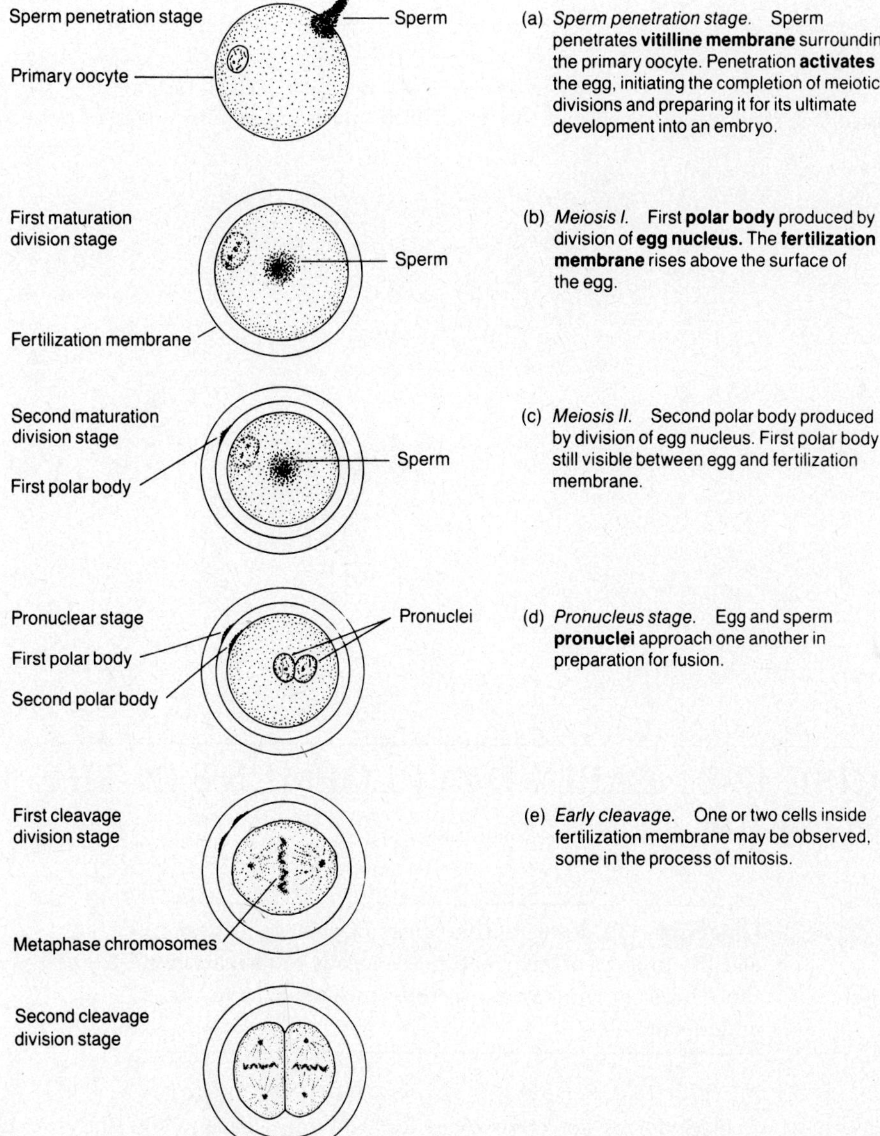

Sperm penetration stage
Primary oocyte
Sperm
(a) *Sperm penetration stage.* Sperm penetrates **vitilline membrane** surrounding the primary oocyte. Penetration **activates** the egg, initiating the completion of meiotic divisions and preparing it for its ultimate development into an embryo.
First maturation division stage
Sperm
Fertilization membrane
(b) *Meiosis I.* First **polar body** produced by division of **egg nucleus.** The **fertilization membrane** rises above the surface of the egg.
Second maturation division stage
First polar body
Sperm
(c) *Meiosis II.* Second polar body produced by division of egg nucleus. First polar body still visible between egg and fertilization membrane.
Pronuclear stage
First polar body
Second polar body
Pronuclei
(d) *Pronucleus stage.* Egg and sperm **pronuclei** approach one another in preparation for fusion.
First cleavage division stage
Metaphase chromosomes
(e) *Early cleavage.* One or two cells inside fertilization membrane may be observed, some in the process of mitosis.
Second cleavage division stage

Figure 13-4 Cross sections through uterus of *Ascaris*.

EXERCISE 13-2 FERTILIZATION IN *ASCARIS*

Objective To describe the processes of sperm penetration, egg activation, polar-body formation, and fusion of pronuclei in the round worm *Ascaris*.

Cross sections through various parts of the uterus of a fertilized *Ascaris* show oocytes and fertilized eggs at various stages of development.

- Find the stages illustrated in Figure 13-4 on the microscope slide your instructor provides. Be able to describe the changes that occur from one stage to the next.

QUESTION

What purpose is served by the raising of the fertilization membrane after a sperm penetrates the egg?

It is used to prevent more sperm from entering the egg

EXERCISE 13-3 EARLY DEVELOPMENT IN THE ECHINODERM

Objective To describe the stages of cleavage divisions and the process of gastrulation that leads to formation of the three germ layers (ectoderm, mesoderm, and endoderm).

The fertilized eggs of echinoderms are convenient for studying cleavage and early development stages because they are relatively large, they contain little yolk (so that division of the gross amount of cytoplasm is fairly equal), and they progress from egg to larval stage in hours or days depending on the species. The earliest stages of development are named according to the number of visible cells (up to the eight-celled stage). The solid ball of many cells is called the **morula,** which becomes a **blastula** when it develops into a hollow ball of cells. The cells of the blastula are called **blastomeres** and the cavity is called the **blastocoel.**

- Your instructor will provide microscope slides of eggs and developing embryos of a sea urchin or sea star. Scan the slide under the compound microscope and locate the stages illustrated in Figure 13-5. In the space next to the figure, make notes that will help you identify the stages.

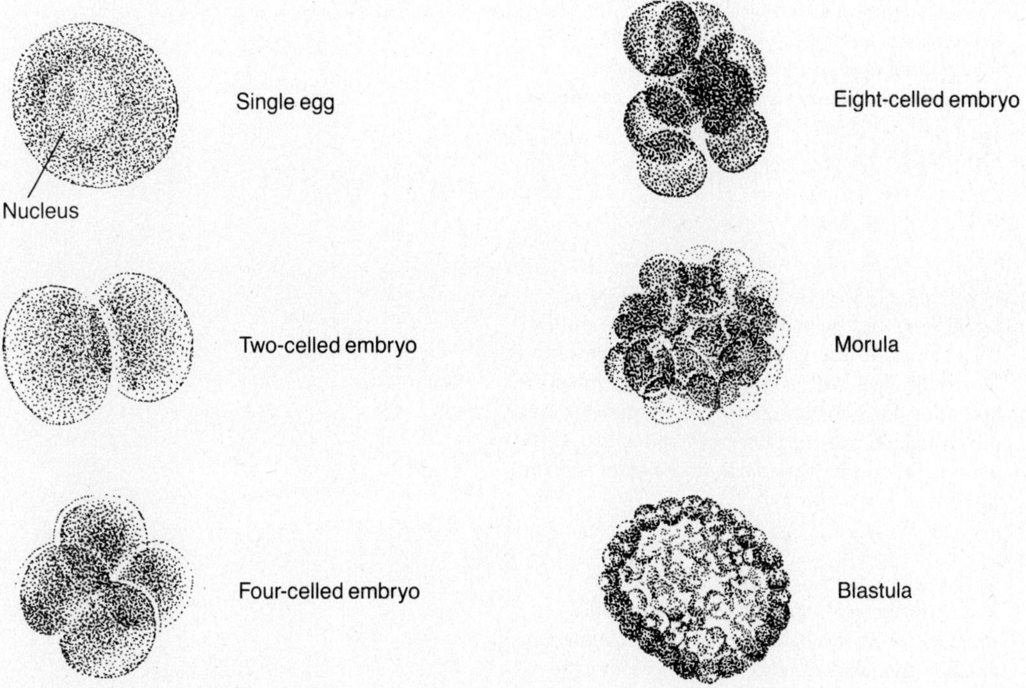

Figure 13-5 Stages in early development of echinoderms.

Gastrulation is the process by which the blastula becomes a complex, three-dimensional organism with three layers of cells. The rates of cell division and growth of the embryo slow down. Cells on the surface move inside the embryo, where they ultimately differentiate into internal organs. Gastrulation is unique in each organism partly because of the effect of different amounts of yolk on an embryo's form. Once gastrulation begins, the blastula is called a **gastrula.**

In the sea star or sea urchin, gastrulation begins with **invagination** of blastoderm cells through the **blastopore,** which becomes the future anus of the animal. In certain other animals the blastopore eventually forms the mouth. This difference in the fate of the blastopore is a fundamental distinction used to classify animals (see Chapter 21 of this manual). In these echinoderms, the stages of gastrulation are clearly visible under the microscope because the embryo is partially translucent.

- Scan the microscope slide of echinoderm embryos for the stages of gastrulation described in Chart 13-2 and make a sketch of an embryo that represents each stage.

Chart 13-2 Stages of gastrulation in echinoderms.

Stage	Sketch
The early gastrula shows a slight invagination into the blastocoel.	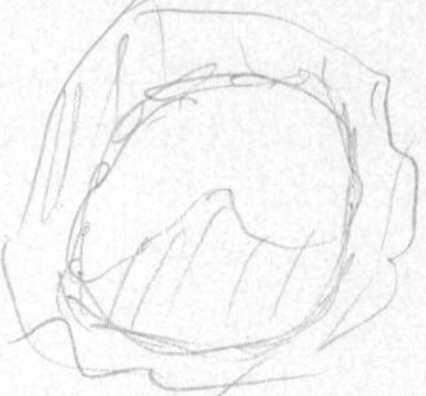
The blastopore is clearly visible as the invagination elongates. At this stage, the invaginated cells are identifiable as **endoderm.** The cells on the outer surface are the **ectoderm.**	
Echinoderms pass through a free-swimming larval stage before settling down to a life on the ocean floor. In the young larva the archenteron is more complex, with a **mouth, stomach, intestine,** and **anus** (former blastopore). The ectoderm has differentiated into various lobes and arms. This larva is called the **bipinnaria** in sea stars and the **pluteus** in sea urchins.	
In the later gastrula, a cavity called the **archenteron** (early gut) is visible inside the endoderm. At the inner end of the archenteron, small outpouches of **mesoderm** represent the start of differentiation of the **coelom** or body cavity.	

EXERCISE 13-4 EMBRYOLOGY OF THE CHICK

Objectives To describe the processes of fertilization, cleavage, gastrulation, and organogenesis in a vertebrate; to describe how the embryo forms from a primitive-streak stage and how the major anatomical structures and embryonic membranes develop.

Chick embryos are ideal for the study of embryological development in vertebrates. They display the major features and processes common to most vertebrates and they are easier to obtain and observe during early stages than are some other vertebrates (such as mammals). In the following exercises you will observe chick embryos that have reached certain classically-defined stages of development. These stages are referred to according to the age of the embryo in hours.

Your instructor will provide you with microscope slides of **whole mounts** of chick embryos at various stages of development. **Serial sections** of embryos will also be available. Serial sectioning involves slicing fixed specimens of embryos like a loaf of bread. Starting at the head, thin slices are pared off with a special cutting tool (called a microtome) and arranged in rows on a microscope slide. Observing changes in the placement of internal structures from one slice to the next provides one with a composite, three-dimensional view of the anatomy of the embryo. Refer to the whole mounts and serial sections as you read the descriptions that follow. Your instructor may also provide you with fertilized eggs containing embryos that are several days old. Instructions for preparing and observing living embryos are provided at the end of the chapter.

A. Fertilization and Early Cleavage

In the hen, oocytes in ovarian follicles accumulate large amounts of yolk. Ova arrested in metaphase of meiosis II are released into the oviduct of the hen. While an ova is in transit through the hen, cleavage divisions begin in the blastodisc, which does not cleave into cells. The thin plate of blastomeres is called the **blastoderm** (Fig. 13-6). The ovum passes through the reproductive tract of the hen, where it is fertilized, egg white (**albumen**) is added, and a calcified shell is secreted to cover it. Approximately one day after fertilization, the egg is laid.

- Examine the whole mount of a **blastodisc,** a small disc of blastomeres that lies on top of the massive yolk in an intact egg.
- Two parts of the blastoderm are distinguishable. The central area, called the **area pellucida,** is separated from the yolk by a cavity and appears lighter in color than the yolk-filled cells that form the **area opaca** at the margin. The area pellucida will form the body of the embryo. The egg is laid while the embryo is a relatively flat plate of blastoderm.

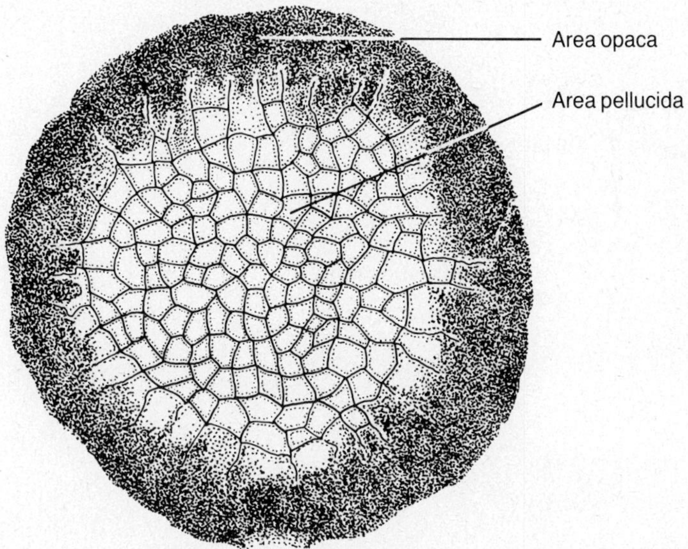

Figure 13-6 Blastoderm of chick embryo.

B. Gastrulation in the 18-Hour Chick Embryo

Gastrulation in the chick is affected by the flat shape of the embryo sitting atop the yolk. A **primitive streak** forms on the blastoderm, visible as a central thickening on the blastoderm of the 18-hour embryo (Fig. 13-7). The primitive streak forms by elongating "forward" toward the **cranial end** of the embryo (where the head forms). The end where the tail forms is the **caudal end.** During gastrulation, cells move down the embryo, through the primitive streak, and spread outward (Fig. 13-8). The first cells to migrate through the primitive streak become the endoderm; they form a layer on the bottom of the embryo. Endodermal cells ultimately form the gut. Cells that migrate inward later become the mesoderm, which gives rise to embryonic precursors of certain internal structures, including the heart, kidneys, and muscles.

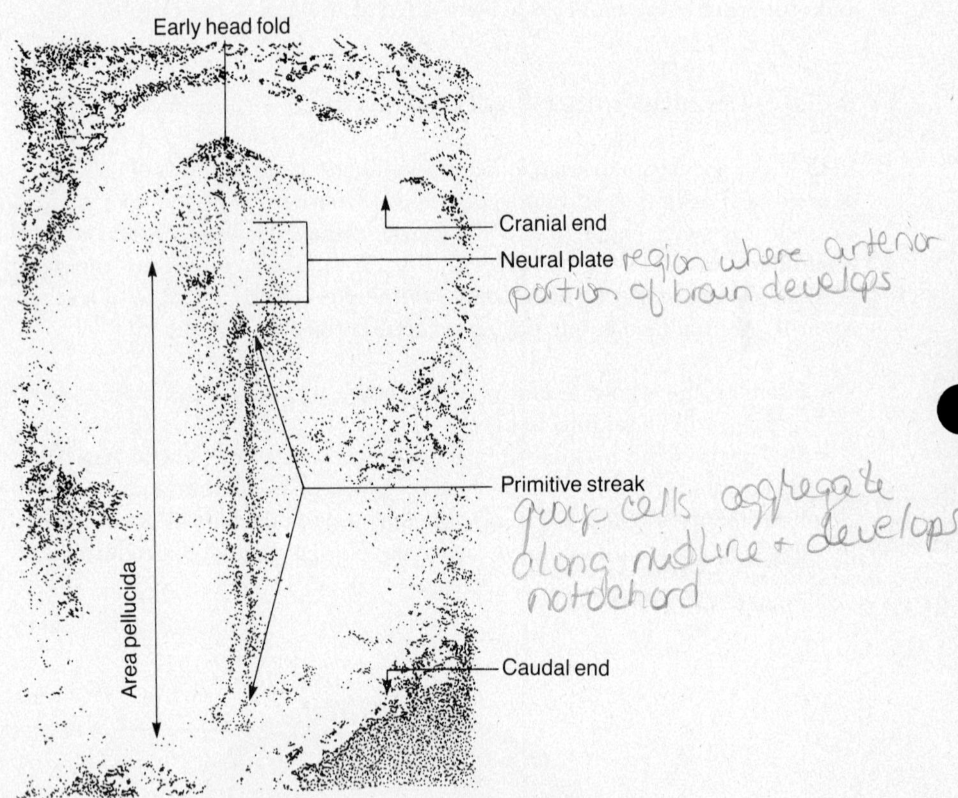

Figure 13-7 Whole mount of 18-hour chick embryo showing primitive streak.

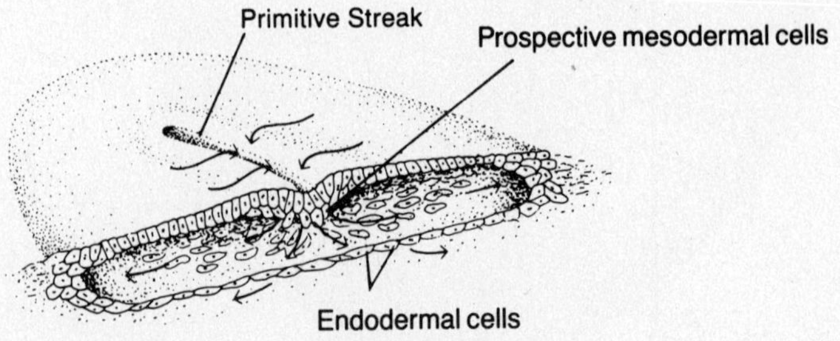

Figure 13-8 Gastrulation in the chick embryo as cells move down into primitive streak.

- Examine the whole mount of the 18-hour chick embryo under the compound microscope. You can also use the stereoscopic microscope to view the entire embryo. Locate the parts of the primitive streak and other structures labeled in Figure 13-7. Some embryos may be slightly more advanced in development than others and show greater cranial development. Some embryos may exhibit the beginning of the **head fold of the body,** which will develop into the head. An ectodermal thickening called the **neural plate** (not visible on the whole mount) covers the cranial portion of the primitive streak.

C. 24-Hour Chick Embryo

- Examine the whole mount of the 24-hour embryo under the microscope(s). After only a few more hours of development than in the 18-hour chick, many details are evident in the embryo (Fig. 13-9). The head fold is enlarged and lies on top of the blastoderm like the finger of a glove. The neural plate is folded to form **neural folds** at the cranial end. The folds border the **neural groove,** which in some embryos may be closed over to form the **neural tube.** Just behind the head fold, an arching line marks the point where endoderm pockets extend cranially (forward) into the **foregut.** Near the middle of the embryo are a series of paired **somites,** derived from **segmental plates** of mesoderm located underneath the slightly folded neural plate in this region.

- What adult structure will the somites form?

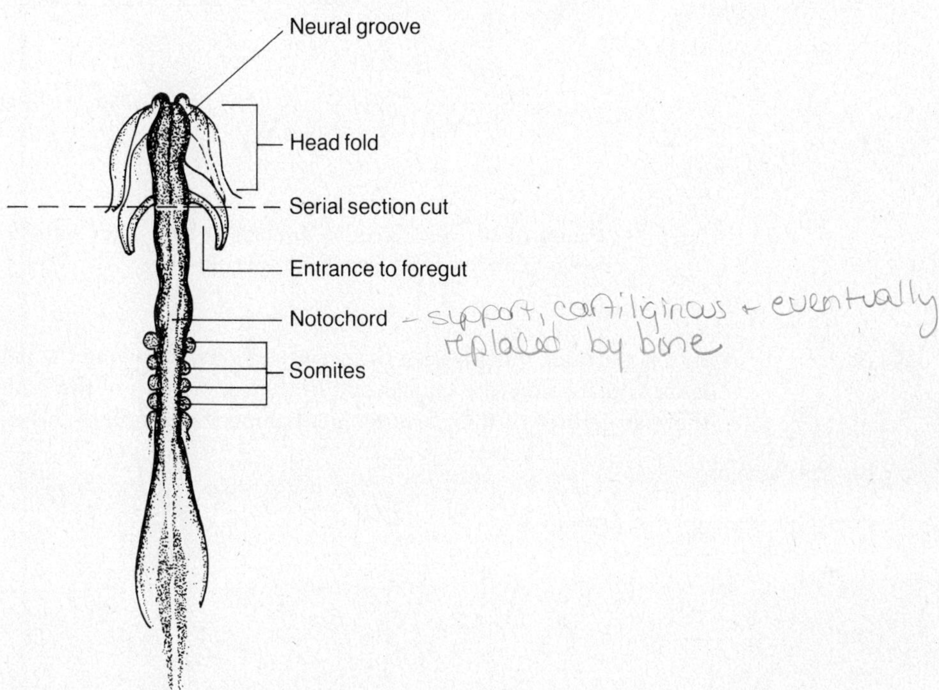

Figure 13-9 Whole mount of 24-hour chick embryo.

- Beneath the neural groove, between the somites, is the **notochord.** It extends nearly the length of the embryo; at the cranial end the notochord may be obscured in whole mounts by the neural folds on top of it. The notochord is replaced by what structures in the adult?

The notochord is replaced by
the spinal cord and the spine

- Examine the slide(s) of serial sections of the 24-hour chick embryo. You won't have time to examine all the serial sections in detail; however, try to locate the section that cuts through the arching entrance of the foregut into the head fold (see the dashed line in Fig. 13-9). Based on Figure 13-9 and the descriptions above, label the structures indicated with lines in Figure 13-10.

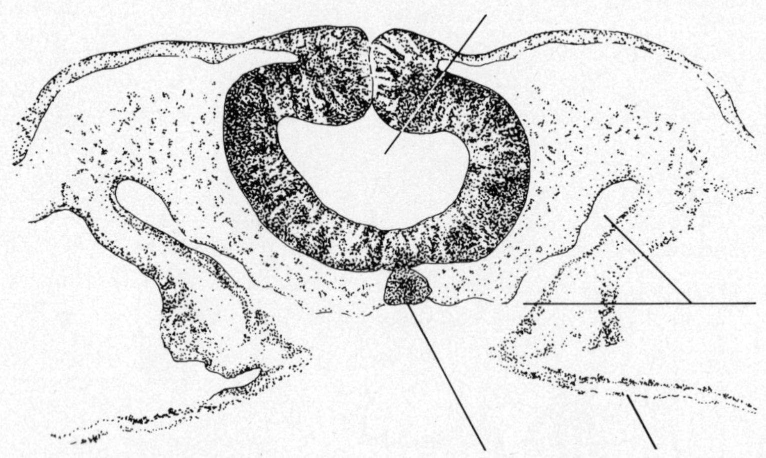

Figure 13-10 Serial section through 24-hour chick embryo near entrance of foregut into head fold (see line in Fig. 13-9).

- If time permits, quickly scan the serial sections, following the path of the notochord and neural folds or plate from the cranial end to the caudal end of the embryo. Describe the changes in these structures or their arrangement along the length of the embryo.

We did not have serial sections

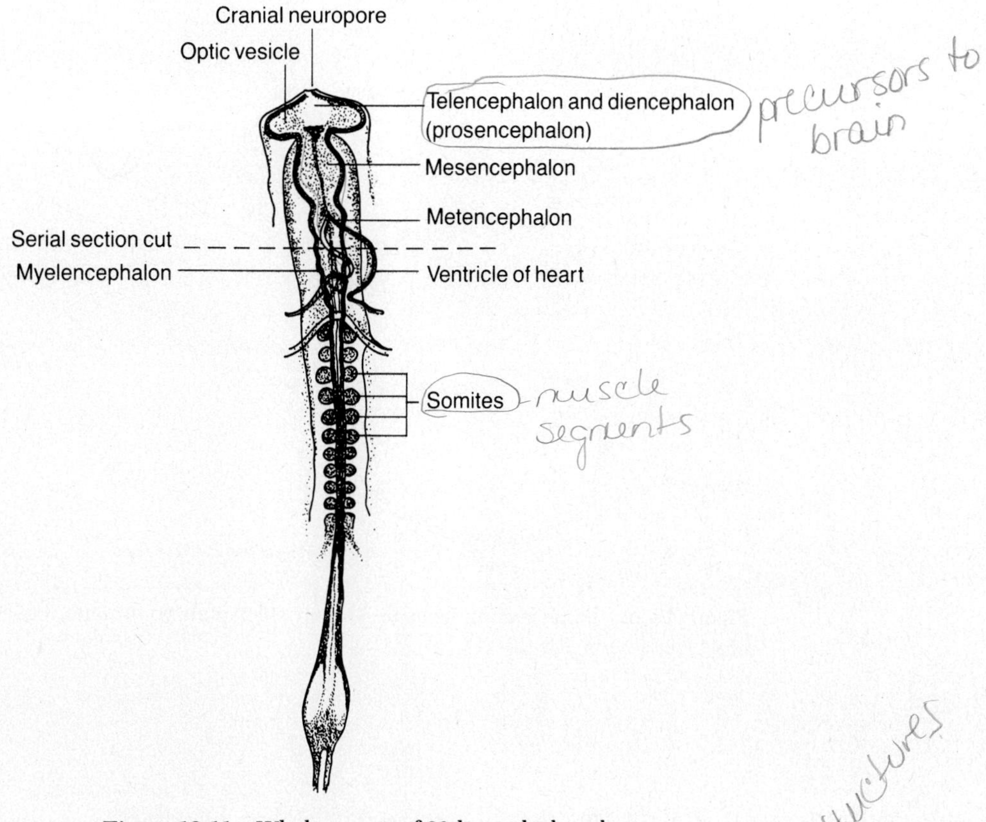

Figure 13-11 Whole mount of 33-hour chick embryo.

D. 33-Hour Chick Embryo

- Examine the whole mount of the 33-hour chick embryo and compare its overall size to that of the 24-hour chick. Under the microscope, the most obvious change in the older embryo is in the cranial region where the brain develops (Fig. 13-11). Here, the neural folds have closed over to form a tube (from above, the sides of the tube look like folds). A **cranial neuropore** is still open at the extreme cranial end of the brain. Two prominent lateral pockets are the **optic vesicles** (future eyes), which are in contact with the surface ectoderm. A series of swellings in the neural tube demarcate parts of the developing brain. Between the optic vesicles is the **prosencephalon,** which will later differentiate into the **telencephalon** and **diencephalon.** Behind them is a swelling called the **mesencephalon,** followed by the **metencephalon** and the **myelencephalon** (Fig. 13-11).

  The heart is located beneath the myelencephalon. The ventricle bends out to the right. (A clearer view can be obtained by turning over the slide.)

  More somites are now visible. How many are clearly developed on your specimen? ____________ In the area opaca at the margins of the area pellucida, clusters of mesodermal cells form **blood islands.** These eventually form a network of blood vessels over the yolk. In front of the head fold is a lighter area called the **proamnion.** This is the only portion of the embryo where mesoderm has not migrated between the ectoderm and endoderm layers.
- Examine serial sections of a 33-hour embryo and locate a section cut through the region of the heart (see the dashed line in Fig. 13-11). Based on your examination of the whole mount and the descriptions, label the structures indicated with lines in Figure 13-12.

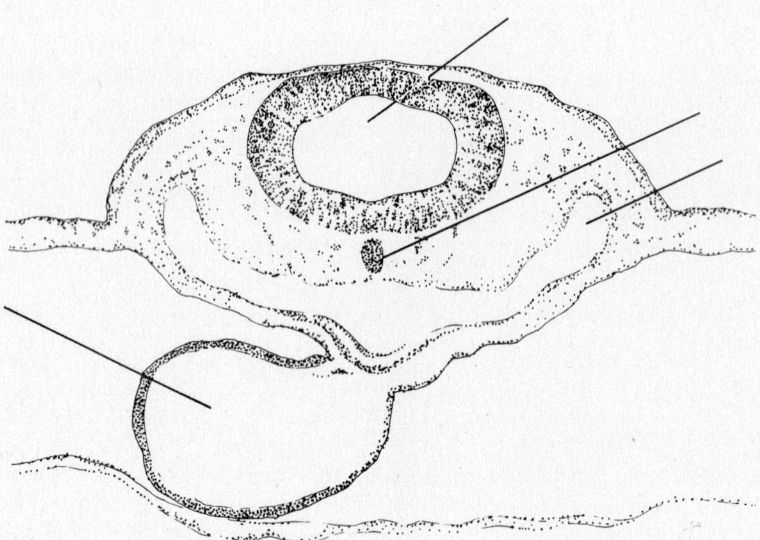

Figure 13-12 Serial section through 33-hour chick embryo through region of heart (see line in Fig. 13-11).

E. 48-Hour Chick Embryo

- Examine the whole mount of a 48-hour chick embryo and compare the size of this embryo with the size of the 33-hour chick embryo. The embryo is both longer and thicker at the later stage, and care must be taken not to damage the slide or the objective by focusing the objective down onto the slide.
- Observe the embryo under low power with the compound microscope and note first the **torsion** df the body; the embryo has twisted to lie on its left side (Fig. 13-13). (Some mental gymnastics may be necessary to orient "right" and "left" with respect to the embryo because the microscope image is reversed.)

More somites have developed in the caudal region, and a distinct caudal **tail bud** is visible. The torsion of the body provides a good view of the anatomy of the brain and heart.

The parts of the brain are now more clearly defined and a distinct **cranial flexure** is evident in the area of the mesencephalon (Fig. 13-13). The optic vesicles are now termed **optic cups,** and each cup has developed an opening, the **optic fissure.** Inside the optic cup is a **lens vesicle,** which forms from an invagination of ectodermal tissue over the cup. Behind the cranial flexure, the **auditory vesicle** is visible as a horseshoe-shaped structure, which will develop into the ear.

The heart is larger and has developed a more noticeable twist. The ventricle is clearly visible as the swollen part of the heart protruding from the embryo. Emerging from the ventricle are three pairs of blood vessels called **aortic arches.** They pass into three masses of tissue called **branchial arches,** which are separated by three splits called branchial grooves (visible as light lines between the stained tissue of the branchial arches). The deep cleft between the first (most cranial) branchial arch and the head is the **stomodeum** (future mouth). The other arches are embryonic remnants of pharyngeal gill arches found in all chordates (see Chapter 22). The aortic arches come together to form a single large vessel not easily seen in whole mounts. This vessel, the **descending aorta,** passes caudally and gives rise to two large **vitelline arteries,** which are clearly visible as they branch

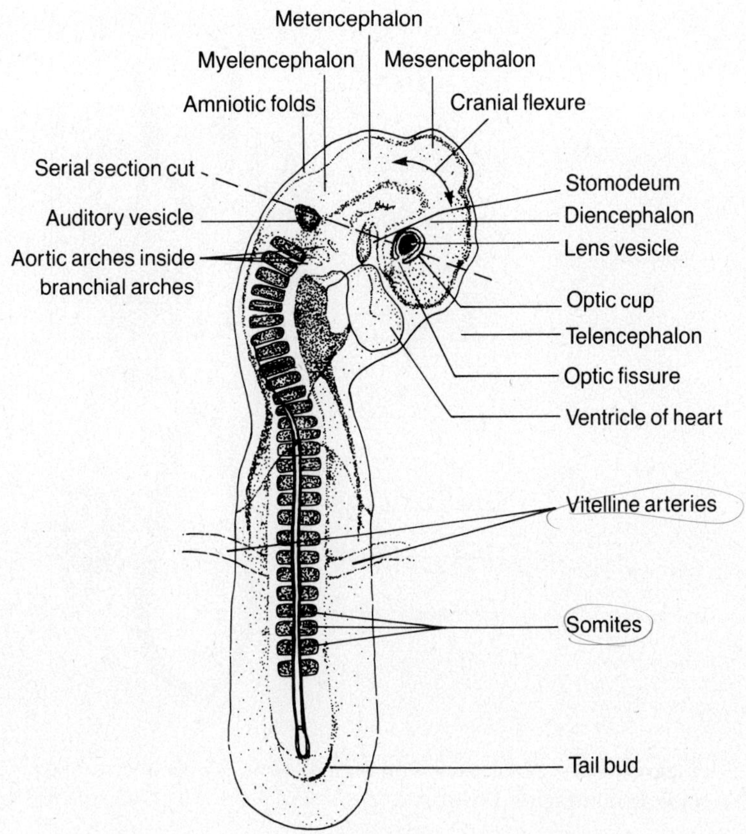

Figure 13-13 Whole mount of 48-hour chick embryo.

off at right angles to the body. Blood in the vitelline arteries flows into a network of blood vessels that absorbs nutrients from the yolk; the blood then flows back into the embryo through **vitelline veins** (not readily visible on whole mount) to the heart. Your instructor may have on display embryos whose circulatory systems have been injected with colored dye; details of the heart and blood vessels are more easily seen on such specimens.

Several embryonic coverings are visible at this stage of development. The **amniotic folds** cover the cranial half of the embryo like a hood (Fig. 13-13). This covering consists of two layers (distinguishable in the serial sections to be observed later). The outer layer is called the **chorion** (sometimes the term **serosa** is used for bird embryos); the inner layer is called the **amnion.** The role of these extraembryonic membranes in protecting and nourishing the embryo will be explained in the next section.

- Examine the serial sections of the 48-hour embryo. The internal anatomy is quite complex at this stage; however, a section through the embryo at the point marked by the line in Figure 13-13 reveals a number of the structures discussed above. Label the structures indicated by lines in Figure 13-14.
- Your instructor may provide you with a freshly prepared living 48-hour chick embryo. Identify as many structures as possible without disturbing the embryo. Notice also that at this stage the heart is beating, and try to follow the movement of blood in the larger vessels.

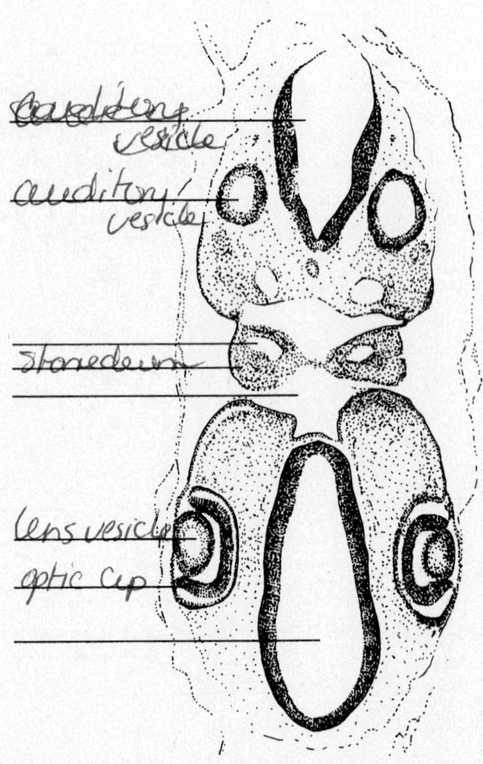

Figure 13-14 Serial section through 48-hour chick embryo at level of line indicated in Figure 13-13.

F. 72-Hour Chick Embryo and Extraembryonic Membranes

- Examine the whole mount of a 72-hour chick embryo. The 72-hour chick embryo is larger and more developed than the 48-hour stage, but few additional structures are visible on whole mounts. Locate the structures shown in Figure 13-15 and compare them to their precursors in the 48-hour chick embryo. Notice that the **cerebral hemispheres** have developed in the telencephalon.

The extraembryonic membranes are well developed at the 72-hour stage. The caudal end as well as the cranial end of the embryo are now covered by the amniotic folds (amnion and chorion). In addition, a small outpouching of the hindgut is visible near the tail bud. This outpouching is the beginning of the **allantois,** which enlarges as it collects urinary wastes from the gut. The embryo now possesses four extraembryonic membranes: the **yolk sac, amnion, chorion,** and allantois. Their development is rather complex, but their arrangement in a late-stage chick embryo is shown in Figure 13-16. The amnion covers nearly the entire embryo except for the **umbilical cord.** At later stages the amnion is filled with amniotic fluid, which prevents the embryo from drying out and also acts as a shock absorber. At this later stage, the now-enlarged allantois is still connected to the hindgut. The yolk sac is depleted as the embryo uses its nutrients for growth. The allantois and yolk sac are connected to the embryo by the umbilical cord. The chorion has grown to surround the embryo, allantois, and yolk sac. Along with the allantois, the chorion absorbs oxygen for the rapidly developing embryo.

G. Fate of the Germ Layers

- Use the information from your textbook (in particular Table 16-1) and the descriptions of chick embryos to determine which germ layer gives rise to each of the structures in Chart 13-3.

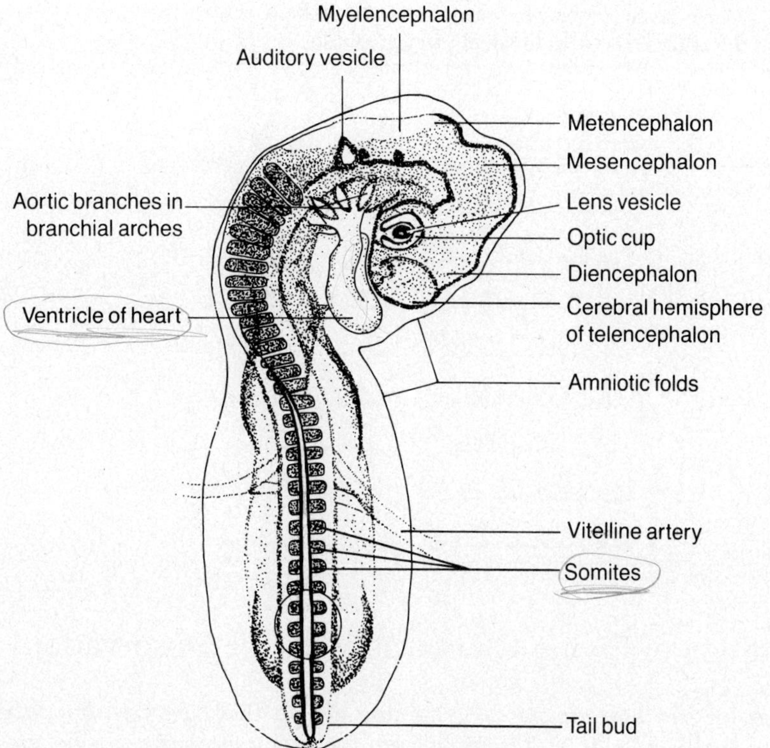

Figure 13-15 Whole mount of 72-hour chick embryo.

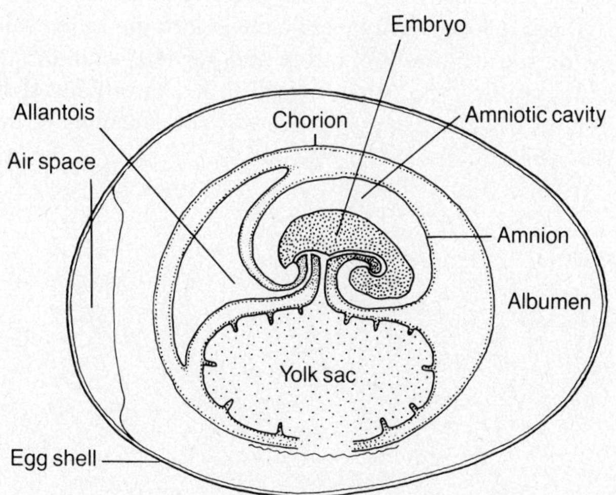

Figure 13-16 Arrangement of extraembryonic membranes in late-stage chick embryo.

Some structures may be derived from more than one germ layer. Complete the chart by writing the germ-layer origin of each embryonic structure and indicate to which adult structure it gives rise. In addition, indicate these derivations directly on the figures of the 48- and 72-hour chick embryos by using colored pencils to underline the labels. By convention, blue is used for ectoderm, red for mesoderm, and yellow for endoderm.

Chart 13-3 Germ-layer origins of structures in the 48-hour chick embryo and the adult structures to which they give rise.

Structure	Germ layer derived from	Adult structure
Neural tube	ectoderm	brain
Optic vesicles	ectoderm	eye
Auditory vesicles	ectoderm	ear
Spinal cord	ectoderm	spinal cord
Notochord	mesoderm	backbone
Somites	mesoderm	muscles
Gut lining	endoderm	gut lining
Ventricle	endoderm	heart

H. Preparation of Living Chick Embryos for Observation

- Your instructor may have on display a number of eggs that have been incubated for 48 hours or more at approximately 38 °C. To observe the living embryos outside the egg, you must provide them with a semi-normal environment. Fill a finger bowl or other deep dish half full with saline solution warmed to about 38 °C. (You can prepare the saline solution by dissolving 1 g of sodium chloride in 100 ml of distilled water.) Carefully crack the egg and submerge it in the saline solution, then gently float the egg contents free in the bowl. Observe the embryo first with the naked eye; then use a magnifying glass or stereoscopic microscope to get a closer look. BE CAREFUL not to focus the objective down into the saline solution or the yolk. Your instructor may provide you with neutral red or another vital stain to make the chick embryo's anatomy more readily visible. Vital stains are absorbed into living tissues without damaging them. (These vital stains will also color your skin without damaging it, but they wear off slowly, so handle them with care.)

The material in this chapter corresponds to Chapter 19 in your text.

14
CLASSIFICATION OF BIOLOGICAL DIVERSITY

Taxonomy is the branch of biology that attempts to categorize the diversity of living things on this planet (and perhaps, in the future, on other planets). The science is more than the practice of naming things, however. Like other fields in biology, taxonomy involves the formulation and testing of theories of how organisms should be classified into groups. The classifications and the groupings change as biologists learn more about the organisms and also as theories about classification change.

Classification schemes have several purposes. One practice purpose is identification. Biologists working in different places and times need a mutually understandable way of referring to organisms they study. They need to be able to identify to what species an organism belongs so that their work can be compared to other studies or so that future scientists can replicate their studies if needed.* Another function of taxonomic classification is to reflect our current understanding of evolutionary relationships. That is, organisms that are close relatives in an evolutionary sense are classified in distinct groups. For example, within the mammals, chimpanzees and humans are classified together in the group called primates, whereas dogs and cats are both in the group called carnivores.

The exercises in this chapter demonstrate these two functions of biological classification. The first exercise introduces taxonomic levels of classification and explains the use of descriptive keys to identify organisms as members of a species. The second exercise demonstrates how characteristics of organisms can be used to construct a **phylogeny,** or diagram, depicting the evolutionary relationships of the organisms. The third and last exercise introduces the five-kingdom classification of biological diversity.

EXERCISE 14-1 DICHOTOMOUS KEYS

Objectives To use a dichotomous key to determine the species of organisms; to construct a dichotomous key for a group of organisms.

*Species names are based on descriptions of a number of specimens by a taxonomist specializing in a group of organisms. New species previously unknown to biologists are added continuously as they are discovered. Old species names are sometimes discarded if new information indicates that the organisms in question are really members of a previously described species.

Biologists often use **dichotomous keys** to identify specimens of plants and animals. Such keys consist of series of paired statements (couplets), only one of which applies to the specimen in hand. For example, the first couplet in a key to a group of flowering plants might read:

1 Leaves broad 2
Leaves long and narrow... 3

Notice that each statement directs the user to another couplet in the key (in this case, couplet 2 or 3) and eventually leads step by step to a final couplet with the identity of the specimen. In biology the term "dichotomous" means "two-forked." In a dichotomous key, the path to identification presents a two-forked decision at each couplet.

Dichotomous keys are artificial; that is, they are usually not meant to reflect evolutionary relationships. The primary function of a key is to correctly identify a specimen. A key may be constructed for any set of specimens: trees in Tucson, ungulates of Kenya, or students in the laboratory. Most often, keys are intended for species identification, but a key may be constructed to identify a specimen to any of the taxa listed in Table 14-1. The following exercises require you to use, or "key out," organisms to the species level and to construct your own key for a set of specimens.

Table 14-1 Major taxa of biological classification applied to the classification of the tiger and cultivated lettuce.

Tiger classification	
Kingdom	Animalia (animals)
Phylum	Chordata (chordates)
Class	Mammalia (mammals)
Order	Carnivora (carnivores)
Family	Felidae (cat family)
Genus	*Panthera* (lions, tigers, leopards, and jaguars)
Species	*Panthera tigris*

Lettuce classification	
Kingdom	Plantae (plants)
Division	Tracheophyta (vascular plants)
Class	Angiospermae (flowering plants)
Order	Campanulatae (bellflowers and composites)
Family	Compositae (composites)
Genus	*Lactuca* (lettuce)
Species	*Lactuca sativa* (cultivated lettuce)

A. Taxonomic categories

Taxonomy classifies organisms as members of a hierarchy of categories or groups. Each category is called a **taxon** (plural: **taxa**). Each taxon is a member of several broader, more inclusive taxa above it in the classification system. A useful analogy is that of the family: You are a member of a family, which together with related families makes up a larger group of relatives, which with other related groups forms a yet larger group, and so on. The species is the lowest level of biological classification in the Linnaean system discussed in your test. Table 14-1 lists the major taxa in biological classification as they apply to the classification of an animal (tiger) and a plant (cultivated lettuce). Note that the taxon "Phylum" is called "Division" by botanists, although both apply to the taxon just below the "Kingdom." Also note that the species name consists of two parts: the genus and the "specific epithet." Genus and species are italicized (or underlined), and all taxa except the specific epithet are capitalized.

B. Using a Dichotomous Key

- Your instructor will provide you with a key to a series of specimens in the laboratory. You might need to refer to the textbook, dictionaries, and reference books to understand terms used in the keys. As you key out a specimen, document the path of decisions made at each couplet by writing in Chart 14-1 the couplet number and the statement that applies to the specimen at hand. If you make a mistake or become confused, this written path will allow you to retrace your steps quickly. Some couplets may present what seems to be an ambiguous choice. If so, place an asterisk next to the confusing couplet and try the most likely path; if this leads to more confusion, come back to the problem couplet and try the other path.
- Check the identification with your instructor. Some keys are easier to follow than others, and some specimens are in better condition than others. Try keying out several specimens whose identity is known to you. If you misidentify them, find the terminal couplet with the correct species name and work backwards through the key until you find where you made the wrong turn. If the key appears to be at fault, discuss with your classmates and instructor how the key could be improved.

Chart 14-1 Keying pathways.

Specimen #	____________	Specimen #	____________
Couplet #	Applicable statement	Couplet #	Applicable statement
____________	____________	____________	____________
____________	____________	____________	____________
____________	____________	____________	____________
____________	____________	____________	____________
____________	____________	____________	____________
____________	____________	____________	____________
____________	____________	____________	____________
____________	____________	____________	____________
____________	____________	____________	____________

C. Constructing a Dichotomous Key

- Your instructor will provide you with a set of leaves or other specimens for which you will construct a dichotomous key. Having used a key yourself, you know how ambiguous wording can lead to erroneous identification. Therefore, use precise, concise language in the key. Limit each statement to short descriptions of easily observable characters of the specimen at hand. Do not offer such statements as "The specimen is a starfish," or "The specimen normally grows in Brazilian rainforests." Follow the format used in the key provided by your instructor. You will probably need to revise the key as you work. Write the final version of your key on a separate piece of paper.

QUESTION

Describe how you constructed the key. What similarities or differences did you look for in organizing the specimens into groups so that you could use the key?

EXERCISE 14-2 CONSTRUCTING A PHYLOGENY

Objective To construct a phylogeny based on monophyletic groups for a hypothetical set of plants.

The underlying principle of most modern taxonomy is evolution: Classification schemes are intended to reflect evolutionary relationships. Put a different way, organisms classified as members of one group share with each other a more recent common ancestor than they share with organisms classified in a different group. Again, human familial relationships provide an analogy to this type of classification. An individual female is a member of a single family of parents and children, and she is also a member of larger groups of more distant relatives with whom she shares even more distant common ancestors.

In theory, we could draw a giant genealogy of all living things on Earth that shows a branching pattern of evolutionary change. Figure 14-1 shows a branching pattern in which the letters represent related species. This kind of diagram is called a "phylogeny" and is based on the idea that an ancestral species gives rise to others through a succession of splittings or dichotomous speciation events. The phylogeny in Figure 14-1 is a nested hierarchy because it contains small groups of organisms (such as A and B) that share a common ancestor (indicated by arrow 1), and these small groups are nested within larger groups (such as A, B, C, and D) that share a more distant common ancestor (indicated by arrow 2).

If phylogenies were as easy to decipher from observing organisms as they are to draw in Figure 14-1, taxonomy would be a very straightforward science. But because there were no witnesses to speciation events in the past, phylogenies must be *inferred* from the characteristics possessed by

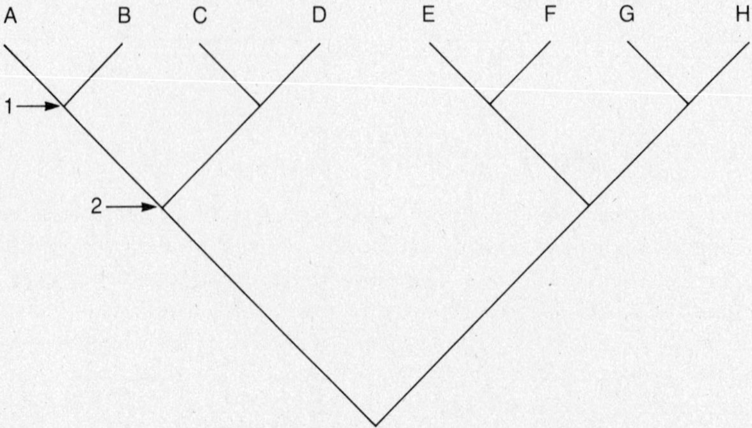

Figure 14-1 Branching pattern of evolutionary relationships.

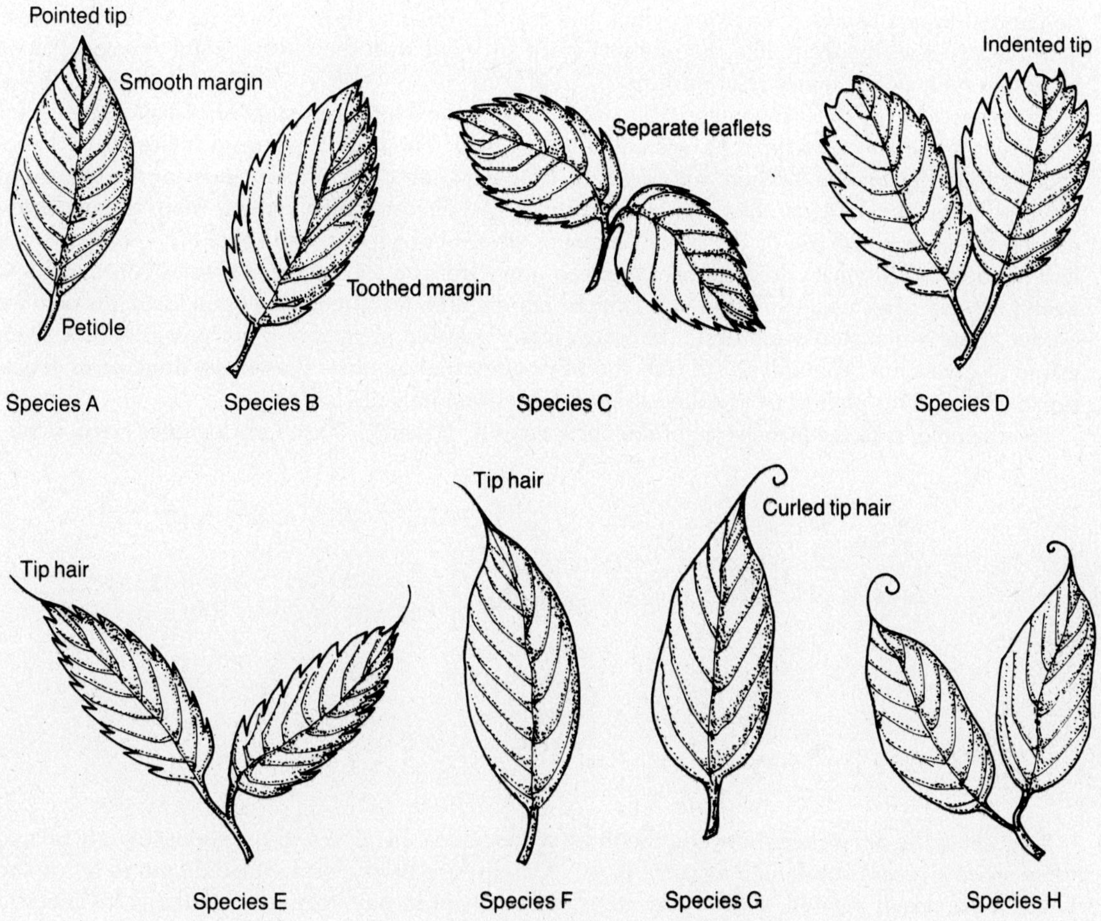

Figure 14-2 Leaf shapes for constructing a phylogeny.

organisms. Different schools of thought exist regarding how one should construct phylogenies. This exercise demonstrates the cladistic method of phylogeny construction, in which the major goal is to identify **monophyletic groups** of the kind diagrammed in Figure 14-1. Monophyletic groups, also called **clades,** consist of all and only the descendants of a common ancestor. For example, A and B in Figure 14-1 constitute a clade; the group consisting of A, B, C, and D also form a clade. But a group of only A, B, and C is not a clade because it does not include *all* the descendants of the common ancestor at arrow 2.

Grouping organisms into monophyletic groups displays the pathway that evolution has taken. Many biologists feel that by deciphering the pathway of evolution, one can better understand the mechanisms of evolution. You will first construct a phylogeny of a hypothetical group of related plant species based on the characteristics of their leaves. Then you will construct a phylogeny for a set of plant species based on a collection of real leaves.

A. Use of Leaf Characteristics to Construct a Phylogeny

The leaf characteristics of the hypothetical group of related plant species is shown in Figure 14-2.* Each species is represented by a letter (A to H). Assume that the entire group of eight species

*An actual group of plant species would differ in more than just leaf characteristics, and one would use all the characteristics to construct a phylogeny. Constructing a phylogeny for them would be too complicated for one laboratory exercise. Taxonomists employ computers to help unravel complicated phylogenies. The reasoning required to construct this simple phylogeny is similar to that for more complicated cases.

descended from a common ancestor, which had leaves similar to those of species A. The task here is to construct a phylogeny like the one in Figure 14-1 but with the letters (plant species) placed to reflect their evolutionary relationships.

Differences between leaf characteristics are the result of evolutionary steps. For example, species A (similar to the ancestral type) has a smooth leaf margin. The leaf of species A is similar to that of species B except for the toothed margin on B. Now we know the common ancestor for the group was similar to species A, so the evolution of B from that ancestor involved one step: the evolution of a toothed margin. Each of the other characteristics (bilobed leaf, tip hairs, etc.) also involved independent evolutionary steps. For example, a move from an ancestor like species A to species C would involve two steps: evolution of a toothed margin and evolution of a bilobed leaf (for now we do not know which step came first). Although many possible phylogenies are possible for a given group of organisms, you will try to find the phylogeny that involves the fewest number of evolutionary steps. This phylogeny is called the most **parsimonious** phylogeny.

For example, take the leaf characteristics of species A, B, and C. Three phylogenies are possible:

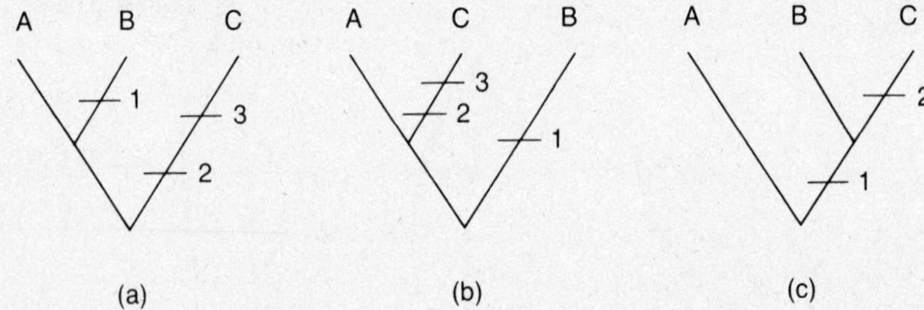

First, note the differences between the three phylogenies. In (a), A and B are most closely related (they share a recent common ancestor); in (b), A and C are most closely related; and in (c), B and C are most closely related. How many steps are involved in phylogeny 1? Assuming an ancestor similar to A, there are 3 steps: (1) B evolved a toothed leaf margin, (2) C evolved a toothed leaf margin in an independent step, and (3) C evolved a bilobed leaf. These steps are shown on the phylogeny by numbered lines. The independent evolution of a characteristic such as a toothed leaf margin in two different clades is called convergent evolution, which results in distant relatives sharing a characteristic that their distant common ancestor lacked.

Phylogeny (b) involves the same three steps as phylogeny (a), but in a different arrangement of branches on the phylogeny. Phylogeny (c), however, involves 2 steps: (1) a toothed leaf margin evolved once in the line leading to both B and C and (2) C evolved a bilobed leaf. Phylogeny (c) is the most parsimonious, so we choose it as the "best" phylogeny. A phylogeny should be viewed as a hypothesis, subject to change if further evidence shows it to be in error.

The situation becomes more complicated with more species and more characteristics. In fact, for the eight species you will use in this exercise, thousands of phylogenies are possible. Luckily, however, you will not have to examine all of them in this exercise. We will simplify matters by using a dichotomously branching phylogeny. Other types of branching are possible, and they imply different kinds of monophyletic relationships. You might try to think of several different types of branching patterns. Try to draw a phylogeny in which each characteristic evolves only once (as the toothed leaf margin evolved only once in phylogeny c). However, in nature similar characteristics can and do sometimes evolve independently in separate lines as shown in the leaf margin example.

- Before you construct a phylogeny, first distinguish between **characters** and **character states.** A character is a particular feature, such as leaf margin. A character state is the *type* of feature shown by a species, such as a smooth leaf margin. Sometimes, a character state is simply the presence or absence of a feature, such as a leaf tip hair. In Figure 14-2, there are three characters: leaf margin, number of leaflets, and type of leaf tip. Each character is expressed in two or more character states. Refer to Figure 14-2 and list the character states for each character in Chart 14-2. Then assign a unique code number to each character state.

Chart 14-2 Character states for Figure 14-2.

Character	Possible character states	Code
Leaf margin	__________	_____
	__________	_____
Number of leaflets	__________	_____
	__________	_____
Type of leaf tip	__________	_____
	__________	_____
	__________	_____

- Next, complete Chart 14-3, describing the character states for species A to H. Write the character state and its code in the columns for each character. The chart, which lists the characters and character states, is called a **data matrix.**

Chart 14-3 Data matrix for species A to H in Figure 14-2.

	Character		
Species	Leaf margin	Number of leaflets	Type of leaf tip
A	__________	__________	__________
B	__________	__________	__________
C	__________	__________	__________
D	__________	__________	__________
E	__________	__________	__________
F	__________	__________	__________
G	__________	__________	__________
H	__________	__________	__________

- Three blank phylogenies are shown in Figure 14-3. Try arranging species A–H on the phylogenies in various ways, by placing species that share one or more character states on the same branch or clade. Use a pencil so you can erase and change your phylogenies. Because

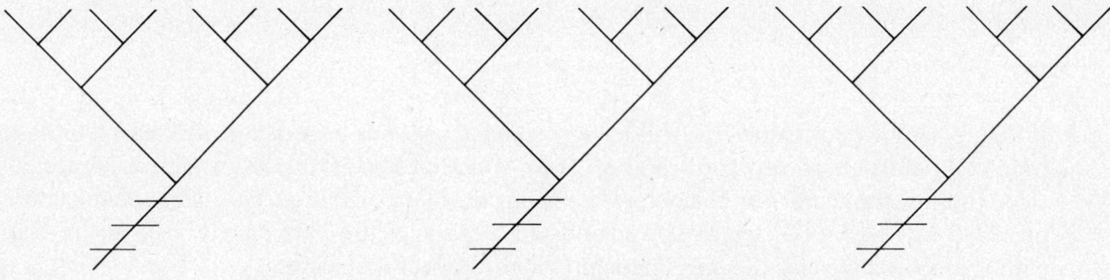

Figure 14-3 Phylogenies for leaf species in Figure 14-2.

we assume the ancestor was similar to species A, the common ancestor at the base of the phylogeny is assumed to have had the character states of species A: smooth leaf margin, single leaflet, and pointed tip. The three bars at the base of the phylogeny should be labeled with your codes for these three character states. Draw in numbered bars on the phylogeny indicating where evolutionary changes (steps) in character states occur. For example, on one of the branches leading to species B, a bar must be drawn indicating a change from a smooth to a toothed leaf margin. Label each bar with the numbered codes you selected for the character states. Drawing a bar for a character state on one branch means that all the species above the bar display that character state, *unless* you draw another bar indicating a reversal.

- Character states may evolve more than once on the phylogeny (toothed margins might evolve separately on two branches) and reversals are possible (toothed margins might evolve on some lower branch, after which a reversal to smooth margins might evolve on a branch above). In fact, you could imagine a phylogeny where two character states changed back and forth many times on a single branch. However, remember that you are looking for the most parsimonious phylogeny, so try to minimize the number of reversals and convergent character states. Calculate the number of evolutionary steps for each phylogeny by counting the number of character-state bars on all the branches. After a few attempts, you will see how placing the character state changes on different branches affects the number of evolutionary steps needed for a phylogeny. Compare your phylogenies with those of other classmates and try to find the most parsimonious phylogeny. Several phylogenies that are very different may be equally parsimonious.

QUESTIONS

Notice that all the leaves in Figure 14-2 have a similar petiole (small branch supporting the leaf). Explain why this character is not useful in constructing a phylogeny.

Species D has a unique, indented type of leaf tip. Explain why a character that is unique to only one species is not useful in placing that species on a particular branch of the phylogeny.

- If time permits, your instructor will have you construct your own data matrix based on leaves from real plants on or near your campus. If so, you might want to look ahead to Chapter 23 to refer to illustrations of leaf characters to use in the data matrix. A few likely characters are provided in Chart 14-4, which you may use to construct the data matrix. Fill in the blanks with character states for the specimens provided by your instructor.

Chart 14-4 Data matrix for leaves from real plant specimens.

	Leaf characters			
Specimen #	Arrangement	Petiole (present/absent)	Margin	Shape

A phylogeny based on real specimens will probably be even more complicated than the idealized example shown in Figure 14-2. Such a phylogeny will likely contain many reversals and evolutionarily convergent character states, and you will have to guess which character states are ancestral. Furthermore, leaves collected from an area like a campus are likely to be from distantly related plants that are not members of a monophyletic group. Therefore, the phylogeny you construct will be artificial. Nevertheless, constructing such a phylogeny demonstrates the difficulty of the process and how complicated evolutionary pathways can be.

- Draw your phylogeny in the space below.

EXERCISE 14-3 THE FIVE KINGDOMS—THE DIVERSITY OF LIFE

Objectives: To provide a brief introduction to the five kingdoms of life and the major morphological features and modes of nutrition of each; to be able to classify a variety of specimens according to kingdom.

The largest and most inclusive group in a classification scheme is the **kingdom.** The textbook uses the five-kingdom classification of R. H. Whittaker, modified slightly to include an additional kingdom called the Archaebacteria (Fig. 14-4). This scheme is an improvement over the original two-kingdom scheme of Linnaeus in which every organism was classified as either animal or plant. Modern biologists now recognize a much wider diversity in complexity of structure and nutritional modes of organisms than Linnaeus knew.

The five-kingdom system reflects major differences between groups of living things, especially the differences between prokaryotic and eukaryotic cells. A major drawback of the system is that it does not reflect patterns of evolution—the kingdoms, with the exception of the Monera, are not monophyletic groups. For example, some large algae (seaweeds) are more closely related to members of the Protista than they are to the vascular plants, with whom they are grouped in the Kingdom Plantae. Therefore, the five-kingdom scheme should be viewed as a convenient way of ordering the bewildering diversity of life forms on Earth, not as a representation of five major branches of evolution. In general, the phyla within the kingdoms do represent monophyletic groups, and it is within phyla that one should look for evolutionary patterns and phylogenies analogous to the one constructed in Exercise 14-2.

- Your instructor will have on display a variety of specimens, which you should be able to classify as members of one of the five kingdoms and describe the rationale for doing so. (The differences between Archaebacteria and other prokaryotes are not evident with a simple microscope.) Record your observations in Chart 14-5.

Chart 14-5 Classifying specimens as members of the five kingdoms.

Specimen	Kingdom	Rationale for placement in kingdom

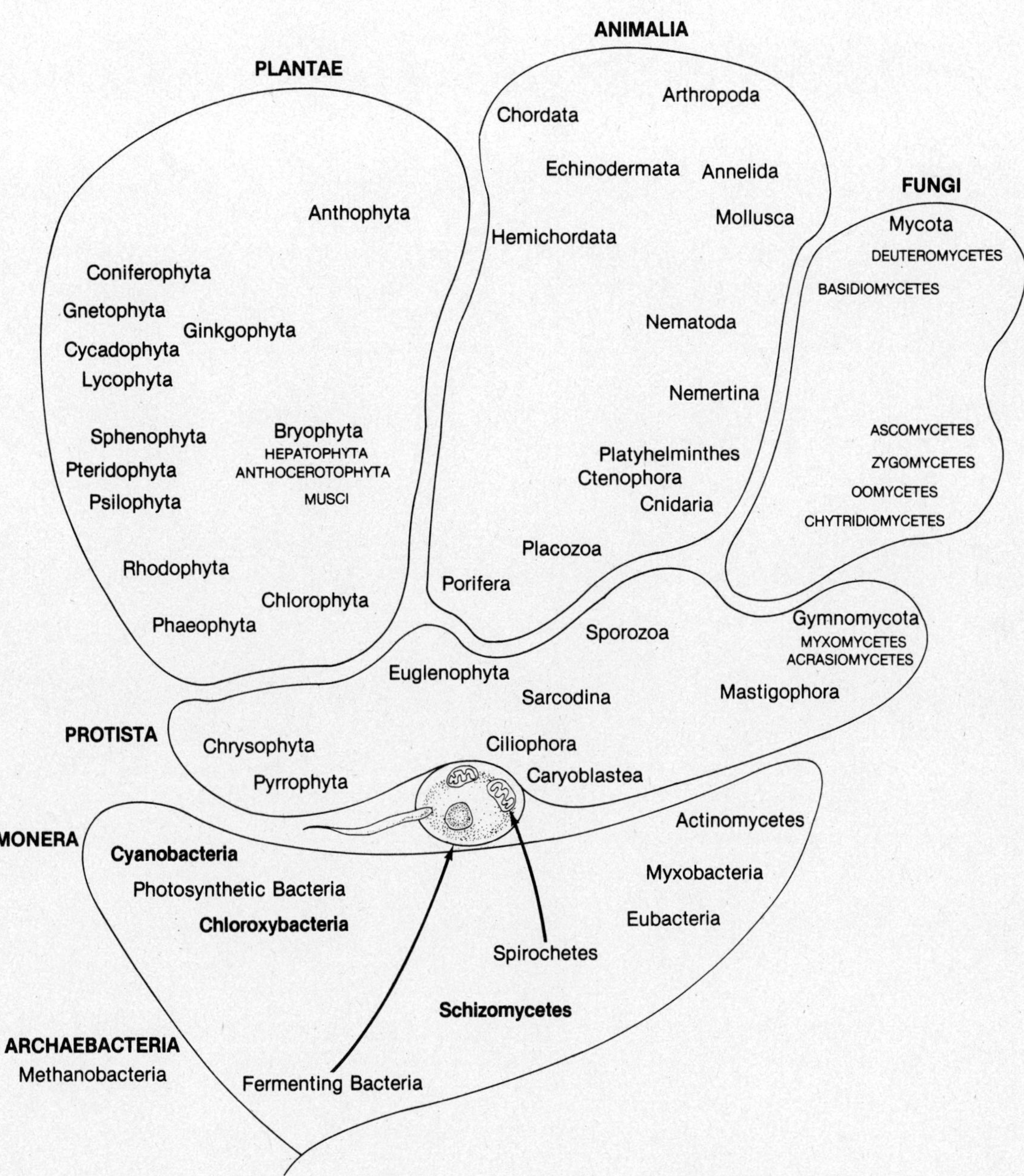

Figure 14-4 Whittaker's five-kingdom classification system.

The material in this chapter corresponds to Chapter 19–20 in your text.

15

KINGDOM MONERA—THE BACTERIA

The Monera, commonly called bacteria, are the simplest living organisms. They possess a prokaryotic structure, meaning that they are cells without any of the membrane-bound organelles (such as mitochondria, nuclei, and chloroplasts) found in eukaryotic cells (see Chapter 5 in this manual). Bacteria are generally smaller than eukaryotic cells and reproduce rapidly through the process of asexual binary fission. Some are capable of primitive sexual processes and pass fragments of genetic material between cells. Because they display these simple traits, bacteria are considered evolutionarily primitive; that is, they are similar to the earliest forms of life on Earth.

But to call bacteria "primitive" belies their remarkable metabolic diversity. Eukaryotic cells, not to mention humans, are Johnny-come-latelies on the evolutionary scene and have no metabolic capabilities that bacteria did not already possess billions of years ago. In metabolic terms, bacteria as a whole can do anything a eukaryote can do and considerably more—for example, some bacteria can fix nitrogen from the gaseous state to produce nitrogenous organic compounds.

Bacteria are ubiquitous, growing on, around, and in nearly everything on Earth's surface. The various types of bacteria are so successful because of their metabolic diversity: They can utilize a wide variety of organic and inorganic substances as energy sources and can grow under a wide range of temperature, pH, and other environmental conditions. Many are disease-causing agents, but others are essential to life for more complex creatures, including humans. For instance, *Escherichia coli* and other bacteria thrive in our intestinal tracts and play a beneficial role in the synthesis of some vitamins, but they can be harmful if they invade other spaces in the body. The bacteria in the stomachs of cows and other ruminants play an essential role in the digestion of cellulose, which the animals themselves cannot break down. The same is true for wood-eating termites, which possess a rich intestinal bacterial population. Certain bacteria grow under conditions of high temperature and pressure in hydrothermal vents on the ocean floor. Various bacteria play key roles in the production of yogurt, certain cheeses, and sauerkraut. And some are important decomposers of organic material and play a critical role in the biogeochemical cycles that maintain Earth's biosphere.

The exercises in this chapter will acquaint you with the variety of organisms in the Kingdom Monera and some of their important characteristics.

EXERCISE 15-1 BACTERIAL DIVERSITY

Objectives To recognize specimens of bacteria in subkingdoms Schizomycete and Cyanobacteria, and to describe some of their key characteristics.

- Your instructor will provide you with both preserved and living specimens of bacteria. Bacteria are grown in culture on nutrient-agar surfaces in petri dishes and in aqueous culture. Make wet mount slides of specimens from aqueous culture. To prepare microscope slides of bacterial **smears** from agar cultures, use the following procedure (Fig. 15-1):

1. Place a drop of sterile water on a clean slide.
2. Hold a wire loop over the flame of a Bunsen burner until it glows red. Be careful not to touch the loop to your skin or any other surface.
3. Lift the lid of the petri dish just enough to insert the loop; touch the loop to a clear area on the agar surface to cool it.
4. Scrape off a tiny bit of bacterial specimen with the loop and mix it into the water drop on the slide. Spread the drop into a very thin film; if the film is too thick you will not be able to see anything.
5. Resterilize the loop by passing it through the Bunsen burner flame and set it aside. The agar plate contains nutrients that will support many types of bacteria in addition to the pure cultures you are to observe. Touching the agar surface with an unsterilized item such as your finger or an unheated wire loop will contaminate the plate. Airborne bacteria will also float onto the agar, so minimize the time you leave the plate uncovered.
6. Air-dry the specimen by quickly passing the slide through the flame face-up for 2–3 seconds.
7. Many bacteria will be difficult to see under the microscope without first being stained. Apply a drop of the stain provided by your instructor. After a time period specified by your instructor (staining time varies for different stains), use a wash bottle to gently wash off excess stain into the sink. Be careful not to stain your skin or clothes.
8. Allow the slide to dry completely, and observe it under the microscope without a cover slip. Use the oil-immersion objective to see more detail. Review Chapter 3 on the use of the microscope before making your observations.

A. Subkingdom Schizomycete

The subkingdom Schizomycete (pronounced shiz-oh-MY-seet) comprises a wide variety of bacteria of diverse form and metabolism. Six major groups of Schizomycetes are listed in Table 20-1 in your text. The Eubacteria, whose name means "true bacteria," is the largest of the six groups. Your instructor will provide you with living or preserved specimens of the three forms of Eubacteria: bacilli (rods), cocci (spheres), and spirilla (spirals). Draw the specimens in the spaces provided in Table 15-1. Label them with the genus name if known and indicate the sizes of the bacterial cells with a scale or magnification index (see Chapter 2 of this manual). Indicate whether the drawing is of living or preserved material, and label the visible structures (cell wall, flagella, and so on). For live cultures, scan the slide for cells undergoing fission (cell division) and draw them. Using your textbook and the materials your instructor provides, supply the information requested in the table regarding other aspects of the biology of these bacterial specimens.

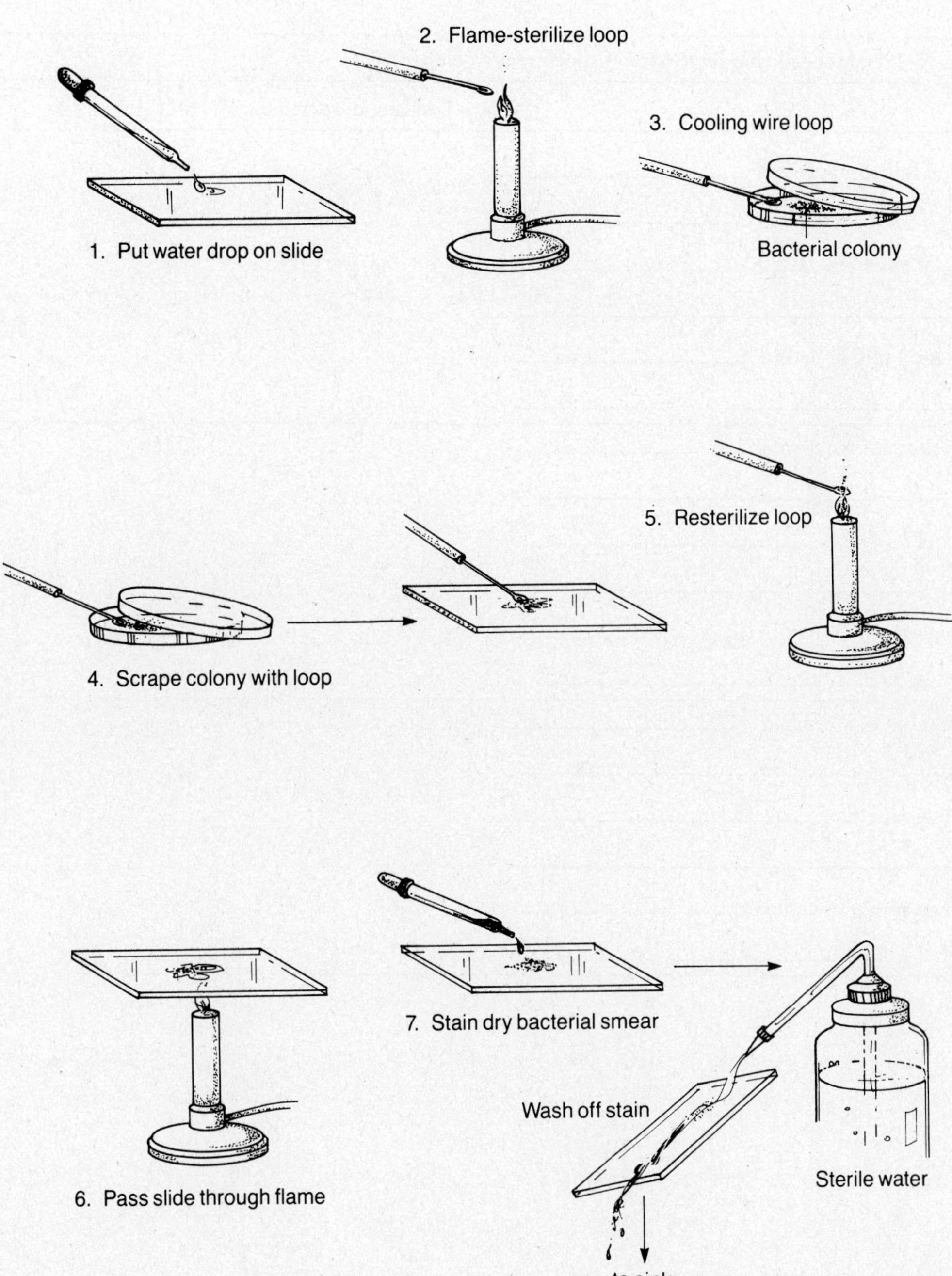

8. Observe slide under compound microscope

Figure 15-1 Procedure for preparation of bacterial smears from agar cultures.

Table 15-1 Observed characteristics of specimens of Eubacteria. 100x

S. marcescens	Drawing of specimen
Mechanism of movement ____________________	longer
Mode of nutrition ____________________	
Ecological role in nature ____________________	
E. Coli — Mechanism of movement ____________________	shorter
Mode of nutrition ____________________	
Ecological role in nature ____________________	darker staining
B. Subtilis — Mechanism of movement ____________________	
Mode of nutrition ____________________	
Ecological role in nature ____________________	

B. Subkingdom Cyanobacteria

The cyanobacteria (pronounced sigh-AN-oh-bacteria) are photosynthetic prokaryotes that differ from photoautotrophic eubacteria in that they possess chlorophyll *a* (a pigment found in eukaryotic green plants and algae) as well as other photosynthetic pigments. The cyanobacteria are sometimes called "blue-green algae," but the term "algae" is now generally restricted to groups of eukaryotic organisms. Cyanobacteria grow in most freshwater habitats and sometimes produce nuisance "blooms" of scum that release toxins into the water or deplete its oxygen supply. Cyanobacteria are also abundant on rocks in the upper intertidal zone of the ocean.

- Cyanobacteria take three basic forms: single cells (unicells), filaments, and colonies. Your instructor will provide you with specimens of each type. Make a drawing of each specimen in the space provided, label the drawings, and provide a magnification scale or index. Using your textbook and the materials your instructor provides, answer the questions about each specimen.

Gloeocapsa

What form(s) does this cyanobacterium display?

Look carefully for a sheath surrounding the cells. If you are observing a live specimen, add a small drop of India ink to the wet mount to render the sheath easier to observe. What is the sheath made of?

Spirulina

What form does this cyanobacterium display?

Are divisions between cells visible?

On what basis has this cyanobacterium been touted as a food supplement?

Nostoc

Make two drawings of this specimen: appearance to the naked eye and appearance under the compound microscope.
Some cells in the *Nostoc* filament are larger than others and appear to be empty. What are these cells and what is their function?

Why is this function important to *Nostoc* and to other neighboring organisms?

Anabaena

- Your instructor will provide you with a specimen of *Azolla*, an aquatic fern that floats at the water surface in ponds and swamps. Observe the fern's tiny leaves under the stereoscopic microscope and make a drawing of the plant in the space provided. Macerate a small piece of *Azolla* on a slide, clear away the larger debris, and make a wet mount slide. You will observe fragments of *Anabaena* filaments that were growing inside the fern. Draw the microscopic

Anabaena filaments as they appear under the compound microscope. Include scale bars for both drawings.

The *Anabaena* is termed a **symbiont** of the *Azolla*. Are *heterocysts* present in filaments of the cyanobacterium? ______________

What are the benefits to the *Anabaena* in this situation?

And the benefits to the *Azolla*?

Azolla is grown in flooded rice paddies in Asia. Explain how this practice can improve rice production.

EXERCISE 15-2 UBIQUITY OF BACTERIA IN THE ENVIRONMENT

Objective To develop an appreciation for the omnipresence of bacteria in nature and, by inference, an appreciation for the natural controls that keep bacterial population growth in check.

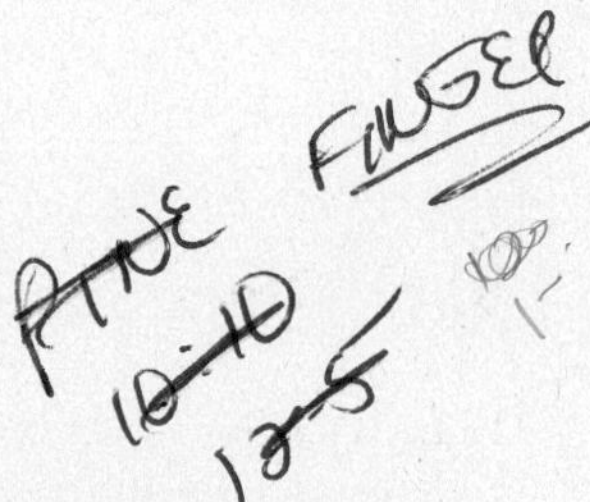

Culture plates

- Approximately one week prior to this laboratory, your instructor will provide you with a series of agar plates. Inoculate them by touching the sterile agar surface with such items as the human tongue, hair, a finger, an orange slice, or a potato chip. Use your creativity to think up items to use. Draw the resulting pattern of colonies growing on each plate and describe them.

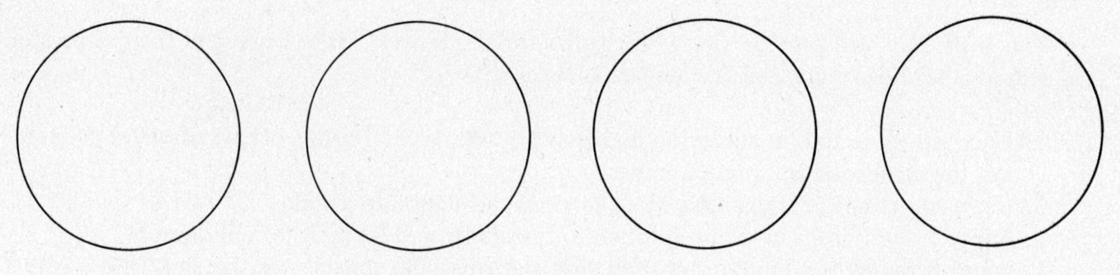

- Either prepare a microscope slide of each culture, or examine the slides provided by your instructor. Describe in Chart 15-1 the predominant types of bacteria observed in each one (rods, spheres, or spirals). Suggest a hypothesis on how bacteria from each source may be normally controlled under normal conditions. (Hint: Your hypotheses can include inferences on the efficacy of sterile technique in surgery and the importance of refrigerators to societal health.)

Chart 15-1 Bacteria on agar plates.

Agar plate	Source of inoculum	Predominant bacterial types	Hypothesized natural control
1.	________	________	________
2.	________	________	________
3.	________	________	________
4.	________	________	________

EXERCISE 15-3 GRAM STAINING AND ANTIBIOTIC RESISTANCE

Objective To employ the method of Gram staining to distinguish between groups of bacteria and to understand how this relates to their resistance to antibiotics.

A. Gram Staining

E. Coli
B. Subtilis

In addition to their forms, bacteria are characterized by their chemical and metabolic characteristics. **Gram staining** is one of the most common methods used to distinguish between two groups of bacteria that differ in the composition of the cell wall. In this test, bacteria are stained first with crystal violet (a purple dye) and then with safranin (a red dye). Gram-positive bacteria retain the purple color of the crystal violet in their cell walls, which are made of a single peptidoglycan layer. Gram-negative bacteria do not retain the crystal violet stain in their cell walls, which have a peptidoglycan layer covered by another lipid bilayer. Gram-negative bacteria do retain the red color of the safranin in their cell walls.

- Your instructor will provide you with two bacterial cultures. Make smears of the cultures on microscope slides, and treat the smears as follows:

1. Place the slide flat on a desktop and flood it with several drops of crystal violet solution. Let the stain soak in for one minute.
2. Use a squirt bottle of distilled water to rinse the stain into a sink.
3. Apply several drops of iodine solution to the smear and let it sit for one minute.
4. Pour off the iodine solution into the sink and rinse the smear over the sink with a squirt bottle of 95% ethanol for 15–30 seconds.
5. Flood the smear with several drops of safranin for one-half minute.
6. Rinse the slide a final time with distilled water and allow it to dry.
7. Observe the slide under the compound microscope. Gram-positive bacteria stain purple; Gram-negative bacteria stain red.

- Record the results of your observations in Chart 15-2.

Chart 15-2 Results of Gram-staining tests.

Bacterial culture	Gram-staining results (positive or negative)
1. E. Coli	negative
2. B. Subtilis	positive

- How do you interpret these results in terms of the composition of the cell wall in each culture?

1.

2.

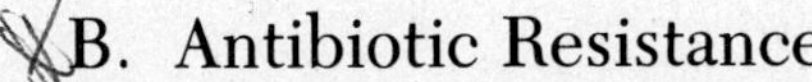

B. Antibiotic Resistance

B. Subtilis

Bacteria might overgrow the organic world were it not for natural controls on their populations. Among these controls are antibiotic substances produced by some bacteria, which use the substances to inhibit the growth of competitors. Numerous antibiotics act by attacking the cell wall of bacteria. The Gram stain is used in medicine to characterize bacteria and predict their susceptibility to various antibiotics. For example, Gram-positive bacteria are readily killed by various types of penicillin, whereas Gram-negative bacteria are sensitive to other antibiotics such as polymixin.

- Examine the Petri plates of bacterial cultures 1 and 2 provided by your instructor. Each plate was prepared by coating the agar surface with a suspension of bacteria. Before significant growth occurred, small paper disks impregnated with various antibiotics were placed on the surface of the agar. The clear area surrounding each disk represents the effectiveness of the antibiotic in inhibiting bacterial growth. Estimate the diameter (in millimeters) of the clear area around each disk and fill in Chart 15-3.

disc 6mm

Chart 15-3 Measurement of the effectiveness of antibiotics on bacterial growth.

Antibiotic disk	Culture 1	Culture 2
1. NA 30	22 mm -6 mm	
2. TE 30	17 mm	
3. TE 30	18	
4. K 30	19	
FD 300	16	

QUESTIONS

Can you draw a general conclusion regarding the antibiotic resistance of culture 1 compared to that of culture 2?

Do any of the antibiotics 1–4 act specifically against only one culture? Against both cultures?

Antibiotics that are specific for a few bacterial types are called **narrow-spectrum** antibiotics. **Broad-spectrum** antibiotics act against a wider variety of bacteria. Comment on the usefulness of narrow- versus broad-spectrum antibiotics in fighting specific and broad-based infections.

Based on the reading in your textbook, what conclusion can you draw regarding cell-wall composition and antibiotic resistance?

The material in this chapter corresponds to Chapter 21 in your text.

16
KINGDOM PROTISTA

Members of the Kingdom Protista are the simplest of eukaryotic organisms. Protists are either **unicellular** or **colonial** and lack the more complex tissues and organs of other eukaryotes. All of the functions necessary to life take place within the confines of a single cell. Protistan complexity is thus unicellular, rather than differentiated into specialized cell types. But despite their morphological simplicity, protists possess fundamental eukaryotic characteristics that relate them more closely to higher plants and animals than to the prokaryotes. The basic eukaryotic features are:

- One or more double-membrane-bound nuclei in a cell.
- Genetic material in chromosomes.
- Ribosomes and nuclear-RNA processing typical of eukaryotic cells.
- Membrane-bound organelles in the cytoplasm (such as chloroplasts, mitochondria, and Golgi complexes).
- A cytoskeleton of microtubules and microfilaments that is involved in a variety of locomotive functions.

In addition, all protists share a characteristic that causes them to be grouped together.

- They are unicells or exist as colonies of virtually identical cells.

As mentioned in Chapter 14 in the discussion on taxonomy, Protista, like other kingdoms, is not a clade or monophyletic group—that is, a group of organisms descended from one common ancestor. Although all protists might have shared a single common ancestor, along with all other living organisms, various clades within the protists arose from different nonprotist ancestors. Lumping the protists into a single kingdom simply because they are all unicellular or simple colonies is an artificial rather than an evolutionary classification. Nevertheless, the kingdom Protista serves as a convenient way of classifying the remarkably diverse world of morphologically simple eukaryotes until scientists better understand their evolutionary relationships.

The following survey of protistan phyla categorizes them on the basis of lifestyle, particularly on the basis of nutritional mode: plantlike protists, funguslike protists, and animal-like protists. The exercises in this chapter will acquaint you with the morphology, reproductive modes, and ecology of representatives of the three categories.

EXERCISE 16-1 THE PLANTLIKE PROTISTS

Objectives To identify the key characteristics of each of the three phyla of plantlike protists, and to describe differences in pigment types, morphology, locomotion, and habitat.

The plantlike protists are so called because they are photosynthetic and contain several types of chlorophyll and other light-trapping pigments. Many are members of the phytoplankton, free-floating unicells or colonies that spend part or all of their lives in freshwater and oceanic habitats. Your instructor will provide living cultures and preserved microscope slides of selected members of the three plantlike phyla. Be able to identify structures labeled in the figures and to define any terms written in boldface in the text.

A. Phylum Euglenophyta

The euglenoid flagellates—the Phylum Euglenophyta (pronounced yew-gleen-AH-fit-uh)—are unicells having one or sometimes two or four flagella (Fig. 16-1). They are found in most types of freshwater habitats: ponds, lakes, ditches, temporary streams, and so forth. Often they are found in waters polluted with animal waste or decaying organic matter. Although they are photosynthetic and possess chlorophylls *a* and *b*, the same photosynthetic pigments of land plants, none are completely **photoautotrophic,** that is, able to survive solely on organic material produced via photosynthesis. Instead, euglenoid flagellates are **photoauxotrophic,** requiring the presence of certain vitamins in the growth medium (often vitamins B_1 and B_{12}) to survive. Most euglenoids, even those that can photosynthesize, can acquire organic nutrients from the surrounding water, a mode of nutrition called **heterotrophism.** Some absorb nutrients through the cell covering, whereas certain types are **phagotrophic** and actively engulf food particles. Because euglenoids are not completely dependent on photosynthesis, some survive even after being induced to give up their chloroplasts by treatment with heat or ultraviolet light. Sexual reproduction has not been observed in members of this phylum; instead, members reproduce by asexual fission.

- Make a wet mount slide of the live culture of *Euglena* provided by your instructor, and observe it with the compound microscope. In the living cell, you should be able to see the **flagellum** protruding from one end of the cell. A reddish **eyespot** lies near the base of the flagellum. Look for the green **chloroplasts,** which may be shaped like disks, stars, or ribbons, depending on the species. If the cells are swimming so rapidly that they are difficult to observe, you can

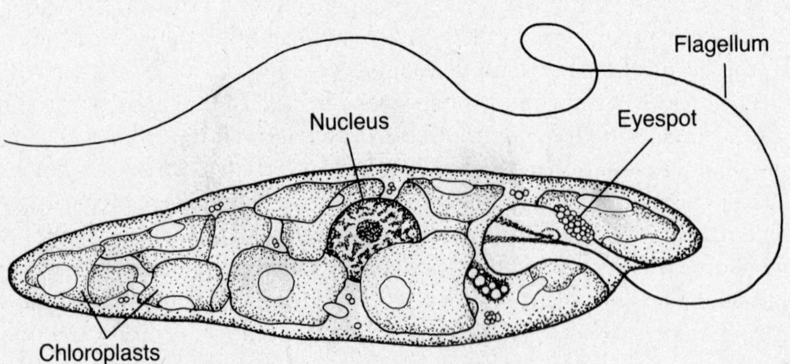

Figure 16-1 *Euglena,* a plantlike protist.

remove the cover slip and mix a small drop of methyl cellulose with the culture fluid. Methyl cellulose is highly viscous and slows the motion of the flagellum so it can be more readily seen. Adjusting the iris diaphragm changes the visual contrast between thin structures in the field of view and may make some features more visible.

- The peculiar motion these cells exhibit is called **euglenoid movement.** Describe euglenoid movement. Does the cell change shape? Is the cell wall rigid? Does the cell have front and back ends?

- *Euglena* are **positively phototactic** to dim light. They swim toward dim light, but they avoid bright light and darkness. Devise a simple experiment using the cultural container or a wet mount slide that would demonstrate such phototactic behavior. Describe the experiment in a sentence or two.

- If possible, conduct the experiment with the help of the instructor. Did the experiment work? Why or why not?

- Protists store the photosynthetic products as various kinds of compounds. Starch is a common storage compound in some protists, as well as in green algae and higher plants (to be studied in later chapters). Lugol's test is used to detect starch. In this test, an iodine solution is applied to the cells. Iodine kills the cells, and although everything appears somewhat darker, the iodine stains starch-containing structures a deep purple. After observing the living culture of *Euglena*, put a drop of Lugol's (iodine) solution (Ch. 4) at one edge of the cover slip and touch the opposite edge with a piece of paper towel to draw the iodine solution under the cover slip. Is starch a storage product of euglenoids? ____________

B. Phylum Pyrrophyta

Members of phylum Pyrrophyta (pronounced peer-AH-fit-uh), whose name means "fire plants," are commonly called **dinoflagellates.** The term "dinoflagellate" means "spinning cell" and describes the swimming motion typical of these protists. Figure 16-2 shows a typical dinoflagellate called *Peridinium*. Species of *Peridinium* occur in freshwater and marine habitats. *Peridinium* is known as an armored dinoflagellate because it is covered by cellulose plates, collectively called a **theca** or **amphiesma.** The arrangement and shapes of these plates vary between genera and species of

Figure 16-2 *Peridinium*, a dinoflagellate.

dinoflagellates. Some dinoflagellates are unarmored and have no thecal plates. *Gymnodinium breve*, a dinoflagellate responsible for some poisonous red tides, is a naked species.

Most dinoflagellates are photosynthetic, and some, like euglenoids, are photoauxotrophic. Like euglenoids, many dinoflagellates are heterotrophic and some lack chloroplasts altogether. Ecologically, dinoflagellates are very diverse. They are important members of the phytoplankton in freshwater and marine habitats. The symbiotic zooxanthellae (pronounced zoh-oh-zan-THEL-ee) found living inside the tissues or body cavities of sea anemones, corals, jellyfish, and snails secrete a portion of their photosynthetic products, which are then used for nutrition by the host animal. In return, the dinoflagellates may be able to utilize nitrogenous wastes from the animal. Symbiotic associations such as this in which both organisms benefit are called **mutualism.** Other types of dinoflagellates accumulate in such high densities that the water turns red (red tides), and some dinoflagellates produce toxins that poison fish and shellfish.

Dinoflagellates generally reproduce through asexual cell division. Occasionally, sexual reproduction occurs; two haploid cells function as gametes and fuse to form a diploid zygote. The zygote then forms a resting stage called a **cyst.** Meiosis in the encysted zygote produces haploid vegetative cells.

- Make a wet mount slide of the culture of *Peridinium* or other dinoflagellate provided by your instructor. Dinoflagellates contain chlorophylls *a* and *c*, but the green color of these pigments is often masked by the yellow or orange color of pigments called xanthophylls. What color are the cells on the wet mount slide? ____________
- Observe the swimming motion of the cells—add methyl cellulose if necessary to slow them down. Describe the motion in the following space and draw arrows on Figure 16-2 showing the direction of movement and spinning in the cell.

- Most dinoflagellates have two flagella, one that projects backward along a longitudinal groove between armor plates and another that wraps around the middle of the cell in a transverse groove. Locate these flagella on the living cell.
- Observe the culture under high magnification. Sketch the cell and include as much detail of the thecal plate pattern as possible. You may be able to find empty thecae and detached plates to help with the diagram.

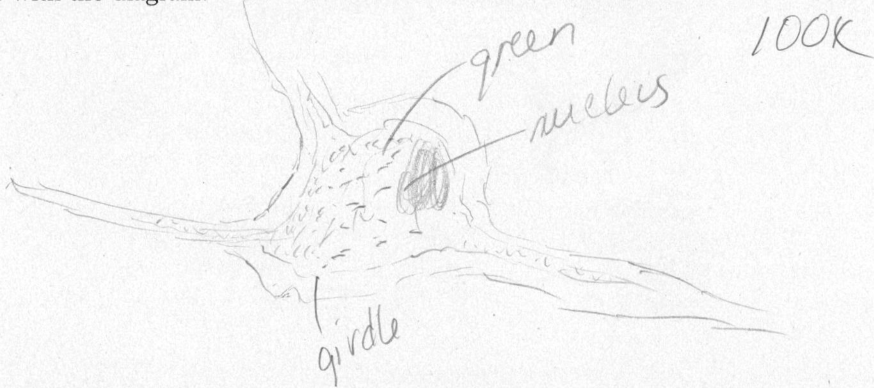

- Add Lugol's solution to the wet mount slide. Is starch a storage product in the Pyrrophyta?

____

C. Phylum Chrysophyta

Like the Pyrrophyta, the Chrysophyta (pronounced kris-AH-fit-uh) contain chlorophylls *a* and *c*, but their beautiful golden hue is due to the abundance of pigments called **carotenes** in their cells. The range of morphology found in this phylum includes unicells, colonies, and a few rare filaments. Several major lines of evolution can be traced in the classes of Chrysophyta. The following exercises deal with members of two classes—the golden-brown algae and the diatoms.

Golden-brown algae

The golden-brown algae occur in a variety of forms, including unicells, colonies, filaments, and flattened masses of cells. In many types, siliceous (glasslike) material is incorporated into cell coverings. Some individual cells are covered with **siliceous scales,** and others are enclosed in a vaselike structure called a **lorica.** Most golden-brown algae produce a **statocyst,** a resting stage with a spiny, siliceous wall. Golden-brown algae are common in freshwater habitats, and some occur in the ocean.

- Make a wet mount slide of the *Synura* culture provided by your instructor. The free-swimming colonies of *Synura* contain many teardrop-shaped cells covered with tiny siliceous scales. The narrow posterior end of each cell points inward so that colonies resemble dense clusters of grapes. Each cell has two flagella that point outward from the colony center. Colonies grow through division of individual cells. Several cells may split off to form a new colony. In sexual reproduction, solitary haploid "male" cells fuse with slightly larger haploid "female" cells within a colony and form a diploid zygote, which encysts inside a spiny siliceous wall. A typical *Synura* life cycle is shown in Figure 16-3.
- Draw a *Synura* colony in the box below. Also draw a single cell viewed at higher power and show the chloroplasts; by adjusting the contrast with the iris diaphragm you may be able to

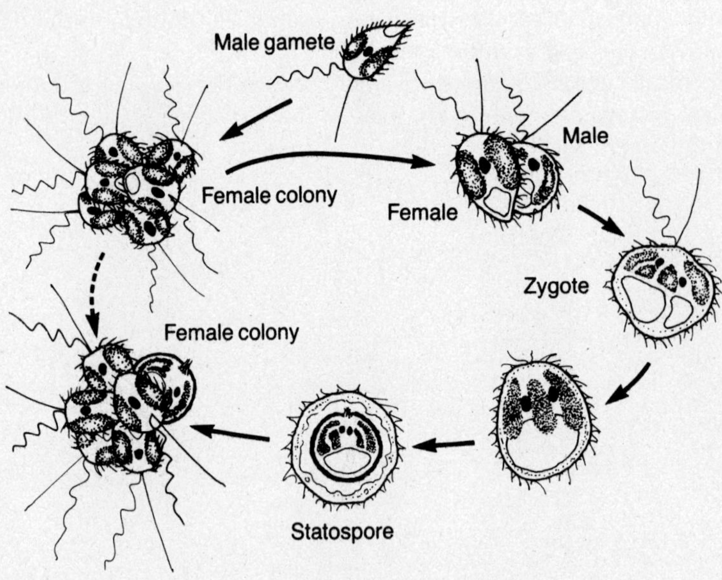

Figure 16-3 Life cycle of *Synura*.

see the thin scale layer around each cell. Include a scale bar. Describe the swimming motion of a colony and include a brief sketch of the motion.

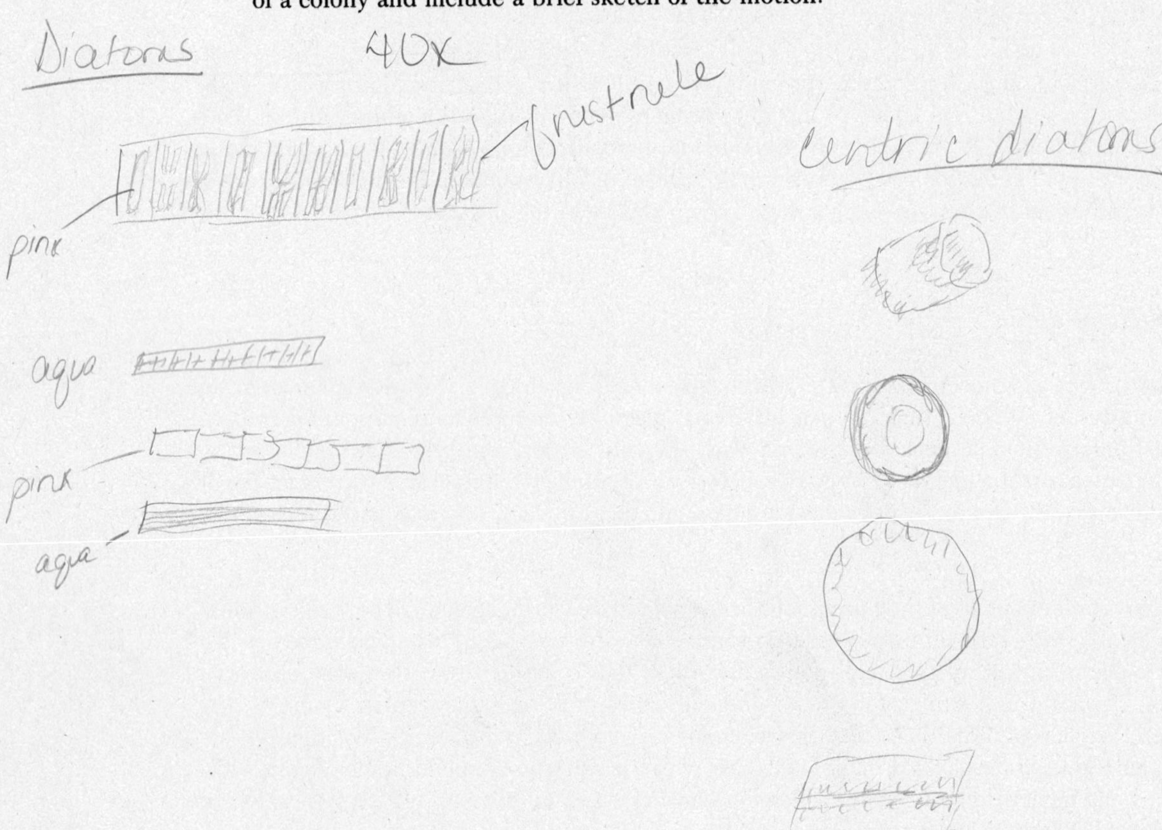

Diatoms

Diatoms are without doubt among the most abundant and widespread eukaryotic organisms on Earth. They are one of the most important primary producers of organic matter in the phytoplankton of oceans and fresh water. In fact, one would be hard pressed to find an aquatic habitat without diatoms.

Diatoms are unicellular, colonial, or pseudofilamentous (chains of separate cells without common cell walls). The diatom cell wall, called the **frustule,** contains silica, a primary ingredient in glass. This rigid, glassy shell encloses the protoplast with its golden chloroplasts. Frustules are symmetrical and often beautifully sculptured with ornate bumps, ridges, or spines (Fig. 16-4). Bilaterally symmetrical diatoms are called **pennate** (Fig. 16-5a); radially symmetrical diatoms are called

Figure 16-4 Diatom frustule viewed with scanning electron microscopy.

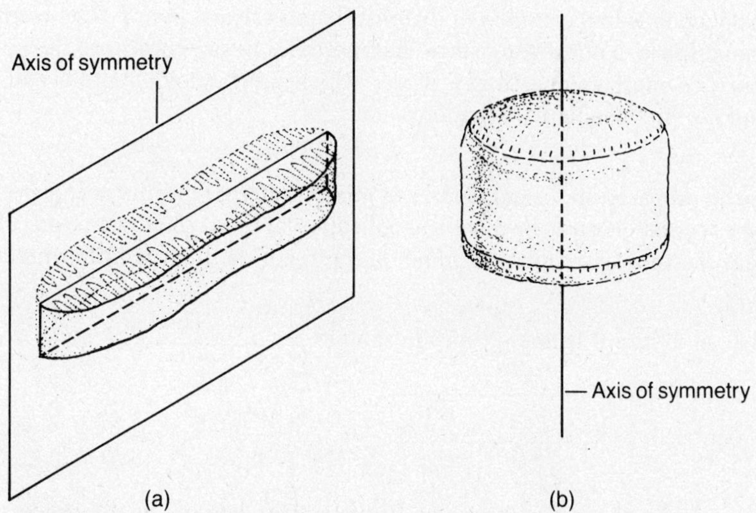

Figure 16-5 Symmetry in diatoms. (a) Pennate diatom with bilateral symmetry. (b) Centric diatom with radial symmetry.

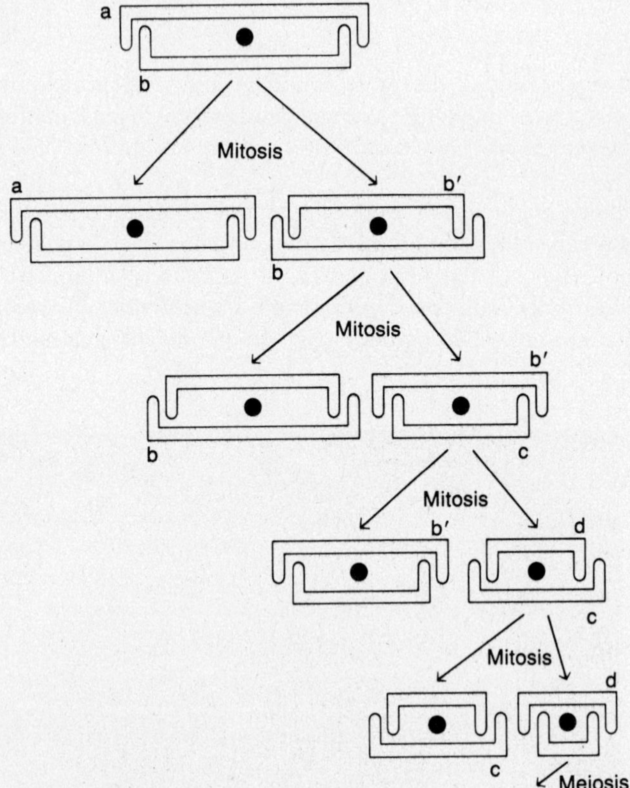

Figure 16-6 Cell division in diatoms.

centric (Fig. 16-5b). A diatom frustule consists of two overlapping halves, or thecae. The **epitheca** fits over the **hypotheca** like the top of a petri dish covers the bottom. When a cell divides, the two parts of the frustule separate, each taking with it one of the daughter protoplasts. Each half of the frustule will become the epitheca of a new diatom. This process is shown in Figure 16-6.

Sexual reproduction is less common in diatoms than is asexual fission. The result of sexual reproduction is an **auxospore**, a nonresting stage that increases in size to restore the cell to its maximum size. In contrast to most golden-brown algae, which are haploid, diatom cells are diploid and undergo meiosis to produce haploid gametes.

- Examine the prepared slides or cultures of mixed diatoms your instructor provides. These may come from several cultures or a natural collection of pond phytoplankton. Count the number of different frustule types in the sample, and categorize them as either pennate or centric.

Total number of different frustule types in sample ______________

Number of pennate types ______________

Number of centric types ______________

- Draw at least two of these pennate and two centric diatoms in the space provided. Include scale bars.

Pennate diatoms **Centric diatoms**

- Pennate diatoms often have a longitudinal groove in the cell wall called a **raphe.** Material secreted through the raphe helps the diatom adhere to the surface and move or glide. Observe the gliding motion of pennate diatoms on the wet mount slide. Describe and draw the gliding motion in several different frustule types. Does cell shape affect the gliding path?

- Your instructor may have some diatomaceous earth on display. This chalky material is made of the empty frustules of fossil diatoms that accumulated over time to form thick layers. Deposits of diatomaceous earth are mined commercially for use in abrasives and polishing compounds, as well as filters for liquids in beer making and sugar refining. Your instructor may have some products on display that contain diatom frustules. In Chart 16-1, make a list of the products and the function that the diatom frustules serve in the product.

Chart 16-1 Products containing diatom frustules.

Product	Function of diatom frustules
1.	
2.	
3.	
4.	
5.	

EXERCISE 16-2 THE FUNGUSLIKE PROTISTS

Objectives To describe the nutritional mode and general habitats of funguslike protists and to describe the differences in morphology and reproduction of the two classes of the phylum Gymnomycota.

Funguslike protists are commonly called **slime molds,** an apt name given their appearance. These protists are nonphotosynthetic; they derive nutrients by ingesting bacteria and other protists and by decomposing organic matter such as fallen leaves and animal and plant remains. Funguslike protists differ from true fungi in that they lack a cell wall around the plasma membrane. Slime molds belong to a single phylum, the Gymnomycota (pronounced GYM-no-my-CO-tuh), with two classes: the Myxomycetes, or true slime molds, and the Acrasiomycetes, or cellular slime molds.

A. Class Myxomycetes

- Observe the culture of *Physarum* provided by your instructor. *Physarum,* of the class Myxomycetes, is a true slime mold consisting of a slimy mass called the **plasmodium,** which is a single cell with numerous diploid nuclei. Contractile proteins of the cytoskeleton allow slime molds to glide or creep from one rotting food source to another. Some true slime molds also prey on living plants. When the slime mold is in a nutrient-poor area, it produces spore-bearing structures called **sporangiophores** (these may or may not be present in the culture). The life cycle of a true slime mold is shown in Figure 16-7. Haploid spores are generated through meiosis and are dispersed by wind and rain. Spores germinate to form flagellated swarm cells, which may fuse to form a diploid zygote. Some swarm cells lose their flagella and become gliding **myxamoebae,** which feed on bacteria or plant debris. Myxamoebae may also act as gametes and fuse to form a zygote, which regenerates the multinucleate plasmodium.
- Use the stereoscopic microscope to observe the plasmodium with transmitted light. Zoom to high power and observe the cytoplasm inside the plasmodium. Describe the movement of particles in the cytoplasm.

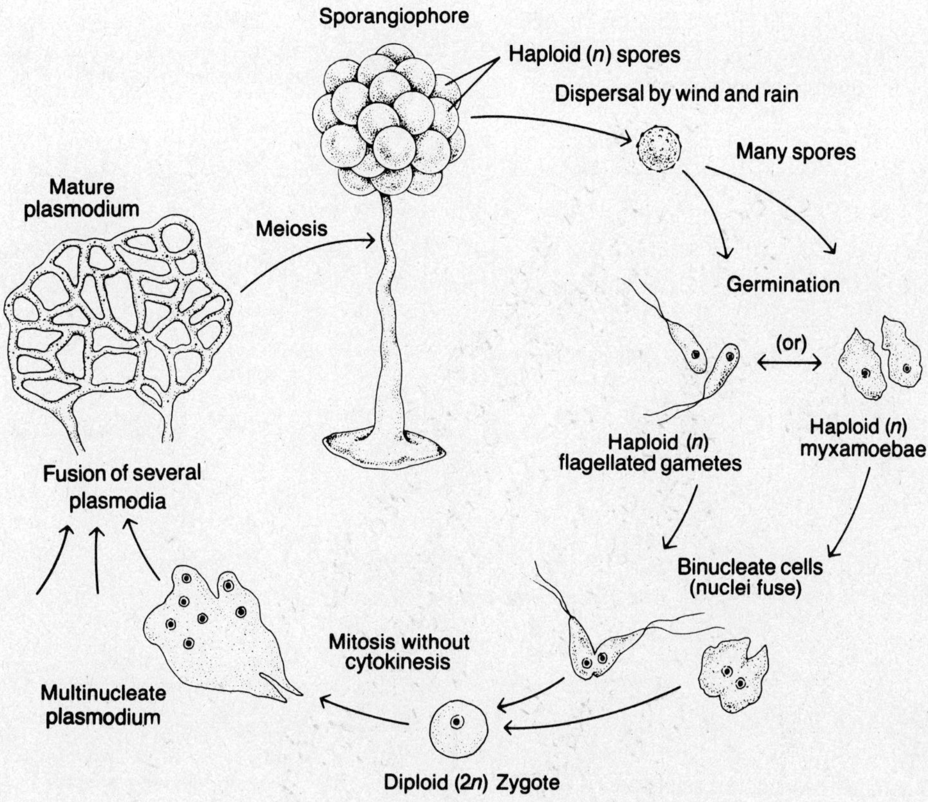

Figure 16-7 Life cycle of a true slime mold.

- This movement is called **cytoplasmic streaming.** Some of the particles involved in cytoplasmic streaming are food vacuoles. How is the movement of food vacuoles useful to the cell?

B. Class Acrasiomycetes

The Acrasiomycetes (pronounced ay-CRA-zeo-MY-seets), or cellular slime molds, are superficially similar to the true slime molds, but they differ in an important respect: They possess a cellular structure throughout the life cycle and remain as amoebae—no multinucleate plasmodium is produced. The *pseudoplasmodium,* a nonfeeding migratory stage, is produced, in which the individual amoebae do not fuse. The stages in the life cycle of *Dictyostelium,* the most studied cellular slime mold, are shown in Figure 16-8. Not shown is the rare sexual reproduction of cellular slime molds, in which amoebae fuse to form a diploid **macrocyst.** The macrocyst undergoes meiosis to produce haploid amoebae.

- Observe the culture of *Dictyostelium* on display. Use the stereoscopic microscope to observe the individual cells of the pseudoplasmodium. Draw the pseudoplasmodium in the space below. **Sporophores** may also be present on the culture plate. If so, remove one and crush it on a

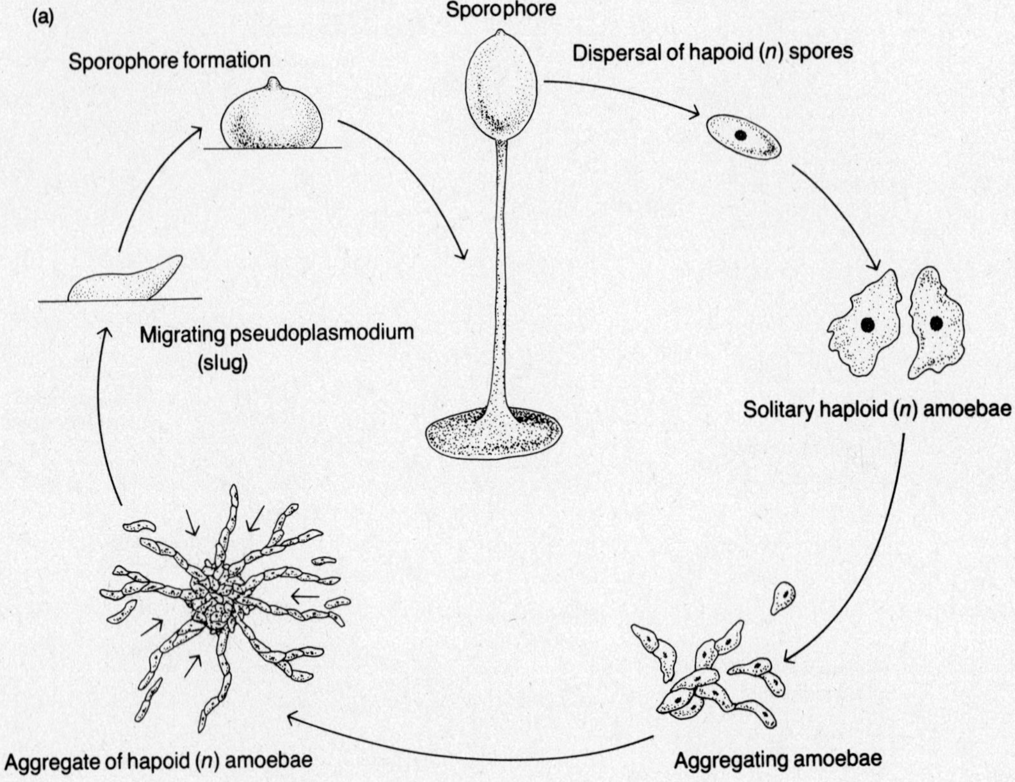

Figure 16-8 Life cycle of a cellular slime mold, *Dictyostelium.*

microscope slide to make a wet mount slide. Are spores visible under the compound microscope? If so, draw several and indicate their size with a scale bar.

- Fill in Chart 16-2 comparing the Myxomycetes and Acrasiomycetes. For each pair of comparable structures listed, name one similarity and one difference between the two classes.

Chart 16-2 Comparison of true slime molds and cellular slime molds.

Myxomycetes	Acrasiomycetes	Similarity	Difference
myxamoebae	amoebae	____________	____________
plasmodium	pseudoplasmodium	____________	____________
sporangiophores	sporophores	____________	____________
zygote	macrocyst	____________	____________

EXERCISE 16-3 THE ANIMAL-LIKE PROTISTS

Objectives To survey groups of animal-like protists and learn the basic characteristics and body structures of each group; to be able to identify representative organisms as members of specific taxonomic groups on the basis of particular traits, including mode of locomotion.

The animal-like protists, also called **protozoans,** are nonphotosynthetic heterotrophs, which ingest food particles, plantlike protists, and each other to survive. Food is digested inside the cell by enzymes in **food vacuoles.** Osmotic balance is achieved by **contractile vacuoles,** which collect and discharge water from the cell.

The animal-like protists are members of a number of phyla, but a convenient way of categorizing them is on the basis of movement. One group, the **Mastigophora,** move by means of whiplike flagella. Protozoans in the group **Sarcodina** move by means of **pseudopods,** which are also used to engulf food particles. The **Sporozoa** are parasites that are nonmotile as adults. The last group consists of a single phylum called the **Ciliophora,** which move by means of the coordinated beating of numerous **cilia.**

Your instructor will provide you with a number of living or preserved specimens of the four groups. The following genera will probably be among those available. For each specimen, you should be able to identify it to a major group and to locate the structures written in boldface.

A. Group Mastigophora

Members of the group Mastigophora (pronounced mass-ti-GAW-for-uh) are also referred to by the common name "zooflagellates" (animal-like flagellates), as distinguished from the phytoflagellates (plantlike or photosynthetic flagellates). Many are harmless symbionts, but one species of *Trypanosoma* (Fig. 16-9) is the infamous zooflagellate that causes African sleeping sickness.

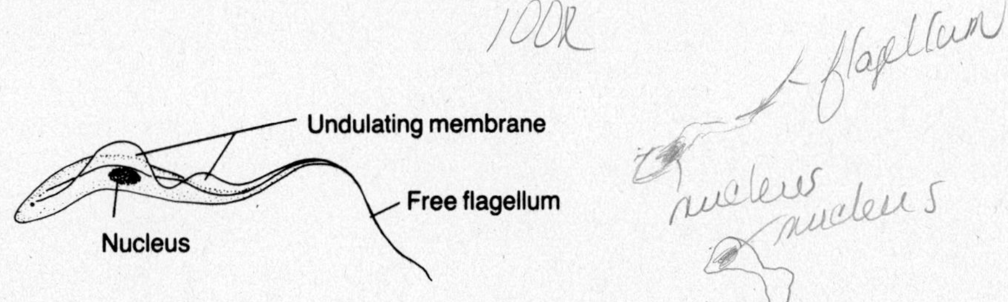

Figure 16-9 *Trypanosoma,* cause of African sleeping sickness.

- Observe the prepared slides of *Trypanosoma* in a smear of red blood cells. In addition to a **flagellum,** this protozoan has an **undulating membrane** that functions in locomotion. The **nucleus** may also be visible.

B. Group Sarcodina

This group of protozoans, Sarcodina, (pronounced SAR-co-DINE-uh) includes various types of amoebae, with variable cell shapes. Some members of the Sarcodina possess elaborately constructed skeletons with long slender spines made of calcium or silica.

- Observe the living *Amoeba* provided by your instructor by preparing a wet mount slide. In the space below, draw an *Amoeba* and describe how it moves using pseudopods. Indicate on the drawing a pseudopod, the cell membrane, the nucleus, and vacuoles (food and water).

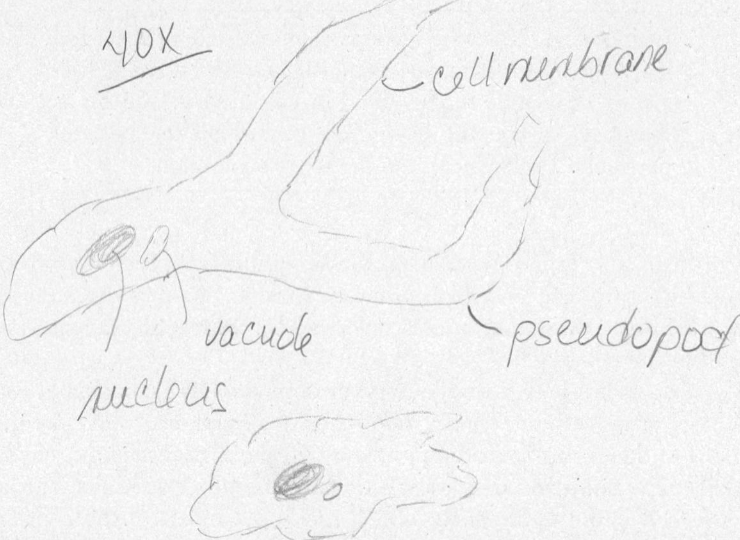

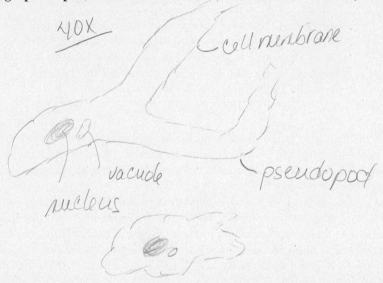

- Observe the prepared slide containing skeletons of foraminiferans and radiolarians. These sarcodines are marine protozoa that live near the ocean's surface. In addition to streaming pseudopods that are used to capture food particles and other planktonic organisms, these protozoans have skeletons of calcium carbonate (foraminiferans) or silica (radiolarians). After the organisms die, the skeletons drift to the bottom of the sea, where they accumulate to form "ooze." Observe the skeletons under high magnification and draw several representatives in the space below. Include a scale bar. Look for the spines and holes in the skeletons through which pseudopods streamed in the living organism.

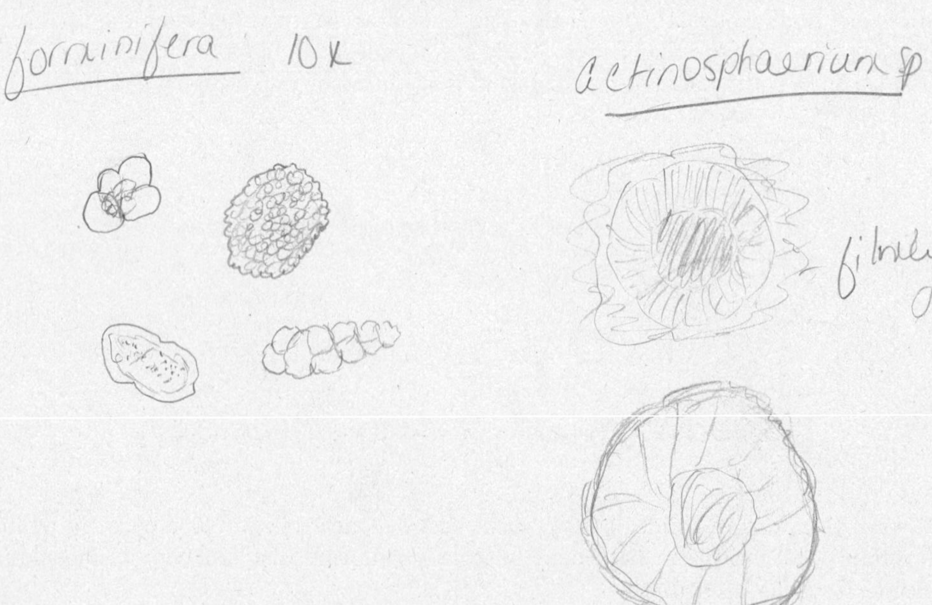

C. Group Sporozoa

This group of parasitic protozoa, the Sporozoa (pronounced SPOR-oh-ZOH-uh), contains the genus *Plasmodium*, which causes malaria.

- Observe the prepared slide provided by your instructor of a blood smear containing *Plasmodium*. You should be able to observe two stages in the life cycle of this sporozoan parasite. The **merozoites** that infect red blood cells appear as small, darkly stained, round bodies strewn among the red blood cells. Once inside red blood cells, the merozoites increase in size and change shape. The growing parasites inside the cells are termed **trophozoites** and are often visible as a distinct **signet ring** stage, which nearly fills the cell. A small round body of nuclear material forms the "gemstone" portion of the signet ring stage. After asexual division of the parasite nucleus, more merozoites are released and spread to other red blood cells.

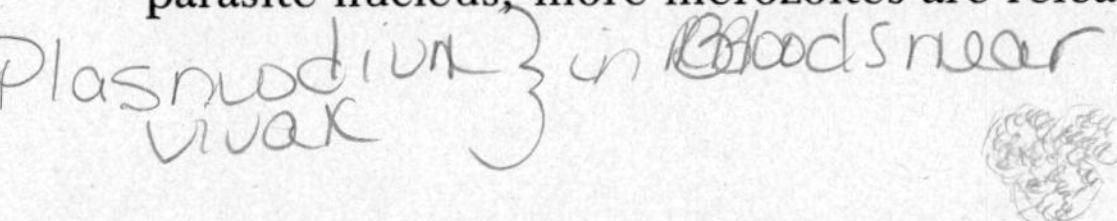

D. Phylum Ciliophora

The protozoans of the phylum Ciliophora (pronounced silly-AH-for-uh) are considered the most complex single-celled organisms. They move by means of rows or bands of cilia moving in a coordinated fashion. Each cell has two nuclei, a **micronucleus** and a **macronucleus.** The micronucleus functions in the unusual sexual reproductive process of **conjugation** (described in your text).

- Make a wet mount slide of the culture of *Paramecium* provided by your instructor. Observe their swimming behavior and describe it in the space below. Sketch the cell, and show the direction of movement.

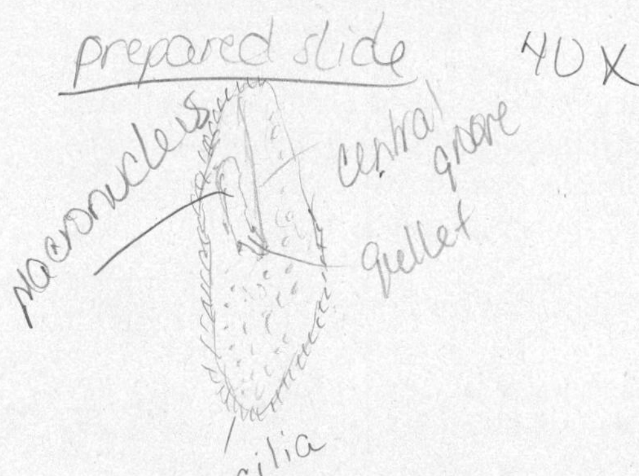

- Find the **oral groove,** or **cytostome,** through which food particles enter the cell (Fig. 16-10). Remove the cover slip and mix in a small drop of methyl cellulose to slow down the *Paramecium*. Observe the beating of the cilia under high magnification. Describe the motion of the cilia.

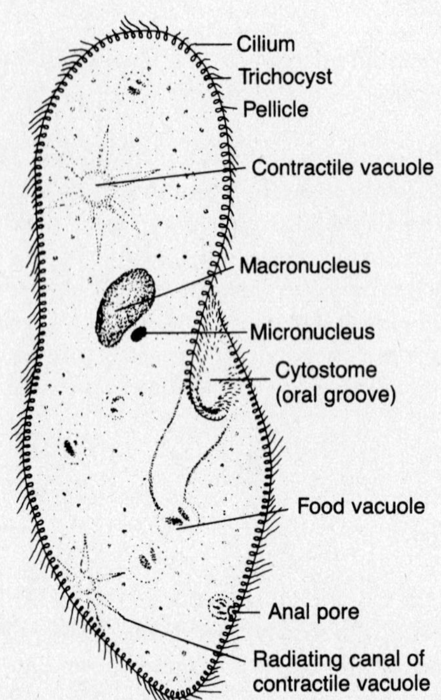

Figure 16-10 *Paramecium*, showing internal and external features.

E. Protistan Evolution

Protists are presumed to have evolved from prokaryotic ancestors, possibly through endosymbiosis of prokaryotic organisms that later evolved into organelles (mitochondria and chloroplasts). The three types of protists discussed in this chapter display a greater complexity of structure than the Monera discussed in Chapter 15, but they share some basic traits with prokaryotes.

- List three general characteristics possessed by some protists that are also found in the Monera.

  1.

  2.

  3.

- List four characteristics of protists that represent evolutionary trends not found in the Monera.

  1.

  2.

  3.

  4.

The material in this chapter corresponds to Chapter 24 in your text.

19
KINGDOM PLANTAE II. THE SEED PLANTS

The seed plants are the largest and morphologically most complex photosynthetic organisms on Earth. The angiosperms, or flowering plants, constitute over 80% of all plant species. The number and variety of products derived from seed plants is remarkable—from wood and medicines to petroleum products from seed plants long dead.

The evolution of seed plants is a story of the conquest of land, and the **seed** is an evolutionary innovation that enabled that conquest. Having studied the life cycles and reproduction of lower plants in Chapter 18, we can now understand the evolutionary origin of the seed from more primitive structures.

Five divisions make up the seed plants: the Cycadophyta (cycads), the Ginkgophyta (ginkgoes), the Gnetophyta (gnetinas), the Coniferophyta (conifers), and the Anthophyta (angiosperms). These five divisions are very different in many aspects, but they share certain characteristics:

1. The megasporangium is protected by an integument.
2. A diminutive gametophyte stage depends on the sporophyte for nutrition and protection.
3. Transport of sperm is not tied to a liquid medium; instead, pollen is moved from male to female reproductive structures by wind or animals.
4. Leaves are large and vascularized.

Unfamiliar terms in this list will be explained and illustrated in the following exercises.

Three of the five divisions of seed plants—Cycadophyta, Ginkgophyta, Gnetophyta—are relatively rare. These three divisions and the Coniferophyta are commonly referred to as the **gymnosperms**, or plants with "naked seeds," because the **ovule** (megasporangium and integument) is exposed on the surface of the sporophyte. In angiosperms, the ovule is enclosed in another structure, the **pistil**, which is evolved from a modified leaf. The angiosperms and gymnosperms used to be considered members of a single division. However, botanists generally believe that the various gymnosperm groups are descended from separate non-seed-plant ancestors and are thus placed in separate divisions.

Objectives To identify living and preserved specimens of seed plants to division, and to describe the key characteristics of morphology and life cycle that distinguish each division; to discuss the adaptations of the seed plants that enabled them to colonize and thrive on land.

EXERCISE 19-1 DIVISION CYCADOPHYTA

You may have seen cycads in ornamental gardens and mistaken their leaves for those of ferns or palm trees. But these plants are neither pteridophytes nor flowering plants. They are gymnosperms and are only distantly related to flowering plants and ferns. Only one genus of Cycadophyta (pronounced sigh-kad-AH-fit-ah) (*Zamia*) is native to the United States, but the sago palm (*Cycas revoluta*) is cultivated widely in warm climates.

- Observe the living and preserved specimens of cycads your instructor provides. Note the relatively short, stumpy stem compared to the large leaves. The leaves are pinnately compound, like fern fronds. They are called **megaphylls**, a term applied to leaves with complex branching vascular systems, in contrast to the simpler microphylls of the Lycophyta.
- Observe male and female conelike strobili of a typical cycad if available (Figure 19-1). Cycads are **dioecious** ("two houses"), meaning that the sexes are separate. These plants are also heterosporous, producing large female and small male spores. The shieldlike structures on the cones are considered to be evolutionary derivations of spore-bearing leaves, or sporophylls. Pull off and examine a shieldlike structure from the male and female cones. Female cones have megasporophylls, each one bearing two ovules (Fig. 19-1a). An ovule consists of the megasporangium and the integuments that cover it. Male cones have microsporophylls and produce microspores in microsporangia (Fig. 19-1b).
- Your instructor will provide you with microscope slides of microspores, pollen grains, sperm, and ovules from a typical cycad. Examine them under the compound microscope and compare them to Figure 19-2. The microspore and its enclosed male gametophyte constitute the pollen grain (19-2a). One of the three cells inside the microspore divides to produce two sperm cells, each bearing a spiral of flagella (Fig. 19-2b).

  Pollen grains are carried by the wind to the ovule where they enter the micropyle, an opening in the integument, and settle on the surface of the megasporangium (Fig. 19-2c). Over a period of several months, the pollen tube grows through the megasporangium toward the eggs in archegonia, which are embedded in the female gametophyte. The pollen tube and its contents constitute the male gametophyte. After fertilization the young embryo develops inside the female gametophyte tissue (Fig. 19-2d). The embryo, female gametophyte, remains of the megasporangium, and mature integument constitute the seed. The integuments mature into the seed coat.

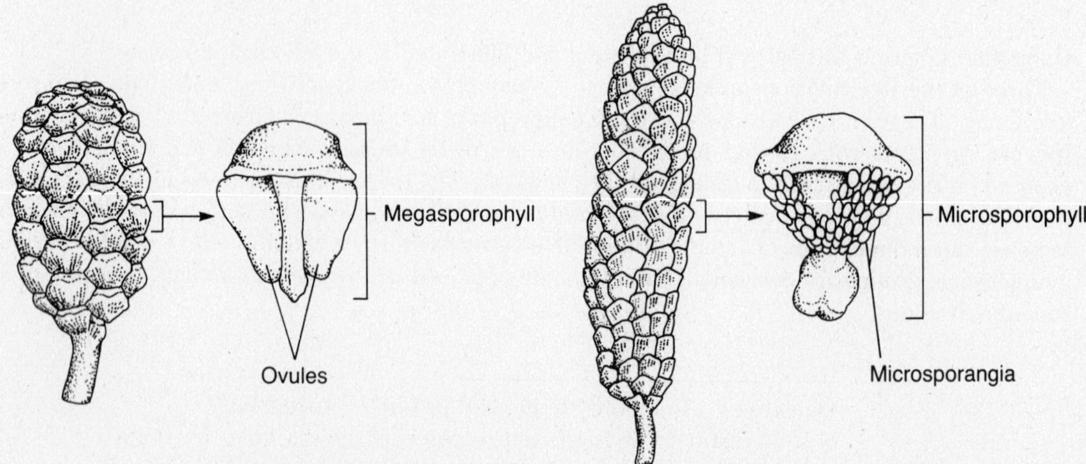

Figure 19-1 *Zamia*. (a) Megastrobilus and megasporophyll with two ovules. (b) Microstrobilus and microsporophyll with microspores.

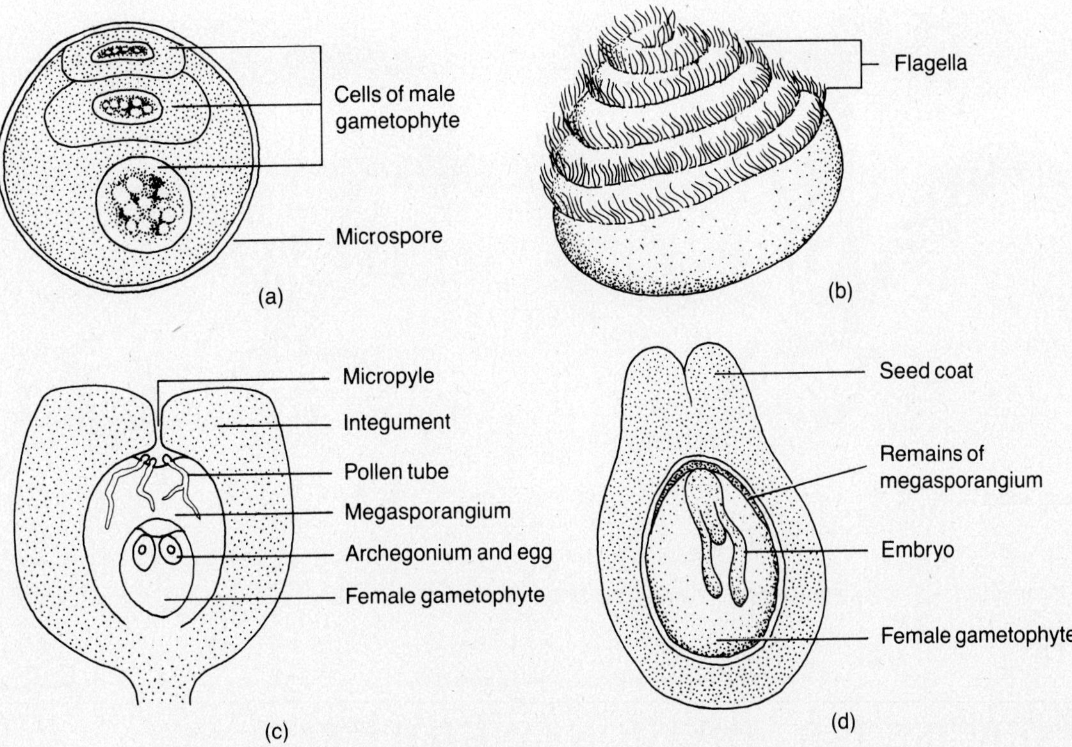

Figure 19-2 *Zamia* male and female gametophytes, and seed. (a) Three-celled pollen grain. (b) Cycad sperm with flagella. (c) Ovule and internal structures with pollen tube. (d) Seed.

EXERCISE 19-2 DIVISION GINKGOPHYTA

The ginkgo (*Ginkgo biloba*), or maidenhair tree, is sole survivor of this once widespread group of unusual plants, the Ginkgophyta (pronounced gink-GAH-fit-ah). Ginkgoes are nearly extinct in the wild, except for those in a small region of eastern China. The trees are widely cultivated, however, so one may see them in many ornamental gardens or even on city streets. Ginkgoes can grow to be large trees, two to three meters in diameter, with many branches; the light green leaves turn a beautiful yellow before being shed in autumn.

- Examine specimens of living or preserved ginkgoes your instructor provides and identify the following structures. The woody, large branches are called *long shoots*; they bear the smaller *short shoots,* which in turn bear the **leaves** and reproductive structures. The ginkgo leaf is unique, with its fan shape and dichotomous branching of the veins (Fig. 19-3). Like cycads, ginkgoes are dioecious and produce microspores and megaspores. Microspores are produced in microstrobili on the short shoots (Fig. 19-3a). Microspores develop into **pollen grains**, each of which contains a four-celled male gametophyte when it is shed. Pollen is carried by wind to the female **ovules**. Like cycads, ginkgoes produce two multiflagellated sperm, which travel through the pollen tube to the egg.

Ovules are produced in pairs on short shoots of the female tree (Fig. 19-3b). After fertilization of eggs, ovules mature into fleshy, plumlike seeds that have a nauseating odor—which is why the male tree is normally cultivated.

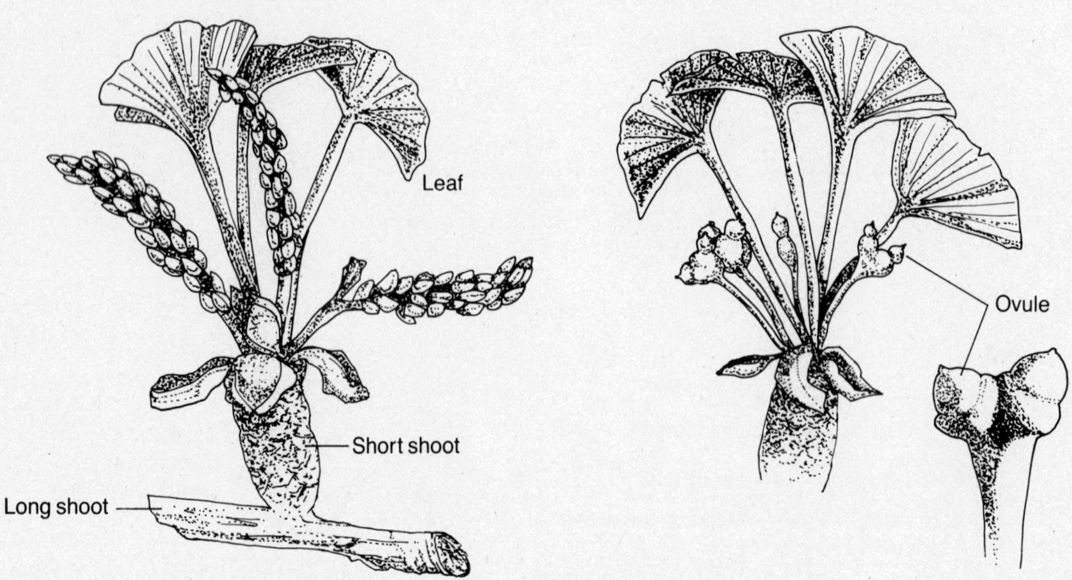

Figure 19-3 *Ginkgo.* (a) Microstrobilus. (b) Megastrobilus.

EXERCISE 19-3 DIVISION GNETOPHYTA

The third division of relatively rare seed plants, the Gnetophyta (pronounced nee-TAH-fit-ah) includes those commonly called **gnetinas**. The division contains three genera that differ greatly in morphology. Two genera, *Gnetum* (a large tree) and *Welwitschia* (a bizarre, stumplike plant with two straplike leaves), are rare and difficult to cultivate. The remaining genus, *Ephedra,* is a small shrub that is native to the southwestern United States.

- Examine the whole mount of *Ephedra* your instructor provides and compare it to Figure 19-4. Note the small size of the leaves; photosynthesis occurs mainly in the ribs of the green

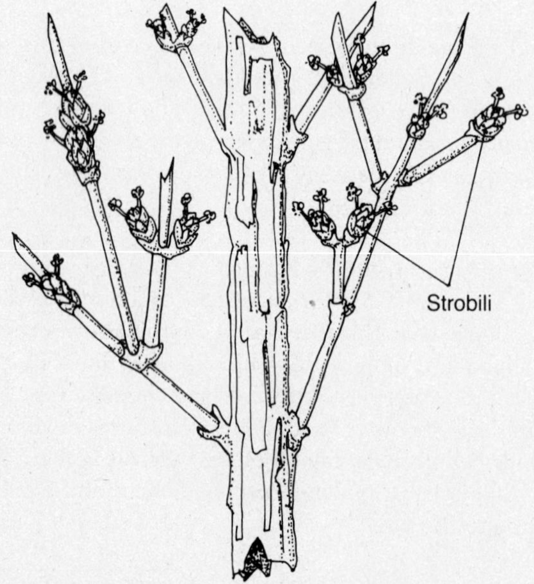

Figure 19-4 *Ephedra* (whole plant).

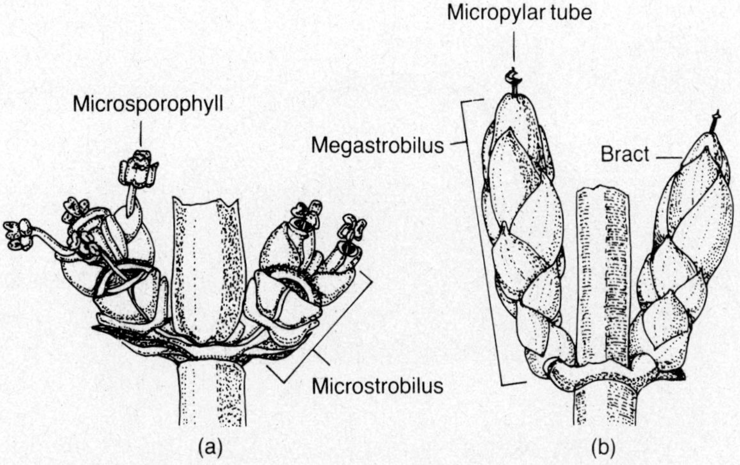

Figure 19-5 *Ephedra*. (a) Microstrobili. (b) Megastrobili.

parts of the stem. The stem also contains true vessel cells with perforated ends. Vessel cells, lined end-to-end inside the stem, conduct water in the plant. (Stem internal anatomy will be covered in Chapter 23.) The Gnetophyta are the only gymnosperms with such cells, a feature that links them evolutionarily with the angiosperms, which also have this advanced water-conducting system. Sexes may be separate (dioecious) or on the same plant (monoecious), depending on the species. Microstrobili and megastrobili occur at the branching points and look somewhat like small flowers. However, the term "flower" is used only for angiosperms.

Pollen are produced on stalked structures that protrude from microstrobili (Fig. 19-5a). Unlike cycads and ginkgoes, Gnetophyta produce nonflagellated sperm (two in each pollen grain). Pollen drift to the ovules on megastrobili (Fig. 19-5b). The ovules are partly enclosed within small bracts. A small micropylar tube sticks out from the bracts and catches the pollen on a sticky pollination droplet. After fertilization, the young embryo develops inside the female gametophyte and megasporangium to form the seed.

EXERCISE 19-4 DIVISION CONIFEROPHYTA

In contrast to other gymnosperms, the Coniferophyta (pronounced con-IF-er-AH-fit-ah), or conifers, are common today and widely distributed in nature. The division includes the familiar pines and firs and many other cone-bearing species. Their commercial importance is obvious in construction materials, wood pulp for paper, and decorative applications. You will study specimens and microscope slides of pine (*Pinus*).

- Examine the specimens of pine branches your instructor provides. The leaves of *Pinus* are commonly called needles, and they are borne singly or in clusters on short spur shoots on the branches. Examine a microscope slide of a cross section of a pine needle, and compare it with Figure 19-6. A **cuticle** covers the epidermis. Openings into the inner parts of the needle are termed **stoma**. A central bundle of **vascular tissue** is surrounded by the **mesophyll**, a layer of chloroplast-containing cells. Circular **resin ducts** are scattered throughout the mesophyll.

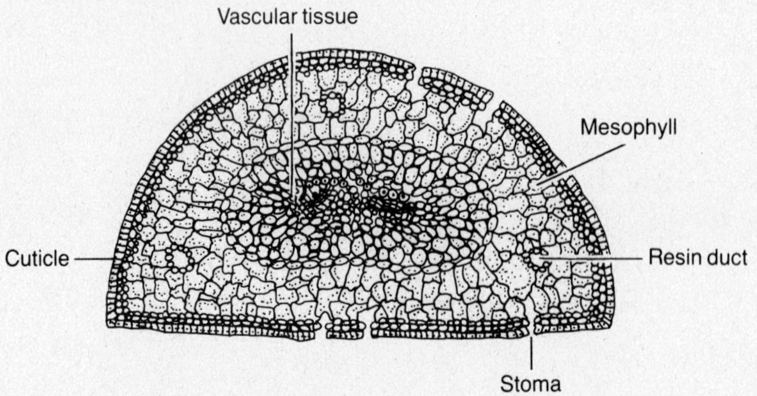

Figure 19-6 *Pinus*. Cross section of needle.

- Pine leaves have a low surface-to-volume ratio. Explain how this adaptation, along with a thick cuticle and stomata, enables them to exist in a dry habitat.

- Like other gymnosperms, pines produce pollen in male (staminate) cones and ovules in female cones. Examine the microscope slides of longitudinal sections of a male cone under the compound microscope. Pollen is produced in pollen sacs (microsporangia) attached to the underside of the microsporophyll of the cone (Fig. 19-7a). The pollen grain consists of four cells inside a wall with two lobes or wings (Fig. 19-7b). The wings increase the surface area of the pollen grain and facilitate wind dispersal of pollen to the female cone. Mature male cones release clouds of pollen if the branches are shaken.
- Examine the longitudinal sections of a female cone (Fig. 19-7c) under the compound microscope. A pair of ovules lies on the upper surface of each woody scale (19-7d). The pollen grain enters the micropyle in the integuments and germinates into a pollen tube through the megasporangium tissue. Inside the megasporangium, the megaspore mother cell divides meiotically to produce four megaspores; only one survives to become the female gametophyte. While the pollen tube is growing, the remaining megaspore divides repeatedly to form the female gametophyte, which consists of a mass of cells and two eggs (Fig. 19-7e). A full year or more after the pollen first arrives on the female cone, the pollen tube finally reaches the egg and a nonflagellated sperm nucleus fertilizes the egg. The embryo nourished by the female gametophyte develops eight or more cotyledons or embryonic leaves. The seed (Fig. 19-7f) consists of the seed coat, female gametophyte tissue, and embryo. You may have eaten pine nuts, which are pine female gametophytes with embryos inside. Each woody scale bears a pair of naked (uncovered) seeds on its upper surface, each seed with a papery wing that aids in seed dispersal.

EXERCISE 19-5 DIVISION ANTHOPHYTA

Flowering plants are the most widely successful and diverse of any division of plants. Often called angiosperms, a term meaning "seeds in a container," Division Anthophyta (pronounced an-THAW-fit-ah) has several unique features. Ovules and developing embryos are contained in the flower, a

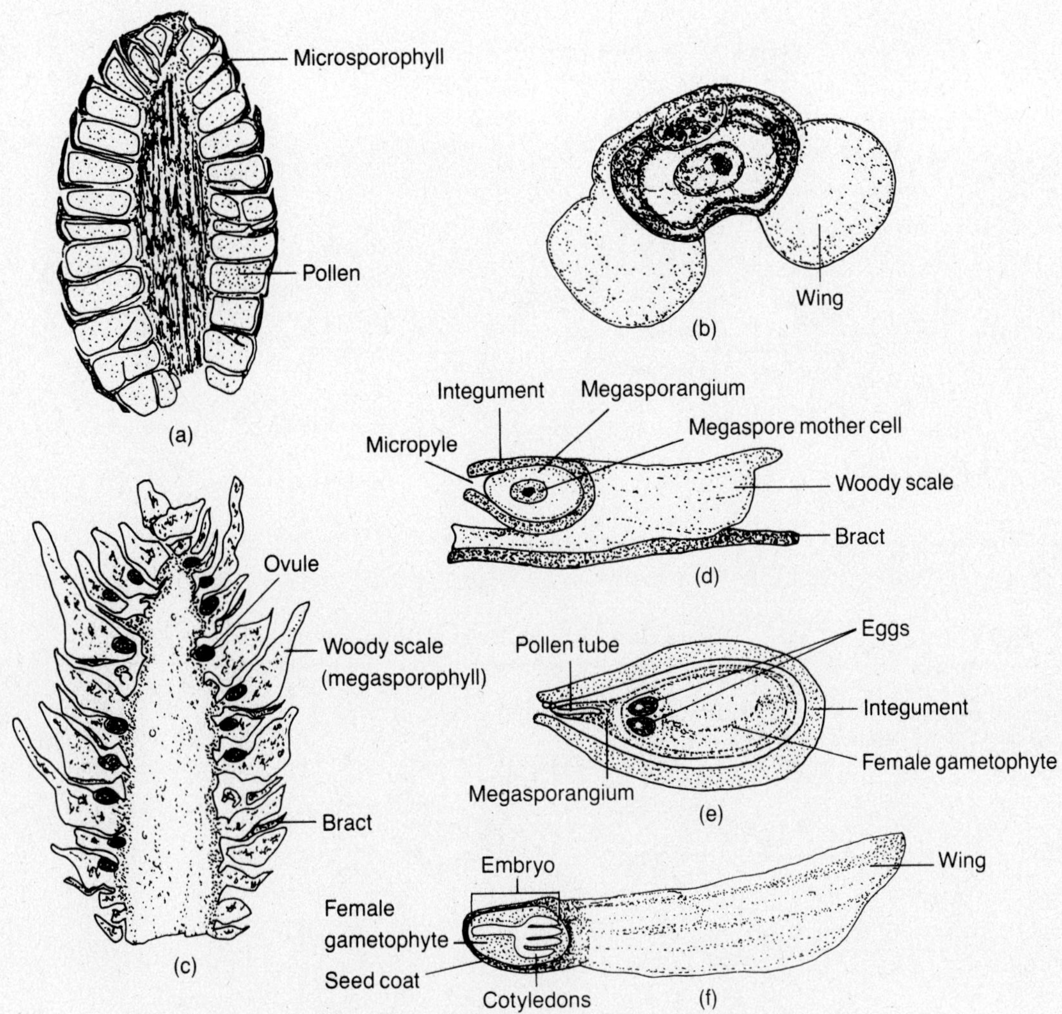

Figure 19-7 *Pinus.* (a) Male cone, longitudinal section. (b) Pollen grain. (c) Female cone, longitudinal section. (d) Ovule on woody scale (megasporophyll). (e) Pollen tube growing toward eggs in female gametophyte. (f) Seed.

structure considered to have evolved from modified leaves into a dizzying variety of shapes, colors, and patterns. Seed containers, or fruits, rival flowers in their variety of colors and forms.

This section will discuss only briefly the salient features of angiosperms. The details of their anatomy and reproduction will be dealt with in Chapter 23.

A. Flowers

The flower is the most distinctive adaptation of the angiosperms. As superficially different as flowers seem to be from the cones of gymnosperms, a close look at their anatomy reveals some similarities.

A typical flower is diagrammed in Figure 19-8. The central axis bears the green sepals and colored petals. Notice, first of all, why angiosperms are described as having "seeds in a container." The ovule, which will become the seed, is completely enclosed by the ovary. The ovary, stigma, and style constitute the pistil, or megasporophyll. Pollen is produced in the anther (cluster of four microsporangia) on the tips of slender filaments. An anther and filament constitute a microsporophyll, or stamen. Pollen is carried by wind or animals to the sticky surface of the stigma. The pollen

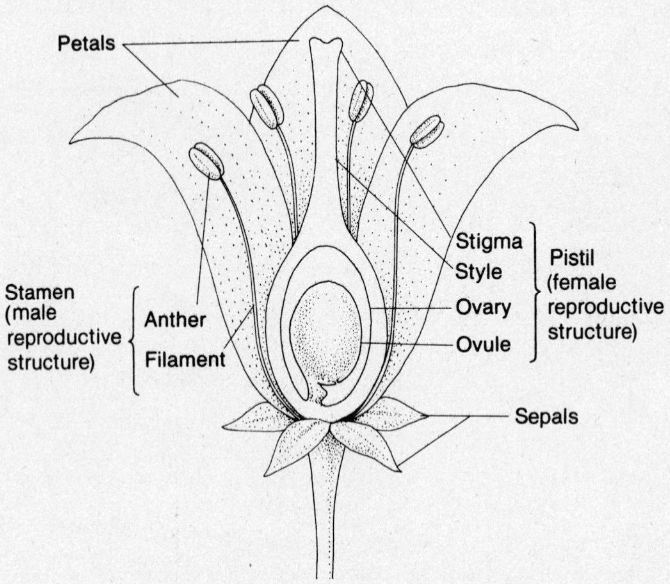

Figure 19-8 Typical flower of Anthophyta.

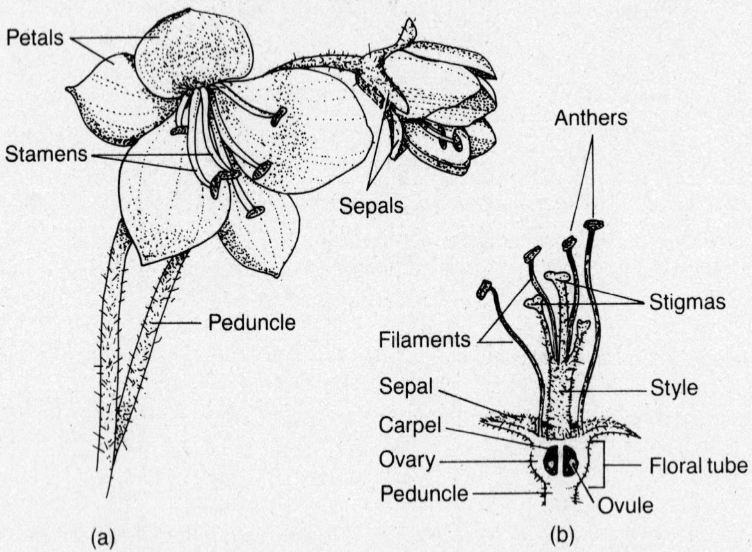

Figure 19-9 Apple (*Malus*) flower. (a) Intact flower. (b) Longitudinal cut through flower.

grain germinates, and a pollen tube grows down through the style and ovary, through the micropyle, and into the ovule to reach the female gametophyte. The male gametophyte consists of the elongated pollen tube and its contents. The pollen tube takes only a few weeks to reach the ovule, in contrast to the months or year that the process takes in gymnosperms. Double fertilization occurs, a process to be discussed in detail in Chapter 24. Briefly, one sperm fertilizes an egg nucleus to form a diploid zygote while another unites with a pair of nuclei in the gametophyte to produce a triploid nucleus. The triploid nucleus forms a tissue called the endosperm, which nourishes the growing embryo.

- Examine the specimen of the apple (*Malus*) flower provided by your instructor (Fig. 19-9a). The flower is supported by the **peduncle**. The five **sepals** are fused at their bases, forming a cuplike covering on the base of the five pink and white **petals**. Continuing the theme of five-parted structures, five **styles** with **stigmas** emerge from the center of the flower. The **stamens**, each consisting of an **anther** and **filament**, extend above the stigmas. Take a razor blade and slice the flower in half longitudinally (top to base) and remove the petals. This cut will expose the **ovary**, which is positioned below the bases of the sepals and petals (the term for this is "inferior ovary"). Inside the ovary are five **carpels**, each containing several **ovules**. The tissue surrounding the ovary is called the **floral tube**, which develops into an important part of the fruit.

- Your instructor may also have on display several other species of flowers. Examine them and be able to identify the structures (in boldface) described for the apple flower. Make any necessary drawings in the following space.

- The Anthophyta are divided into two groups, the dicotyledons and monocotyledons, often simply called dicots and monocots. These groups differ in the number of embryonic leaves present on germlings and in other characters as well (Table 19-1). Use the information in Table 19-1 to classify the flowers and leaves of the flower specimens examined previously. In Chart 19-1, list the characteristics for each specimen that lead you to call it a dicot or monocot.

Table 19-1 Monocots and dicots: Differences obvious and subtle.

Characteristic	Dicotyledons	Monocotyledons
Usual arrangement of flower parts (sepals, petals, stamens)	Multiples of fours or fives	Multiples of threes
Number of cotyledons (seed leaves)	Two	One
Usual pattern of leaf venation	Network	Parallel
Usual arrangement of vascular bundles in young stem	Circle	Scattered
Usual presence of secondary, or woody, growth	Present	Absent

Chart 19-1 Classification of flower specimens.

Specimen name	Type	Reasons for classifying
1. ____________	____________	____________________________
2. ____________	____________	____________________________
3. ____________	____________	____________________________
4. ____________	____________	____________________________

B. Pollination

- Scrape some pollen from the anthers of three of the flowers you sketched in the previous section and make a wet mount slide of each. Draw the pollen in the spaces that follow. Describe any differences in size, shape, and surface texture you observe.

- If the time of year is right and flowers are blooming during this part of the course, visit a nursery, botanical garden, or landscaped part of the campus. Make observations of the pollinators that visit at least two different kinds of flowers. Choose flowers that differ in shape or color. Make your observations in the early morning. Observe one or more flowers on the same plant and record the number and kinds of pollinators, if any, that visit the flower(s) during a 15-minute interval. Fill in Chart 19-2, using common terms for pollinators (large bee, yellow butterfly, etc.). Note the behavior of the pollinators.

Chart 19-2 Observations of pollinators visiting flowers.

Flower type	Species (if known)	Pollinators observed and behavior
1. ________ Drawing	________	a. ________ b. ________ c. ________ d. ________
2. ________ Drawing	________	a. ________ b. ________ c. ________ d. ________

Continued on p. 238.

Chart 19-2 **(continued) Observations of pollinators visiting flowers.**

Flower type	Species (if known)	Pollinators observed and behavior
3. ______________ Drawing	______________	a. ______________ b. ______________ c. ______________ d. ______________
4. ______________ Drawing	______________	a. ______________ b. ______________ c. ______________ d. ______________

- Summarize any differences in pollinator species between flower types, as well as differences in pollinator behavior. Do the pollinators carry pollen on their bodies? Does it appear that the pollinators effectively transfer pollen from their bodies to the stigmas?

Remembering that the observations were made in an environment influenced by humans, would you expect these pollinators and plants to be adapted to each other?

C. Fruits

A fruit is the ripened ovary and the other structures that surround it at maturity. As the colors and patterns of flowers are adaptations for pollination, the shapes, colors, and other characteristics of fruits affect seed dispersal. The wall of the ovary is modified to become the fruit wall, or pericarp. Pericarps come in various textures and colors, and fruits are classified according to these and other characteristics. The pericarp is often differentiated into several layers: an outer exocarp, a middle mesocarp, and an inner endocarp.

- Examine the apple fruit provided by your instructor. This fruit type is called a **pome**. First, examine the intact fruit and note the remnants of any floral parts. The peduncle, or "stem," may still be attached to the base. The brown, papery remnants of the sepals are at the other end of the apple. The apple itself is the highly modified floral tube and enclosed ovary of the flower (Fig. 19-9). The red or green skin of the apple is called the **epidermis**.
- Pair up with another student or group and cut one apple in half vertically from peduncle to sepals (Fig. 19-10a) and the other apple transversely (Fig. 19-10b). Examine this no doubt familiar sight. The white flesh of the apple below the epidermis is floral tube tissue. Inside this layer of tissue is a region of tougher carpellary tissue, the core, containing the carpels and seeds (mature ovules). In the apple cut transversely, note the five carpels arranged in a star shape, surrounded by the five-lobed carpellary tissue. The lobes alternate with the "points" of the carpels. Outside the tips of the carpels are the remnants of **petal bundles**, vascular tissue that supplied the petals. On the outer edge of each carpellary tissue lobe is a **sepal bundle**.
- Your instructor will provide you with a selection of fruit types, many of which you will be familiar with, though you may not know the scientific terms applied to them. Fruits are categorized according to whether they are formed from one or more ovaries or flowers, whether they are dry or fleshy, and whether they split open at maturity (dehiscent fruits). These

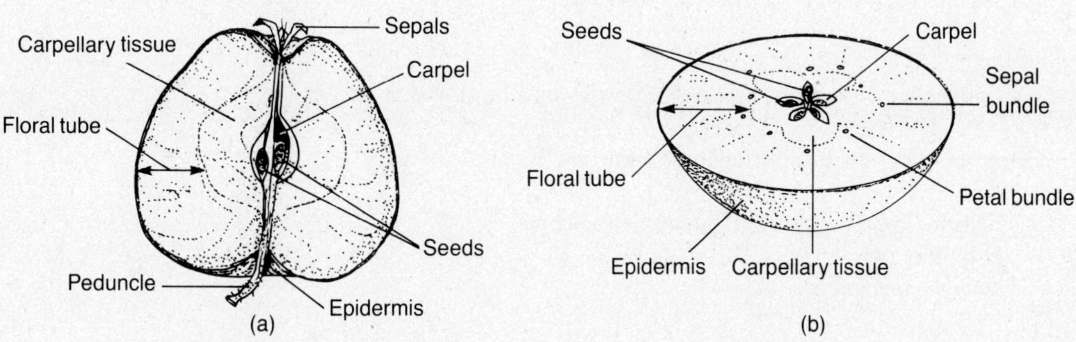

Figure 19-10 Apple fruit (pome). (a) Vertical section. (b) Transverse section.

categories are based on characteristics of the fruits and should not be confused with a taxonomic classification system. Fruit types are defined below, and an example of each type is provided. You should be able to categorize the fruits on display into the appropriate types, and list them under "Display specimens" in the following list.

Simple fruits consist of a single ripened ovary plus any adherent parts such as sepals, stamens, etc. Simple fruits may have many seeds. Most angiosperms have simple fruits, which are further categorized as follows:

Fleshy fruits have a pericarp that is soft and fleshy at maturity. Most of the structures we usually think of as "fruits" fall into this category. The most common types of fleshy fruits are:

Berry—exocarp skinlike, mesocarp fleshy, and endocarp slimy or juicy.
Example: grape
Display specimens:

Hesperidium—a berry with a leathery rind.
Example: orange
Display specimens:

Pepo—a berry with a more or less hard rind.
Example: watermelon
Display specimens:

Drupe—exocarp a thin skin, mesocarp fleshy, and endocarp hard and stony (a "pit").
Example: peach
Display specimens:

Pome—endocarp papery, forming a core with several seeds; outer fruit composed of thickened receptacle tissue.
Example: apple
Display specimens:

Dry fruits have a pericarp that becomes dry and hard at maturity.

Dehiscent dry fruits split open at maturity. Examples are:

Legume (pod)—splits open along two seams.
Example: pea
Display specimens:

Capsule—consisting of two or more fused carpels and splitting open at maturity.
Example: lily
Display specimens:

Indehiscent dry fruits do not split open at maturity. Examples are:

Grain (caryopsis)—does not split open at maturity, contains single seed, seed coat fused to pericarp.
Example: corn
Display specimens:

Nut—a one-seeded fruit with a very hard pericarp.
Example: walnut
Display specimens:

Aggregate fruits consist of clusters of several or many ripened ovaries produced by a single flower and borne on same receptacle.
Example: raspberry
Display specimens:

Multiple or compound fruits consist of clusters of several or many ripened ovaries produced by several flowers in the same inflorescence.
Example: pineapple
Display specimens:

Summary

Fill in Chart 19-3 on p. 242 comparing structures and processes in the five divisions of seed plants.

Chart 19-3 Comparison of the five divisions of seed plants.

Division	Leaf type	Spore-producing structures	Dioecious and/or monoecious	Means of pollen dispersal	Seeds naked or enclosed	Embryo nourished by gametophyte/ sporophyte
Cycadophyta						
Ginkgophyta						
Gnetophyta						
Coniferophyta						
Anthophyta						

20
KINGDOM ANIMALIA I. THE PRIMITIVE INVERTEBRATES

This chapter begins discussion of organisms commonly called "animals." It is the first of two chapters in which we consider the multicellular animals known as invertebrates, creatures without backbones. Like the term "algae," "invertebrates" is a term that applies to a diverse assemblage of organisms. Table 25-1 of the text lists 32 invertebrate phyla, which together contain several million species. (Remember that "phylum" is used for animals in the same way that "division" is used for plants.) These 32 phyla are probably not descended from a single protistan ancestor; it is highly likely that various groups arose from different protists. The only traits common to the millions of invertebrate species are heterotrophism and **multicellularity**. However, certain evolutionary trends and adaptations *are* clearly shown in the invertebrates—trends in anatomical structure, physiology, reproduction, behavior, and development. These trends will be emphasized in this chapter and the next, which cover nine major phyla. This chapter deals with four phyla of primitive invertebrates.

Definition of an Animal

Like many other terms, "animal" is one used so often that we take its meaning for granted. Without consulting a dictionary, write three statements in the spaces below that would enable someone to categorize any organism as an animal. Phrase the statements as concise, grammatically correct sentences that describe the organism.

1.

2.

3.

Refer to these statements as you proceed with your observations of the invertebrate phyla. Do not go back and change them—you will have the opportunity to do that at the end of this chapter. The objective here is to demonstrate the difficulty of defining the term "animal" in the face of so much diversity in the animal kingdom.

EXERCISE 20-1 PHYLUM PORIFERA

Objectives To describe the general morphology, reproduction, and feeding modes of specimens of porifera, and to describe the primitive tissue layers of which sponges are made.

The Porifera (pronounced pore-IF-fur-ah), or **sponges**, are considered by most biologists to be the simplest animals living today. Sponges are sessile (stationary), aquatic organisms that extract their food from the surrounding water. Most sponges are marine, but a few live in fresh water. Flagellated cells set up a current through the sponge body, and food particles are captured as the water stream passes through them. This mode of feeding is called filter feeding and occurs in many invertebrates in addition to sponges.

Tissues such as endoderm, mesoderm, and ectoderm formed in higher animals during embryological development (Chapter 13) are absent. Sponges, however, are composed of several different cell types arranged in distinct cell layers. Sponges are capable of reproducing asexually by the budding of new individuals from the tissue of existing ones. Fragments of sponges may also break off and form new sponges. Some freshwater and a few marine sponges produce asexual **gemmules**, small masses of cells with a hard covering. Although you will not directly observe budding in the laboratory, evidence of it is observable in clusters or spreading masses of sponges growing on one rock. Sexual reproduction in sponges occurs when sperm and eggs are produced by special cells in the same sponge. Sperm are dispersed between sponges by water currents. The fertilized egg develops into a flagellated larval stage.

- Examine the specimens of sponges provided by your instructor. Describe and sketch the diversity of body types displayed.

- Are some of the sponges symmetrical? ____________ What kind of symmetry do they display? ____________ Write a one-sentence definition for this type of symmetry.

- Examine the microscope slides of *Grantia* under low power with the compound microscope. This is a very small (1–2 cm long), vaselike sponge. On a longitudinal section of the entire sponge (Fig. 20-1) the pathway of water can be traced. Water enters the outer openings of the **incurrent canals**, passes across the tissue layers of the sponge and into the **radial canals**, and from there enters the large central **atrium**. Water from all the radial canals flows up and out through a single common large opening termed the **osculum**.
- Switch to higher magnification and examine the tissue layers in the sponge wall. The **epithelium** covers the outer surface of the sponge, including the walls bordering the incurrent canals. The internal surfaces of the radial canals are covered by flagellated cells called **choanocytes**. These collar-shaped cells have flagella whose beating induces the current of water that flows through the sponge. Food particles are filtered and ingested by the choanocytes, but the digestion does not occur here. Food particles are passed to mobile **amoebocyte** cells in the middle tissue layer termed the **mesenchyme**, where digestion occurs in food vacuoles, much as in protozoa. Food is transported around the body of the sponge by the mobile amoebocytes. This system of food ingestion, digestion, and distribution is very primitive compared to that in all other animals. In addition to amoebocytes, the mesenchyme contains the egg cells, which are fertilized by sperm taken in by choanocytes.
- The nonliving components of the skeleton are also found in the mesenchyme. Fibers of a type of collagen (which gives the sponge its flexible texture) and hard **spicules** made of calcium carbonate or silica make up a skeleton that can be flexible or rigid. Look for the spicules of *Grantia*, which are relatively simple spines. In other sponges, spicules look like grappling hooks, crystal lattices, and spiked martial-arts weapons. Speculate on the structural and defensive functions of spicules.

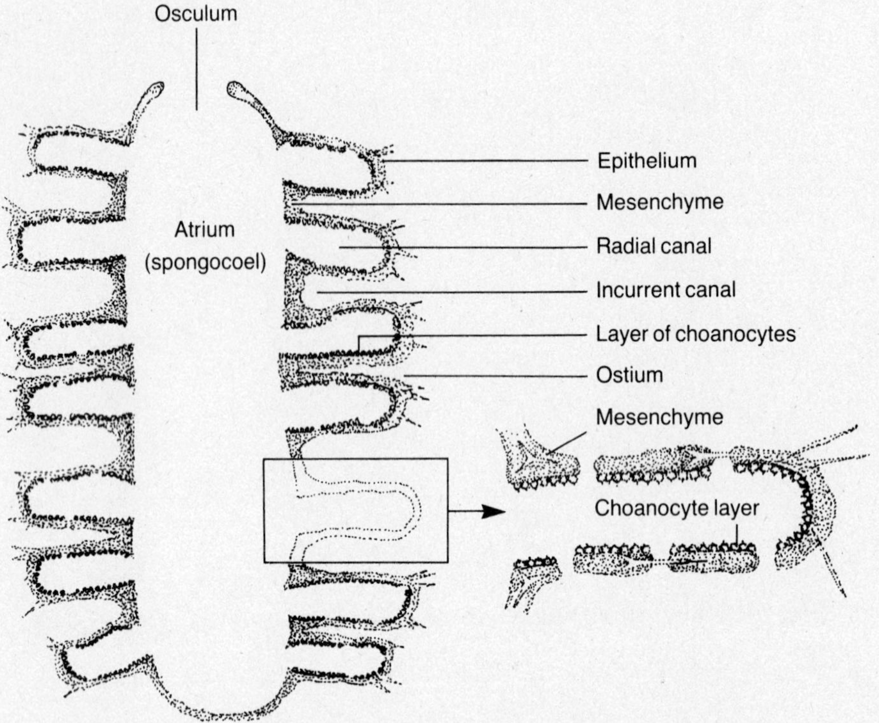

Figure 20-1 *Grantia*, sponge. Cross section and longitudinal section.

EXERCISE 20-2 PHYLUM CNIDARIA

Objectives To describe the symmetry and tissue level of anatomical organization of specimens of Cnidaria; to describe alternation of generations in this phylum; and to describe the capture-feeding mode of these animals.

The Cnidaria (pronounced nye-DAR-ee-ah) or **coelenterates** represent a step up in complexity compared to the Porifera. This group includes aquatic organisms such as sea anemones, corals, jellyfish, and other similar albeit less familiar animals. They exhibit radial symmetry, but have more complex tissue types, physiology, behavior, and life cycles than sponges.

As in the Porifera, three cell layers make up the body wall in coelenterates. But in this group the cell layers form more integrated tissues. The outer **epidermis** is skinlike and provides a relatively tough, flexible body covering. The middle cell layer is termed the **mesoglea**, which contains jellylike material and muscle fibers in some coelenterates. The inner **gastrodermis** lines an internal cavity in which digestion occurs. In contrast to sponges, in which digestion occurs in food vacuoles, digestion in the Cnidaria is extracellular. The size of food items is thus considerably larger in coelenterates than in sponges.

Some members of this phylum go through an alternation of generations in their life cycle (Fig. 20-2). One stage is called the **polyp**, which is stationary and anchored to the substrate (Fig. 20-2a). The polyp buds off **medusae** (Fig 20-2b), the other stage in the life cycle. Eggs and sperm are usually produced by different medusae, which are thus termed dioecious. Although the term "alternation of generations" is used for this process as well as the various life cycles of algae and higher plants (Chapters 18 and 19), the underlying mechanisms are different: Plant generations alternate between haploid and diploid stages, whereas polyps and medusae are both diploid, and the gametes are the only haploid stage in the life cycle.

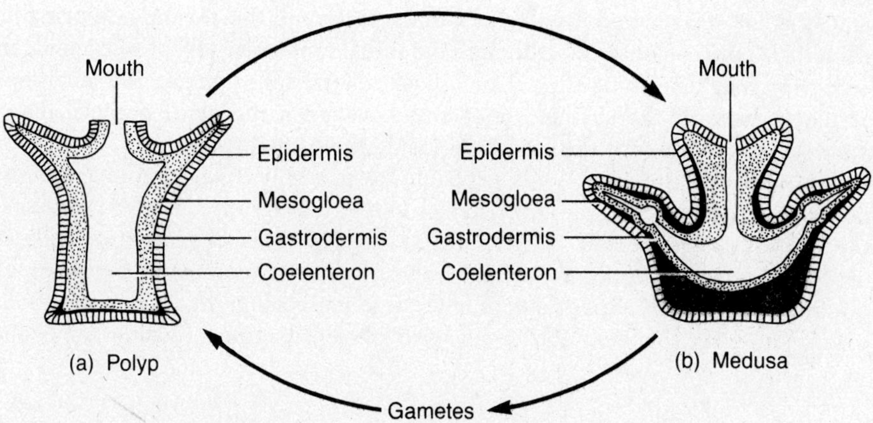

Figure 20-2 Alternation of generations in hydrozoans.

The Phylum Cnidaria is divided into three classes. The class **Hydrozoa** contains organisms that have both a colonial polyp stage and a solitary medusa stage. The class **Scyphozoa** comprises the jellyfish, which have large medusae and small polyp stages. The class **Anthozoa** includes the corals and sea anemones, which lack the medusa stage entirely. You will observe specimens of each of these classes.

A. Class Hydrozoa

- Use the stereoscopic microscope to observe the living specimens of *Hydra*, a freshwater hydrozoan that is unusual for the class because it lacks a medusa stage. It does, however, have the virtue of being easy to culture and study in the living state. The *Hydra* will be provided in shallow observation dishes of water. Do not remove the *Hydra* from the dishes, and try to disturb them as little as possible—when startled they tend to contract into tiny lumps for long periods of time. Sketch the specimen and label the following structures. The organism is attached to the dish with a **basal disk** or **foot**. The polyp can move slowly by sliding on the foot or somersaulting across the substrate, and it can also detach and secrete a gas bubble on the basal disk and float to a new site. The **stalk** may appear solid but is actually a hollow cylinder surrounding the **gastrovascular cavity** or **coelenteron**. Observing the animal with transmitted light reveals the hollow nature of the stalk. The apex is ringed by flexible **tentacles** with hollow centers that are connected to the coelenteron of the main stalk. At the center of the ring of tentacles is the **mouth**, which opens into the coelenteron.

- Using a pair of forceps, very gently drop a dead brine shrimp on the tentacle of a *Hydra*. If the animal is not too startled it will curl a tentacle around the shrimp and bring it toward the mouth and into the coelenteron. Although the initial tentacular response is rapid, the ingestion of the shrimp may take some time. Come back several times during the laboratory period to check the process. If the shrimp appears to have been ingested, observe the *Hydra* with transmitted light to observe the food item inside the coelenteron.
- As you manipulated the animal you probably observed it changing the shape of its stalk in several ways to become shorter and fatter or longer and thinner. *Hydra* possesses two sets of muscle threads or **myonemes**. Muscle threads in the bases of epidermal cells are oriented longitudinally (along the long axis of the polyp), while myonemes in the inner gastrodermis are oriented transversely. Speculate on how these muscles might act in opposition to produce the changes in body shape you observed. Use labeled diagrams to show the changes in body shape.

- Cnidarians possess a primitive nerve net that allows them to respond to tactile stimuli. Take a rested, undisturbed *Hydra* and touch it lightly with a glass probe at the structures listed below. Allow the polyp to relax between touches. Describe the response of the polyp to each stimulus.

  tentacles:

  mouth:

  stalk:

  foot:

  Does stimulating some structures elicit more response than stimulating others? Suggest a reason for these differences.
- Use the compound microscope to examine the longitudinal section of *Hydra* that your instructor provides (Fig. 20-3a). At high magnification you should be able to identify the gastrodermal, epidermal, and mesogleal layers of the body wall. Small, bumplike regions on the tentacles are sites where nematocysts are located. A typical nematocyst is shown in Figure 20-3b. These harpoonlike cells shoot barbs, loops, or sticky filaments to capture prey. How do nematocysts enhance the function of the tentacles?

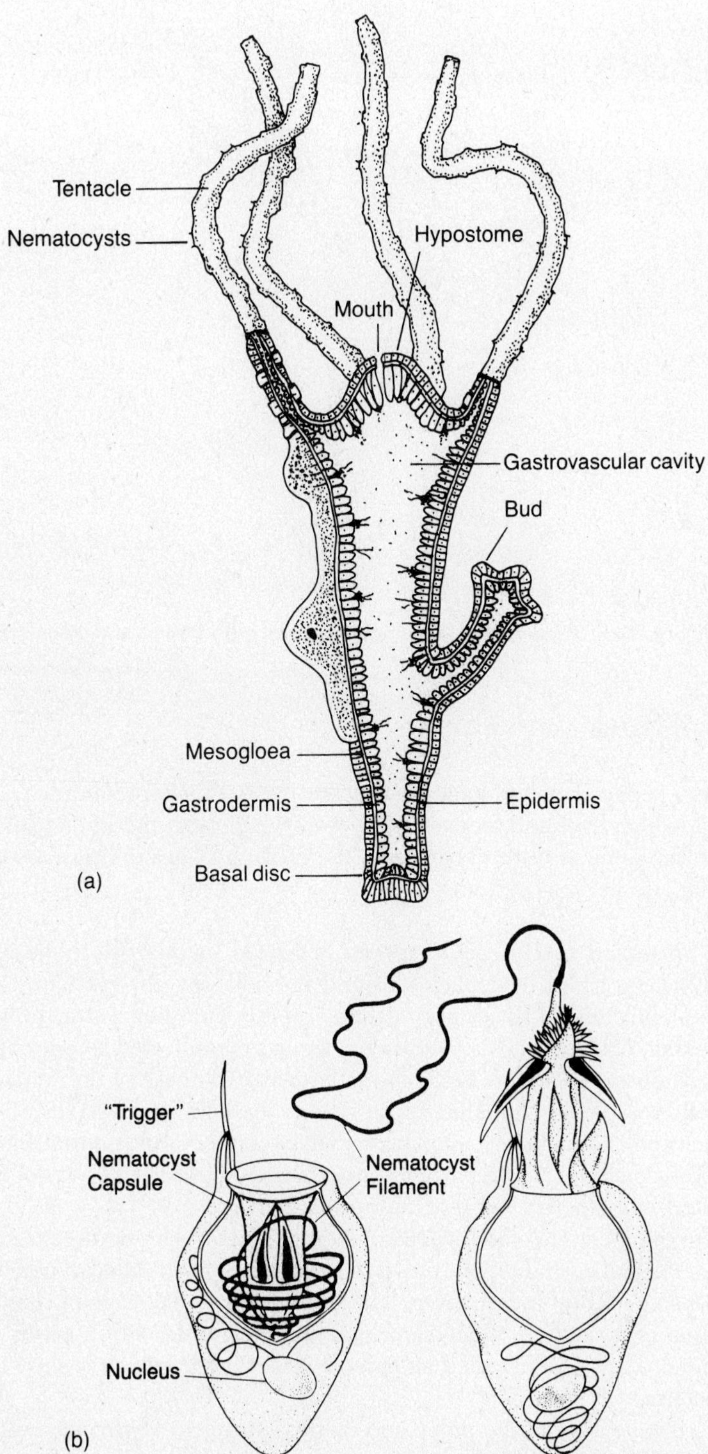

Figure 20-3 *Hydra*, freshwater polyp. (a) Longitudinal section of polyp. (b) Nematocyst.

- *Obelia* is a typical representative of a colonial hydroid (Fig. 20-4). Observe the microscope slides of *Obelia* polyps. This stalked colonial hydroid consists of numerous individual feeding polyps connected by a common coelenteron. *Obelia* has a typical hydrozoan life cycle, in which the polyp alternates with the medusa stage. Medusae are produced as buds in specialized branches termed "gonangia."

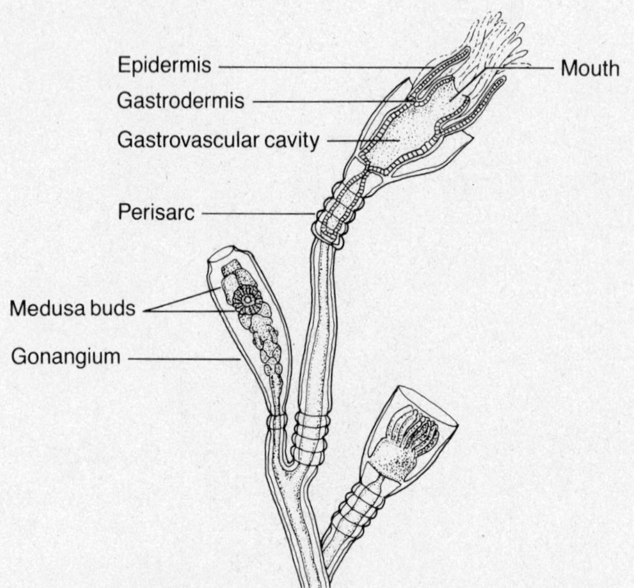

Figure 20-4 *Obelia*, stalked colonial hydroid with polyps and gonangia.

B. Class Scyphozoa

Scyphozoans have a reduced polyp stage in the life cycle. The predominant stage is the free-swimming medusa, which lives and feeds in open water. Although the body plan and tissue layers of scyphozoans are the same as in the Hydrozoa, the medusa stages of this class have more highly developed muscular and nervous systems.

- Examine the preserved specimens of *Aurelia*, a typical scyphozoan medusa (Fig. 20-5). The adult medusa bears a fringe of tentacles around the bell (Fig. 20-5a). Circular muscles in the bell propel the living animal by jet propulsion—rapidly pumping water through the mouth in a steady succession of squirts. This medusa has a more complicated sensory apparatus than the other organisms observed so far. Eight indentations at the base of the tentacular ring on the rim of the bell are sites of **rhopalia**, sense organs for light and balance. Food particles are caught in mucus on the tentacles. The **oral arms** sweep food off the tentacles, and flagella in the grooves of the arms carry the particles into the mouth. Other species of scyphozoans have highly poisonous nematocysts, used to capture larger prey.
- Other stages in the life cycle of *Aurelia* can be examined on the microscope slides provided by your instructor. Sexual reproduction results in a tiny larval form called a "planula," which settles onto the substrate and becomes a polyp. The diminutive polyp stage in the life cycle is called the **scyphistoma** (Fig. 20-5b), which develops into a **strobila** with a series of saucer-shaped buds (Fig. 20-5c). Each bud is called an **ephyra** (Fig. 20-5d), which is shed to become a free-swimming medusa.
- Compare the relative sizes of the polyp and medusa stages in Hydrozoa and Scyphozoa.

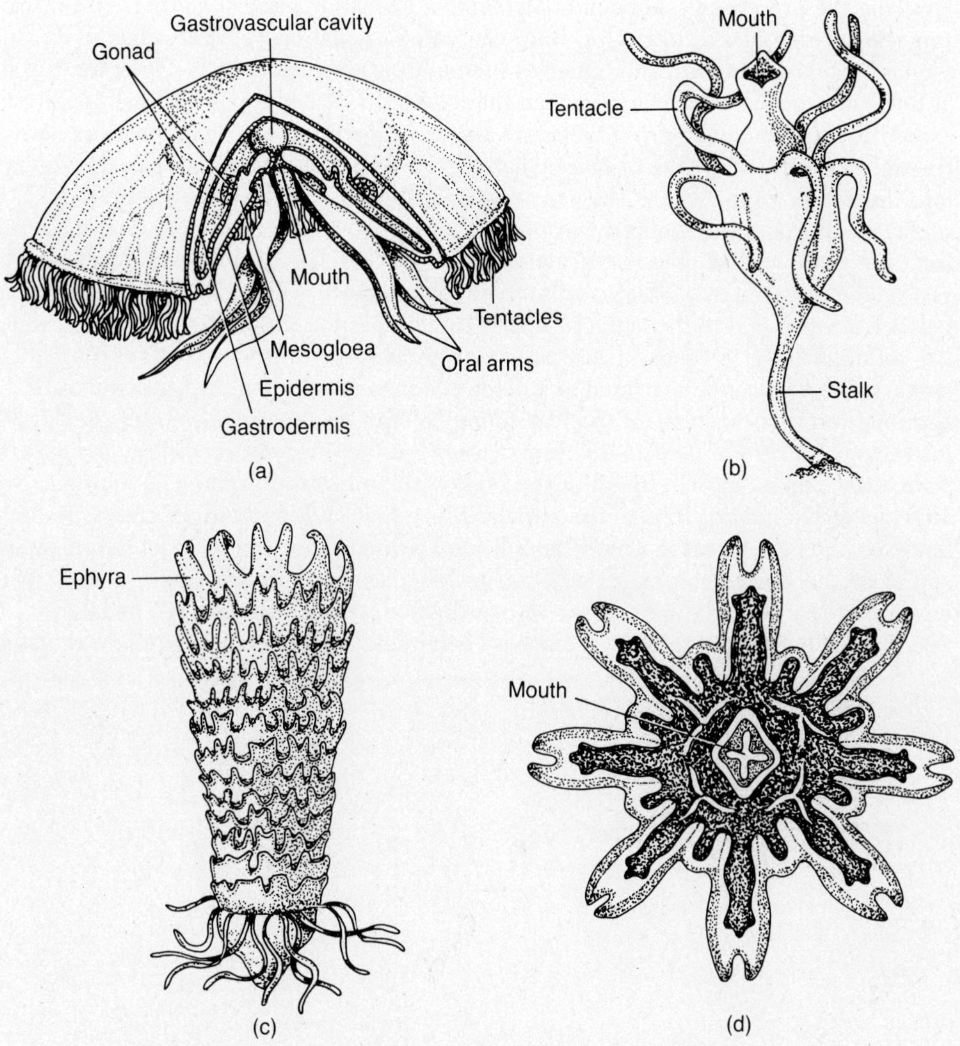

Figure 20-5 *Aurelia,* jellyfish. (a) Adult medusa. (b) Scyphistoma polyp. (c) Strobila with ephyra. (d) Ephyra.

- Speculate on the advantages to a scyphozoan of having a more highly developed nervous system compared to that of the hydrozoan polyps.

C. Class Anthozoa

This class includes the sea anemones and corals so abundant in the oceans. Members of this class lack the medusa stage altogether. The polyps may be solitary or colonial, and organisms may reach great sizes. Large sea anemones in the Pacific Northwest of the United States can be several decimeters tall. But the most remarkable Anthozoan structures—in fact, the largest biotic structures on Earth—are the coral reefs of tropical seas. These reefs are made from the living and dead remains of the calcium carbonate skeletons of coral colonies.

- Examine the preserved specimen of *Metridium*, a small sea anemone (Fig. 20-6a). Notice the superficial resemblance to *Hydra*: Both consist of a **pedal disk** that attaches to the substrate, a cylindrical body column, and tentacles surrounding an apical mouth. However, the structure of this anthozoan is more complex than that of *Hydra*. Cut the polyp in half longitudinally to expose the internal anatomy. The mouth opens into a tube, the actinopharynx, that leads to the coelenteron below. One or more ciliated grooves in the actinopharynx carry food particles into the coelenteron, where they are digested and absorbed by the gastrodermis. Primary septa extend from the actinopharynx out to the body wall; secondary and tertiary septa extend from the body wall in toward the actinopharynx. These septa divide the coelenteron into a series of compartments, which are interconnected because the primary septa do not extend below the lower end of the actinopharynx. Gonads are located in the ends of the septa below the actinopharynx. Strands of acontia are connected to the gonads. These strands contain nematocysts and can be extruded in a defensive manner if the animal is disturbed.
- Examine the cross sections of the *Metridium* column on microscope slides provided by your instructor (Fig. 20-6b). Locate the three tissue layers: epidermis, mesoglea, and gastrodermis. Notice the fibrous muscle tissue in the body wall and in the septa. The muscular system in *Metridium*, like that of *Hydra*, has circular transverse and longitudinal fibers. In *Metridium*, however, the muscles act in a more complicated fashion. They can contract the ring of tentacles and close the actinopharynx, in addition to lengthening or shortening the body. Anemones move in a very slow gliding manner by coordinated muscle action in the pedal disk.
- Speculate on the advantage to the anemone of being able to completely close off the actinopharynx.

EXERCISE 20-3 PHYLUM PLATYHELMINTHES

Objectives To describe the organ level of organization in specimens of the Turbellaria, as well as their cephalization and bilateral symmetry; to identify typical members of the three classes and describe their adaptations to a free-living or parasitic life style.

This phylum exhibits a distinctly greater structural complexity than that found in sponges and cnidarians. The Platyhelminthes (pronounced PLAT-ee-hell-MINTH-eez), or flatworms, display the **organ level** of anatomical organization. Flatworms have muscle fibers, excretory organs, and reproductive organs. They also show **cephalization**, the presence of a distinct front end with specialized sense organs and a nerve center. Like many other organisms that show directional motion, flatworms have **bilateral symmetry**, instead of the radial symmetry generally found in sedentary animals.

There are three classes of flatworms, one free living (Turbellaria) and two parasitic (Trematoda and Cestoda).

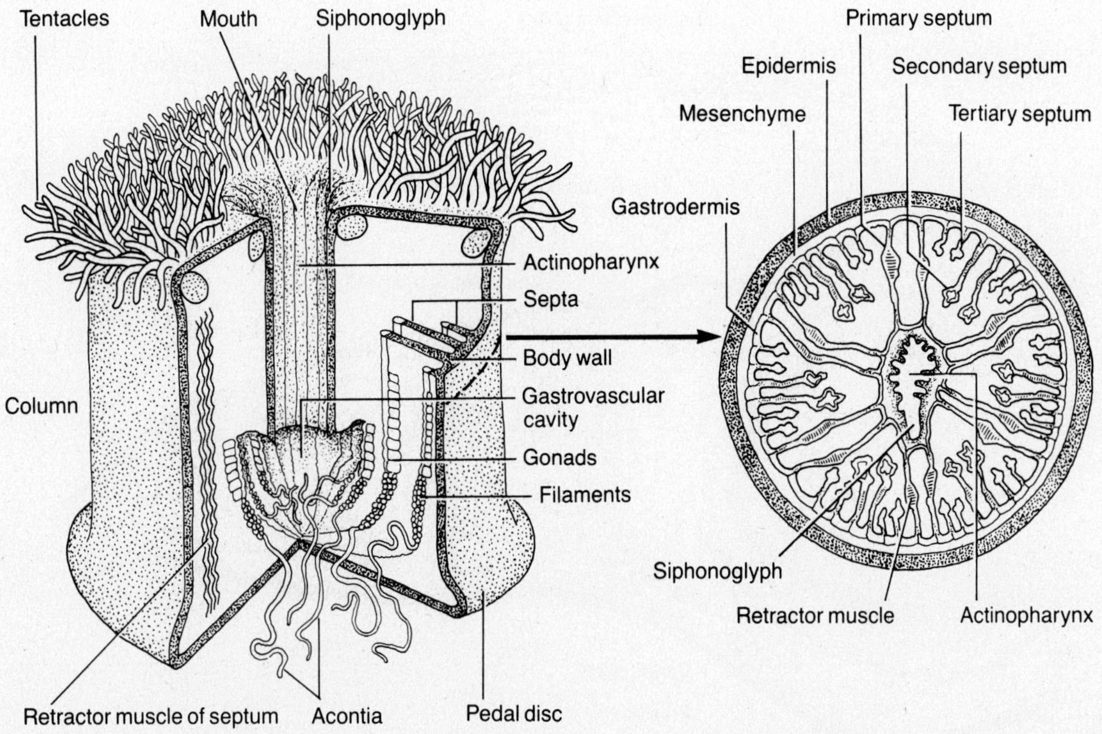

Figure 20-6 *Metridium*, sea anemone. (a) Intact animal. (b) Longitudinal section.

A. Class Turbellaria

The free-living flatworms are generally aquatic; their flattened, undulating bodies are well suited for swimming and hiding in crevices and under rocks. The name "flatworms" is an apt one, and these creatures have a paper-thin profile. Despite a nearly two-dimensional appearance, they possess an internal differentiation of organ systems considerably more complex than the phyla examined so far.

- Use the low-power objective of the compound microscope to examine the whole mount microscope slides of *Planaria* provided by your instructor. *Planaria* is an easily cultured turbellarian whose behavior has been well studied. The body of the worm is elongate and bilaterally symmetrical about the long axis: The left and right sides are mirror images (Fig. 20-7a). The front end has a pair of flared lobes, or **auricles**, on the sides. Near the auricles are a pair of **eyespots** that have a somewhat cross-eyed appearance. Near the eyespots are nerve ganglia, but they are not readily seen on the prepared slides.
- The whole mount slide may be of an animal whose gastrovascular cavity has been rendered visible by being filled with dark material. If so, the elaborately branched network of this cavity will be clearly visible. The entrance to this network is near the center of the lower, or ventral, surface of the worm. Turn the slide over if necessary to see the **mouth**, which leads into the muscular **pharynx**.
- Next, examine the microscope slides of cross sections through the pharyngeal region of a *Planaria* (Fig. 20-7b). The large tubular pharynx in the center rests inside a cavity, the **pharyngeal pouch**. The pharynx is protrusible—it is extended for feeding (described in the following material). Other branches of the gastrovascular cavity are visible as circular, hollow

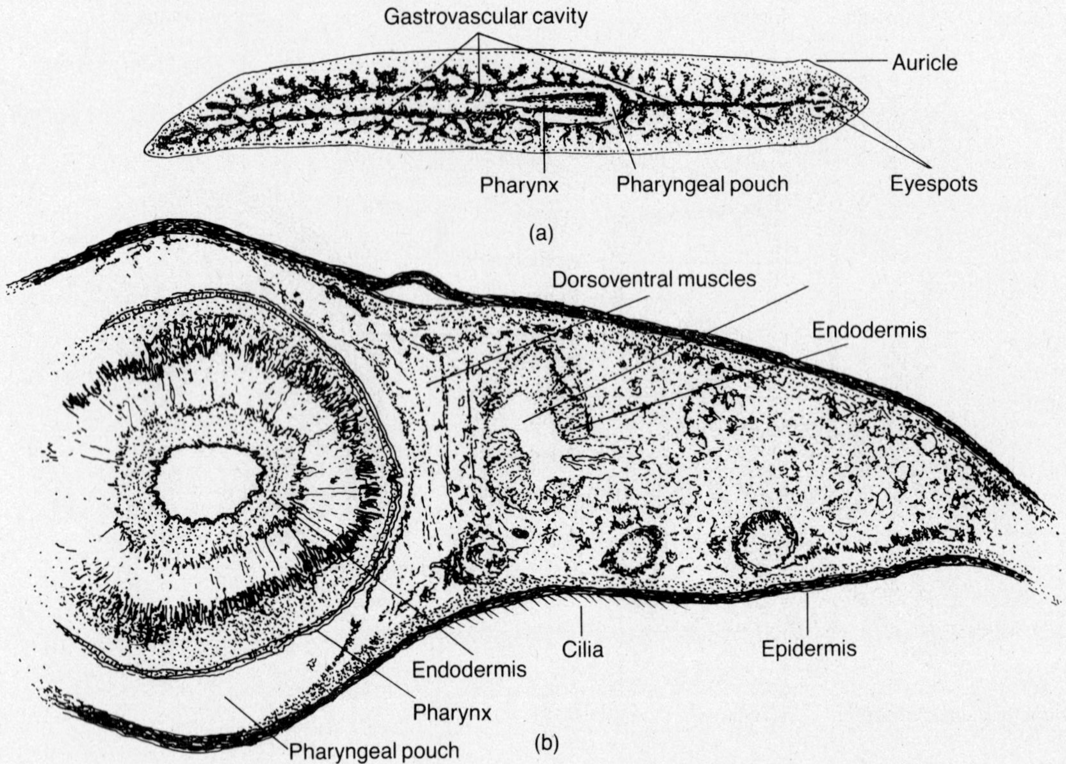

Figure 20-7 *Planaria*, flatworm. (a) Whole worm. (b) Cross section through pharynx.

tubes. These tubes and the pharynx are lined by gastrodermis. Look closely at the epidermis on the upper and lower surfaces. Which surface is ciliated? ______________

- Speculate on why this surface is ciliated.

Planaria lacks a true body cavity between the gastrovascular cavity and the epidermis. The tissue filling the interior of the worm is called **mesenchyme**, and it contains various types of muscles that run longitudinally, between the dorsal and ventral surfaces, and in a circular fashion around the body. Some of these muscles may be visible as strands of fibers in the cross sections.

Unfortunately, the two other organ systems (excretory and reproductive) are not easily observed on living animals or prepared slides. Most turbellarians are hermaphrodites, bearing ovaries and testes. The reproductive system is pictured in Figure 25-12 of the text. The excretory system consists of a network of tubes and specialized excretory **flame cells** called a **protonephridial system**. These tubules and flame cells are located around the periphery of the worm's body, not unlike the arrangement of the reproductive system.

- If live *Planaria* are available, observe their behavior in a shallow dish of water. Describe the swimming motion relative to the external structures you observed with the microscope. If possible, put a few tiny bits of finely chopped meat in the dish and observe the orienting movements of the worms and their feeding behavior. Record your observations and any drawings in the space below.

B. Class Trematoda

The Trematoda, or flukes, are parasitic flatworms that infect a number of vertebrates, including humans. Like many parasites, they devote a great deal of body mass to reproductive tissue in certain phases of their life cycle, and reproductive structures are readily observable with the compound microscope.

- Examine the microscope slides of the adult stage of the Chinese liver fluke, *Clonorchis sinensis* (Fig. 20-8). This trematode lives in the bile ducts of the human liver and consumes tissue of the host; it is a particular problem in the Far East. The outer surface of the fluke is termed the **tegument** and lacks cilia. The more narrow, tapered end contains the pharynx and **oral sucker** that the fluke uses to attach to the host. Extending back from the pharynx are two slender tubes of the intestine, both of which end at the posterior end of the animal. A ventral sucker lies just forward of the mass of female reproductive tubules.

Most of the tubular structures in *Clonorchis* are part of the male or female reproductive systems. The dark mass of folded tubules in the anterior and central part of the fluke make up the **uterus**,

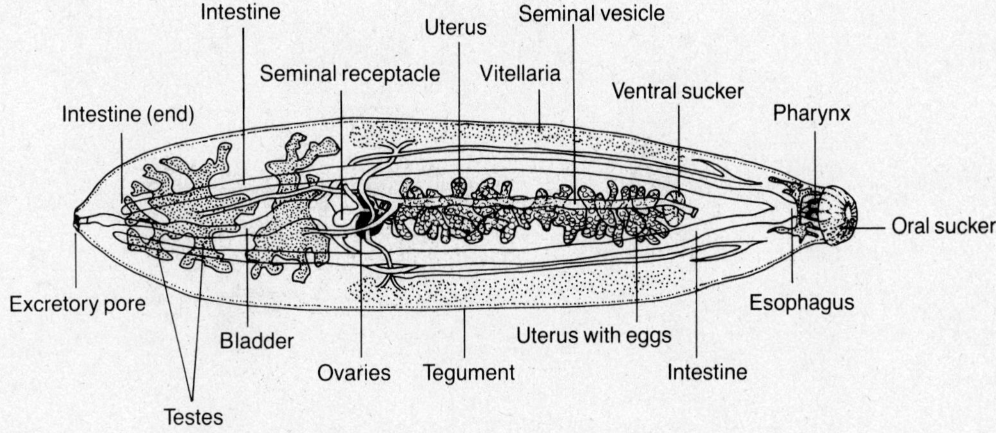

Figure 20-8 *Clonorchis sinensis*, Chinese liver fluke. Whole mount.

which may contain thousands of eggs. Eggs originate in the ovaries, which appear as a dark globular mass at the posterior end of the uterus. The branching network of tubules in the posterior portion are the testes, where sperm are produced. The **seminal receptacle**, a light-colored sac posterior to the ovaries, receives sperm from another worm through a system of copulatory canals. The granular materials near the edges of the worm are **vitellaria**, which function in yolk production for the eggs.

Like other turbellarians, the trematodes have a protonephridial excretory system consisting of tubules and flame cells. An **excretory pore** at the posterior end connects with the **bladder**, which may be obscured by the testes in your specimen. The bladder connects fluid from a series of ducts that run along the sides of the worm.

C. Class Cestoda

Members of the class Cestoda are commonly known as **tapeworms**. They are also parasites but have an even more modified anatomy than flukes in that they lack a gut; all nutrients are absorbed through the epidermis of the worm, which resides in the gut of vertebrates. The absence of a gut in this group of flatworms is believed to have come about through the evolutionary loss of this relatively advanced structure, which was unnecessary in a parasite living in the nutrient-rich environment of the digestive tract of a host.

- Examine the microscope slides of a tapeworm of the genus *Taenia*. There are two basic parts to the worm: a **scolex** (Fig. 20-9a) on the anterior end that attaches to the intestine by means of a ring of hooks and suckers; and a long chain of **proglottids** (Fig. 20-9b), which are little more than packets of reproductive organs. Each proglottid is basically like all the others, and therefore the ribbonlike body is not considered to be truly segmented (a feature of Annelida, Chapter 21). Gravid proglottids (ripe with eggs, Fig. 20-9b) break off from the worm and disperse the eggs outside the host. Meanwhile the scolex remains attached to the gut lining and manufactures more proglottids.

Like other turbellaria, the excretory system is a protonephridial system of tubules and flame cells, but these are not easily seen on the slide specimens. Likewise, the nerve cords and ganglia are reduced, as are longitudinal and circular muscles. The gut is lacking entirely. Because of the habitat of these parasites (anoxic gut interior), their metabolism is usually anaerobic and produces carbon dioxide and organic acids (Chapter 8), although the worms can use oxygen for respiration if it is available.

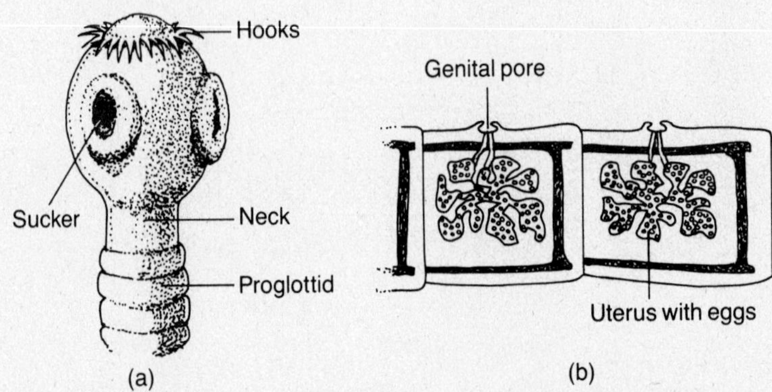

Figure 20-9 *Taenia*, tapeworm. (a) Scolex. (b) Proglottids.

EXERCISE 20-4 PHYLUM NEMATODA

Objectives To describe the pseudocoelom of members of the Nematoda and to describe the location of the major organs within the pseudocoelom of *Ascaris*, a typical parasitic roundworm.

Nematodes, commonly called roundworms because of their profile in cross section, are incredibly abundant (if inconspicuous) animals. A biologist once hypothesized that if everything on Earth suddenly vanished except for the Nematoda (pronounced nee-ma-TOAD-ah), one could still get a fairly good picture of what Earth was like just from the shapes that the ubiquitous creatures outlined.

Like other parasites, roundworms have large and well-developed reproductive organs. In addition, they are the first phylum of invertebrates considered so far to have a body cavity, or closed space surrounding the internal organs. The body cavity of nematodes is called the **pseudocoelom** ("false coelom"). The nematode pseudocoelom is a derivative of the embryonic blastocoel (Chapter 13) and is bounded on one side by gut tissue or epidermis and on the other by mesoderm tissue. (A true coelom, found in structurally more complex phyla to be discussed later, is bounded on all sides by mesoderm tissue.) Functionally, the pseudocoelom acts like a true coelom, holding the gut and reproductive organs in a cavity containing the organism's own body fluids. Circulation and gas exchange in nematodes occur by diffusion, but wastes are disposed of through excretory canals. Nematodes also have a simple brain and dorsal and ventral nerve cords.

- Examine the preserved specimens of *Ascaris*, a large roundworm that is a parasite in the gut of vertebrates (Fig. 20-10a). What is the texture of the outer surface of the worms?

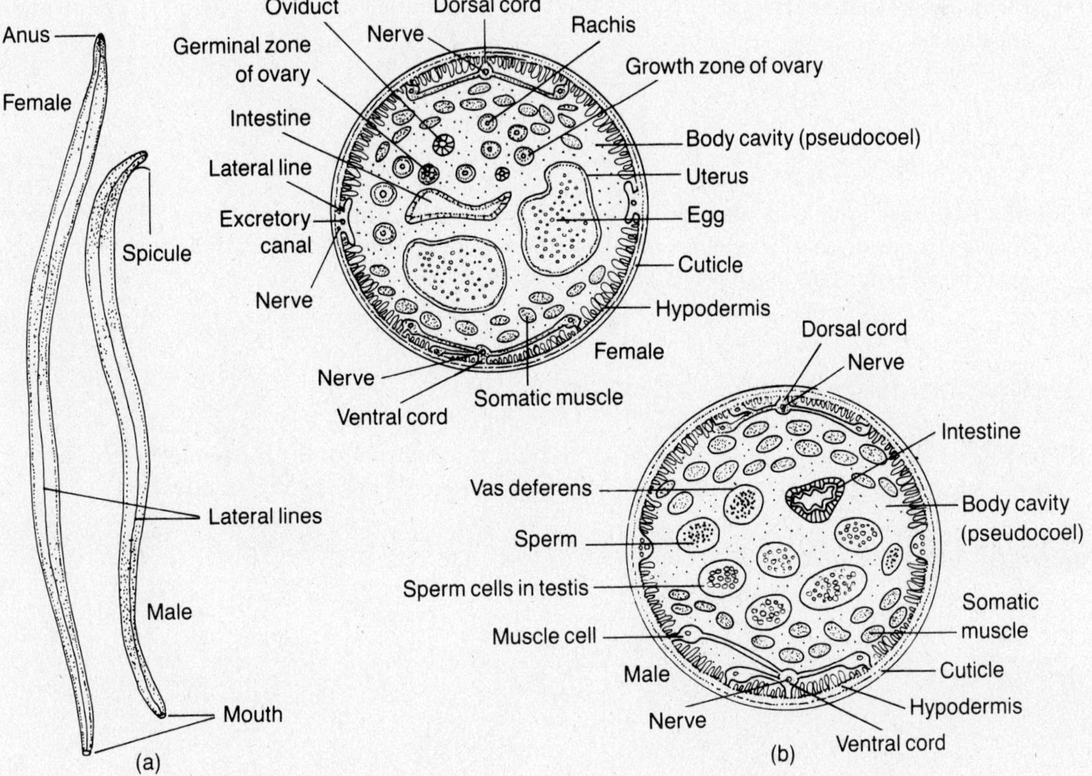

Figure 20-10 *Ascaris*, roundworm. (a) External anatomy of male and female worms. (b) Cross sections of male and female worms.

______________ Roundworms are covered by a multilayered, nonliving cuticle that is impermeable and somewhat rigid. Speculate on the advantages of a cuticle with these properties to these parasites.

- The **lateral line** running the length of the worm contains excretory and sensory structures. Unlike the Turbellaria, *Ascaris* is dioecious. Observe the differences in external anatomy between male and female roundworms, and locate the curved anal end and **spicule** of the male.
- Use the compound microscope to observe cross sections of male and female *Ascaris* (Fig. 20-10b). You will recognize some of the internal organs because they are similar in appearance to comparable structures in the Turbellaria. Near the center of the worm, the intestine often appears folded or flattened. The intestine runs straight from the pharynx to the anus. Small, circular profiles of the tubular ovary are dorsal to the intestine in the cross section of the female worm. Larger circles below the gut are loops of the uterus, filled with eggs. Analogous circular profiles in the cross section of the male worm are loops of the vas deferens, containing sperm. Notice that these structures lie free in a cavity, the pseudocoelom. Fluid is maintained under pressure inside the pseudocoelom; this is why the gut is flattened in cross section. Pricking the intact body wall with a pin produces a squirt of fluid. Speculate on how maintaining this fluid pressure helps the worm control body shape and movement.

Bundles of muscles are visible near the dorsal and ventral surfaces of the worm. Two nerve cords, dorsal and ventral, are visible. A system of excretory canals is difficult to see in slide specimens.

Summary

- You have now examined specimens from four phyla of primitive invertebrates. The four phyla display trends toward increasing complexity in several aspects of form and function. Summarize your observations on these phyla by filling in Chart 20-1.

Definition of an Animal—Revisited

Refer to your three criteria for defining an animal that you recorded at the beginning of this chapter. Would you change any of them? If so, describe how you would change them and why.

1.

Continued on p. 260.

Chart 20-1 Characteristics of the primitive invertebrate phyla.

Phylum	Common name	Level of organization	Type of symmetry	Cephalization (present/absent)	Site of digestion	Body cavity (if any)	Parasitic or free-living	Sense organs	Special features of phylum
1.									
2.									
3.									
4.									

2.

3.

The material in this chapter corresponds to Chapter 25 in your text.

21
KINGDOM ANIMALIA II. THE ADVANCED INVERTEBRATES

The five invertebrate phyla covered in this chapter represent two distinct groups, the **protostomes** (Latin for "first mouth") and the **deuterostomes** (Latin for "second mouth"). These names refer to the formation of the mouth in embryological development. In protostomes, the blastopore, the first opening into the gastrocoel, becomes the mouth; in deuterostomes, the blastopore becomes the anus, and the mouth is formed at another opening. Other differences in development that correlate with these patterns of mouth formation are detailed in the text and summarized in Table 21-1. Because of these differences, the protostomes and deuterostomes are considered to represent two separate lines of evolution.

The differences between the protostomes and deuterostomes listed in the table may seem minor at first glance—after all, what does it matter whether the blastopore becomes the mouth or anus? But such variations arise in fundamental processes of growth and development. As a result, the variations are considered to represent evolutionary changes that occurred at a major branching point in the animal evolutionary tree.

The protostome lineage includes three major phyla whose members are probably familiar to you: Annelida, Arthropoda, and Mollusca. These phyla and the deuterostome phylum Echinodermata are covered in this chapter. The other major deuterostome phylum is the Vertebrata, which you will study in Chapter 22.

Table 21-1 Differences in characteristics of protostome and deuterostome lineages.

	Protostomes	Deuterostomes
Fate of blastopore	Becomes mouth	Becomes anus
Cleavage of embryonic cells	Spiral	Radial
Control of development	Determinate	Regulative
Origin of coelom	Splitting of mesoderm (schizocoelous)	Outpouching of mesoderm (enterocoelous)

Protostomes

EXERCISE 21-1 PHYLUM ANNELIDA

Objectives To identify specimens of the annelids to the three classes of the phylum, and to describe segmentation and the trochophore larva; to describe the true coelom present in members of this phylum and the major organ systems within this body cavity.

The Annelida (pronounced an-EL-i-duh) are the segmented worms. Most familiar are the earthworms, but the phylum also includes segmented marine worms and the leeches, a group of predatory worms with a highly specialized anatomy.

Annelids have a true **coelom**. In appearance, the coelom is a fluid-filled body cavity similar to the pseudocoelom of nematodes (Chapter 20). However, the origins of these body cavities are quite different. The pseudocoelom develops from the remnant of the embryonic blastocoel, and is lined on one side by mesoderm tissue and on the other by gut tissue or epidermis (see Figure 25-16 in the text). A coelom, as found in members of the phyla described in this chapter, is lined completely by mesoderm. In protostomes, a solid mass of mesoderm splits and forms the coelomic cavity. Like a pseudocoelom, a coelom can function as part of a hydrostatic skeleton. In addition, the coelom is associated with the circulation of gases, nutrients, and metabolic wastes.

Other advanced characteristics that make their first appearance in annelids are a closed circulatory system and segmentation of the body. These features will be discussed in the sections dealing with each of the annelid classes: Oligochaeta (earthworms), Polychaeta (marine worms), and Hirudinea (leeches).

A. Class Oligochaeta

The freshwater and terrestrial annelids are members of this class. The most familiar is the common earthworm, *Lumbricus*. This and other oligochaetes play an important ecological role in mixing and aerating the upper layers of soil. Charles Darwin devoted his last book to a study of their behavior and ecology.

- Examine the preserved whole specimens of *Lumbricus* your instructor provides (Fig. 21-1a). The segments are clearly visible, except for a region called the **clitellum**, which girdles several segments and secretes the mucus that holds copulating worms together. The clitellum is closer to the anterior end of the worm, the first segment of which is termed the **prostomium**. The clitellum secretes material that encloses worms in a protective cocoon. The upper, or **dorsal**, surface of the worm is darker than the **ventral** surface. Note the short, prickly **setae** on the ventral surface of each segment. The setae help the worm grip the soil during locomotion. Near the setae on each segment are pores for excretory organs, or **nephridia**. A protective **cuticle** covers the entire animal.
- Place the specimen dorsal side up in a dissection pan partially filled with water. Pin down the head near one end of the pan, then extend the body down the center of the pan and pin down the middle of the worm. Use scissors to cut along the midline of the dorsal surface from just behind the clitellum, forward to the anterior end. As you cut, spread open the body wall and pin it down at several points to expose the internal organs. You may have to partially cut through some of the **septa** between segments to open the body wall. The major organ systems and segmentation pattern of the body are now visible (Fig. 21-1b).

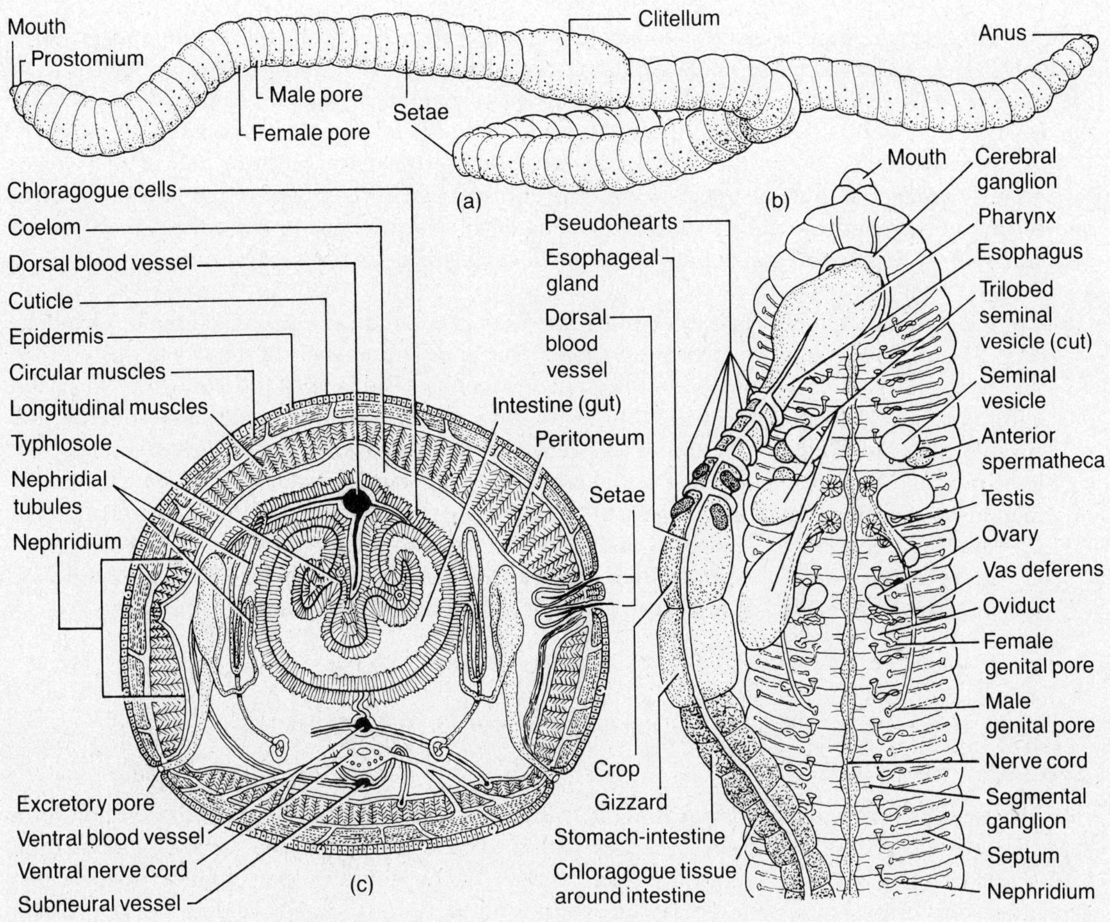

21-1 *Lumbricus*, earthworm. (a) Whole worm. (b) Internal anatomy of dissected worm. (c) Cross section of segment.

The interior of the body is divided into compartments corresponding to the external segments. Each compartment is a segment of the coelom, which is lined by the **peritoneum**, tissue derived from mesoderm. Each segment contains a pair of **nephridia**. One end of each nephridium extends through the septum into the next anterior segment. The other end opens to the outside through an excretory pore. The segmentation of annelids is different from that of the Cestoda (tapeworms) discussed in the previous chapter. Whereas the proglottids of tapeworms are basically a series of reproductive packets, in annelids the reproductive organs are restricted to certain segments of the worm (to be described later). Thus, the segments in *Lumbricus* represent a series of body compartments, each containing a set of muscles, blood vessels, excretory organs, and nerve cell ganglia; a few segments bear specialized appendages or mouth parts. Such "specialized" segmentation allows for larger body size, as well as more effective locomotion.

The gut also exhibits some segmentation. From anterior to posterior the following parts are discernible: **mouth**, **pharynx**, narrow **esophagus**, **crop**, **gizzard**, and segmented **intestine** (Fig. 21-1b).

A dorsal blood vessel lies above the gut and a ventral blood vessel lies below it. Blood flows toward the anterior end in the dorsal vessel and toward the posterior end in the ventral vessel. Small branches supply blood to each segment. The dorsal blood vessel contracts to pump blood, and several **pseudohearts**, which encircle the esophagus, also assist in pumping. The blood of *Lumbricus* contains hemoglobin, which functions in oxygen transport. In some annelids, oxygen transport is a function of the coelomic fluid.

Earthworms are hermaphroditic but do not self-fertilize. Two copulating worms inseminate each other. Sperm are produced in two pairs of small **testes** in segments 9 and 10 and stored in the pair of large three-lobed **seminal vesicles** found in segments 9 to 12. From there, the sperm move through the **vas deferens** to the male genital pores in segment 15. After copulation, sperm from the other worm are stored in the **seminal receptacles** in segments 9 and 10. Eggs are produced in the **ovaries** in segment 13, and pass through the **oviduct** to the female genital pores in segment 14.

The **cerebral ganglia** lie on the dorsal surface of the gut near the anterior end of the worm. Nerve cords connected to the ganglia encircle the anterior end of the pharynx and join the **ventral nerve cord** underneath the gut in your dissection. Push aside the gut to trace the ventral nerve cord posteriorly. **Segmental ganglia** appear as small thickenings on the ventral nerve cord.

- Use the compound microscope to examine the microscope slide of a cross section of *Lumbricus* (Fig. 21-1c). The section you observe will probably come from a part of the worm posterior to the internal organs you dissected in the previous section. The **cuticle** and **epidermis** form the outer layer of the body wall. Inside this layer are two muscle layers: **longitudinal** muscles and **circular** muscles. The inner boundary of circular muscles is covered by the peritoneum, which lines the fluid-filled coelom. The coelom acts as a hydrostatic skeletal system, which the two muscle layers squeeze in different ways to cause the burrowing motion of the earthworm. Setae may also be visible in the segment you observe. If you have observed a live earthworm move in the laboratory, or if you remember how earthworms move from previous observations, speculate on how the two muscle layers and setae function in movement.

In the center of the cross section is the gut, which has a generally circular profile, except for a deep inward fold on the dorsal surface. This fold is termed the **typhlosole**, and it increases the digestive surface in the gut. Lining the outer surface of the gut is a layer of **chloragogue** cells, which function in digestion. The dorsal and ventral blood vessels are adjacent to the dorsal and ventral surfaces of the gut. Below the ventral blood vessel is the ventral nerve cord. A small subneural blood vessel may also be visible. On either side of the gut you may see the irregular outline of nephridial tubules cut in various planes.

B. Class Polychaeta

Polychaetes are marine worms; some are sedentary tube-dwellers, and others crawl about under rocks in the intertidal or subtidal zones. Similar in some respects to oligochaetes, polychaetes have well-developed excretory, digestive, circulatory, and nervous systems. In addition to the difference in habitat (freshwater or terrestrial for oligochaetes, marine for polychaetes), the appendages on the head and segments are much more developed in the polychaetes than in the earthworms.

- Examine specimens of the marine segmented worm, *Nereis* (Fig. 21-2). *Nereis* is a free-living worm that lives in the rocky intertidal zone. The body is segmented, like that of *Lumbricus*, but the appendages on the head and segments are more elaborate. The pharynx is protrusible and bears a pair of hooklike jaws. On the dorsal surface of the head are four eyes and various tentacles and smaller antennalike appendages. Each segment bears a pair of lateral, paddlelike, fleshy appendages called **parapodia**. The parapodia each bear several clusters of long setae.
- Keeping in mind the difference in habitat between *Lumbricus* and *Nereis*, speculate on the advantage of greater cephalization and parapodia on the body segments in *Nereis*.

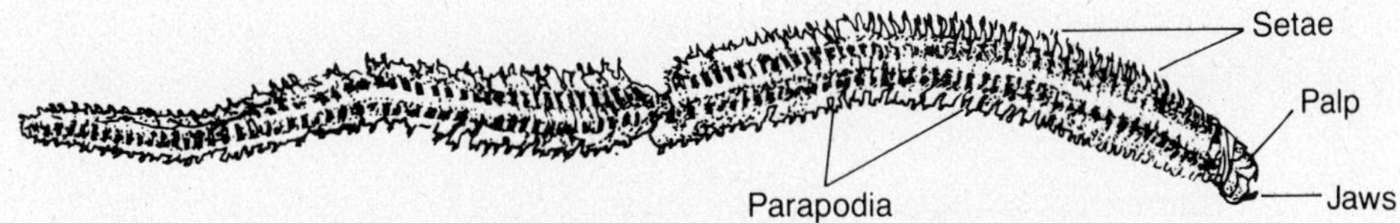

Figure 21-2 *Nereis,* marine worm. Whole worm.

C. Class Hirudinea

Leeches are segmented worms that are highly specialized predators. Some are adapted to take blood meals from vertebrate or invertebrate prey, while others prey on small snails, insects, and amphibians. Despite a specialized anatomy, leeches share with other annelids the features of a coelom, segmentation, and well-developed excretory, digestive, circulatory, and nervous systems.

- Use the compound microscope to examine the specimens of *Hirudo* or other common leeches (Fig. 21-3). Although segmentation of this blood-sucking leech is evident, the number of apparent segments is greater than the actual number. This is because each segment has about three transverse grooves (annuli) on the surface. On the head end are an anterior sucker and a pair of very small ocelli (light detectors). A large posterior sucker is used for locomotion and for attachment during feeding. When feeding, *Hirudo* secretes an anticoagulant that keeps the wound from clotting. The medical practice of "leeching" or bleeding patients was abandoned long ago. However, some surgeons have recently begun using leeches to drain blood from congested tissues following surgery.

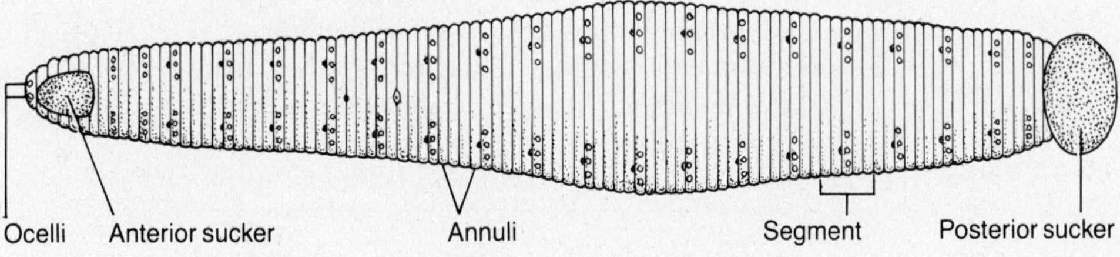

Figure 21-3 *Hirudo,* leech.

- *Hirudo* is extremely sensitive to stimuli that reveal the presence of prey: vibrations in the water, olfactory cues from skin oil or blood, and even shadows passing overhead. If your instructor has live leeches on display, devise simple experiments to test the responsiveness of the leeches to these stimuli.

D. Annelid Larvae

- Polychaete worms pass through a larval stage called the **trochophore** (Fig. 21-4). Your instructor may have prepared slides of trochophores on display. The swimming trochophore lives and feeds in the plankton, and it possesses a mouth, stomach or midgut, and anus. Swimming is accomplished by means of a girdle of cilia called the **prototroch**, an **apical tuft** of cilia, and a posterior tuft of cilia called the **telotroch**. Trochophore larvae are also found in members of the phylum Mollusca, a fact that indicates that annelids and molluscs shared a common ancestor.

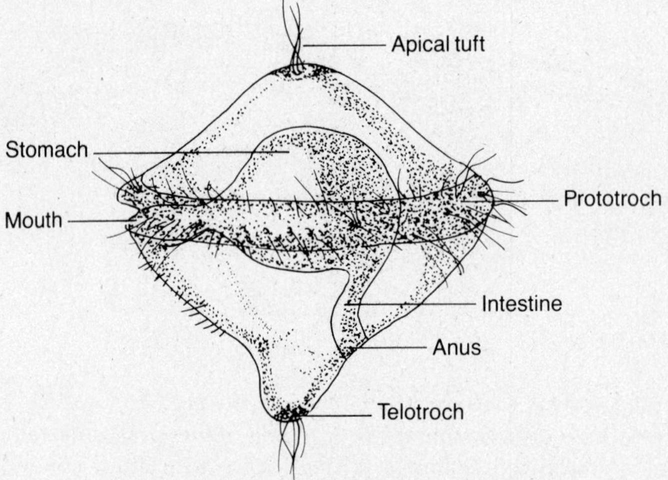

Figure 21-4 Trochophore larva of Annelida.

EXERCISE 21-2 PHYLUM ARTHROPODA

Objectives To describe the complex type of segmentation found in the arthropods, as well as the hemocoel and exoskeleton and how they differ from similar structures in the Annelida; also, to identify selected specimens as members of the three major subphyla and to describe their distinguishing characteristics and habitats.

The diversity and sheer numbers of arthropods on Earth are truly amazing. Phylum Arthropoda (pronounced arth-ROP-oh-duh or ARTH-row-PO-duh) contains more species than all other animal phyla combined. Members include the crustaceans, spiders, mites, and insects. Like annelids, arthropods have a segmented body design, bilateral symmetry, and a similar nervous system. The major differences between the two groups that you should keep in mind as you examine specimens of arthropods are:

1. Arthropod body segments are highly modified and may bear specialized appendages that serve a variety of functions, such as locomotion, feeding, and reproduction.
2. Internal segmentation is absent in arthropods, and although the coelom is present early in development, it is later replaced by a blood-filled hemocoel.
3. The arthropod body is covered by a rigid exoskeleton, which consists of a series of hard plates or rings connected by softer, flexible membranes; the hard parts provide protection and attachment points for muscles involved in complex motions.

You will observe specimens of each of the three major living subphyla of arthropods. (Members of a fourth group, the trilobites, are abundant in the fossil record but are now extinct.)

A. Subphylum Chelicerata

This subphylum of arthropods contains such seemingly unrelated organisms as horseshoe crabs, spiders, mites, ticks, and scorpions. Chelicerates have two major body parts: the cephalothorax (composed of the fused head and thorax regions) and the posterior abdomen. The first pair of appendages next to the mouth are called *chelicerae*; they evolved from a pair of walking legs into pincers or claws in most living chelicerates. The second ancestral pair of walking legs have also been modified by evolution into feeding appendages called *pedipalps*. Four pairs of actual walking legs are attached to the cephalothorax. There are no legs on the abdomen.

- A specimen of *Argiope* (Class Arachnida) or other large spider will be used to represent the chelicerates. Use the stereoscopic microscope to examine the external anatomy of the spider (Fig. 21-5). Each of a pair of **compound eyes** on the dorsal surface of the cephalothorax is composed of a multiple-lens area that focuses light on many individual light receptors. Each **chelicera** consists of two segments, one of which is a **fang**. The fangs contain pores connected to poison glands. Few spiders are able to penetrate human skin with their fangs, but of those that do, several (such as the black widow, *Lactrodectus mactaus*, and the brown recluse, *Loxosceles reclusa*) possess powerful toxins. The **pedipalps** join the cephalothorax posterior to the chelicerae; they are used to hold food, and in males they serve as a copulatory organ. Four pairs of **walking legs** are attached to the **sternum**. On the anterior part of the ventral surface of the abdomen is the **epigastric furrow**, a transverse groove associated with reproductive and respiratory structures. In the center of the groove is the genital opening, or **gonopore**. In front of this opening is a hard plate called the **epigynum**, which contains openings into the seminal receptacles. At the edges of the groove are **spiracles**, openings into the **book lungs**. These respiratory organs, which are not visible from the outside, are composed of chambers with hollow, leaflike plates; air circulates in the hollow space and transfers oxygen to blood on the other side of the thin plates. Another spiracle and the **spinneret** are located at the posterior end of the abdomen. The spinneret and associated silk glands are used in web weaving.

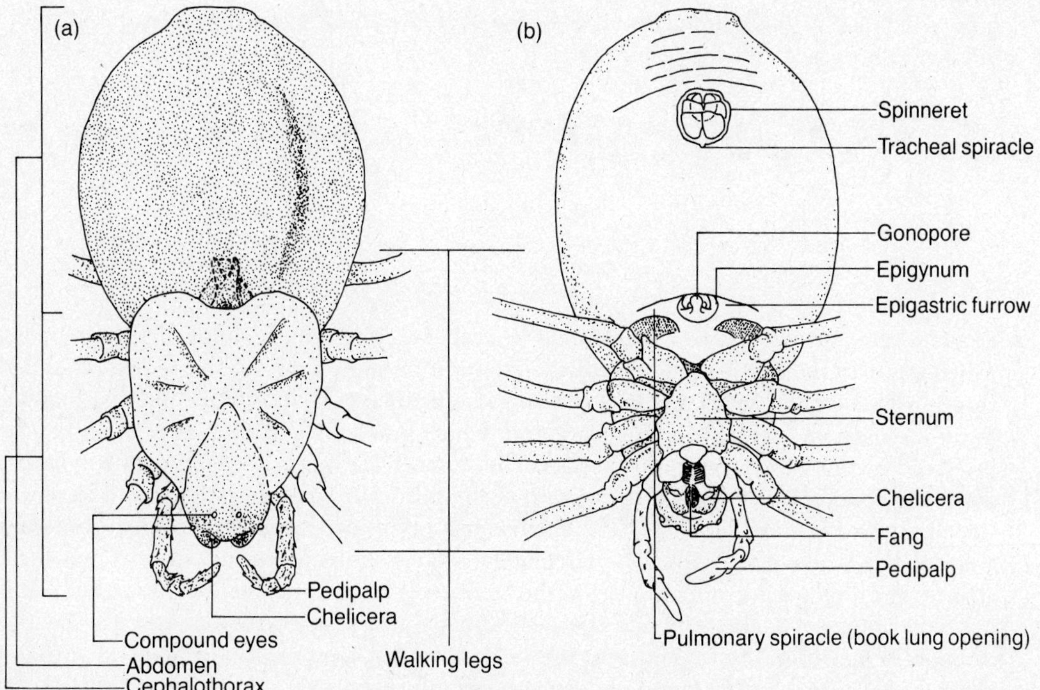

Figure 21-5 *Argiope*, spider. (a) Dorsal view. (b) Ventral view.

B. Subphylum Crustacea

The Crustacea are a large group of freshwater and marine arthropods, which includes shrimps, crabs, and lobsters, as well as the less appetizing barnacles, pill bugs, and sow bugs. Crustaceans have two pairs of sensory antennae on the head; posterior to them is a pair of mandibles, jawlike mouthparts for chewing. Several additional pairs of modified appendages called maxillipeds are attached behind the mandibles. The thorax is covered by a carapace made mostly of chitin, a tough polysaccharide material, although the carapace of some larger crustaceans is hardened with calcium. Respiration in these aquatic animals is accomplished by well-developed, featherlike gills that are usually inside the exoskeleton in chambers where water is pumped over them. Like most other arthropods, crustaceans outgrow their exoskeletons and go through several periods of molting of the old exoskeleton; each molt is followed by a vulnerable period before the new covering hardens. (Soft-shelled crabs are newly molted animals with soft exoskeletons.) Molting is controlled by hormones secreted by glands in the eyestalks.

- Your instructor will provide you with a specimen of *Cambarus*, a crayfish. Examine the external anatomy (Figs. 21-6a and b). The body is divided into three parts: **head**, **thorax**, and **abdomen**. On the head are two large **antennae**, along with four smaller **antennules**. Stalked eyes lie on either side of the **rostrum**, an anterior extension of the **carapace**. On the ventral surface of the head are the **mandibles** and several types of feeding appendages. The carapace covers the thorax and encloses the gill chamber. Five pairs of large **walking legs** attach to the underside of the thorax. The female genital openings are found at the bases of the third pair of walking legs; the smaller male genital openings are at the bases of the fifth pair of walking legs. The abdomen is divided into segments bearing pairs of swimmerets, small fringed appendages used in swimming. In males, the first pair of swimmerets have long anterior extensions for sperm transfer during copulation. The tail segment bears a telson and two lateral uropods, which are fused into a flattened tail fan that provides thrust in swimming.
- To expose the internal organs of *Cambarus*, use a pair of scissors to cut through the carapace along a line extending from the eye to the uropods on each side of the animal. Lift off the top of the carapace and cut away the sides to expose the gill chamber. Observe the featherlike gills, which are actually branches off the base of the walking legs. How does the form of the gill increase surface area for respiration?

- Examine the internal organs of *Cambarus* (Fig. 21-6c). The mouth opens into the esophagus, which leads to the **cardiac portion of the stomach** on either side of the thorax. A sheetlike anterior gastric muscle extends forward from the cardiac portion of the stomach. Just lateral to the stomach on each side is a **green gland**, which functions in excretion of the dilute urine produced by these freshwater crustaceans. The stomach leads into a long **intestine**, which runs down the abdomen to the anus at the base of the telson. A large **digestive gland** lies on each side of the stomach and intestine. The crayfish has a typical arthropod circulatory system with a dorsal **heart** above the gills. The circulatory system is open; that is, blood flows through arteries and empties into open sinuses of the hemocoel surrounding the various organs. Returning blood flows over the gills into the pericardial sinus, a space surrounding the heart (cut through in your dissection), and into the heart through several pairs of holes, or **ostia**. The **ventral nerve cord** can be found underneath the internal organs on the ventral surface of the animal. A series of thickenings in the nerve cord represents the ganglia that supply nerves to the segments and relays messages to and from the brain, which is a large ganglion ventral to the esophagus in the head.

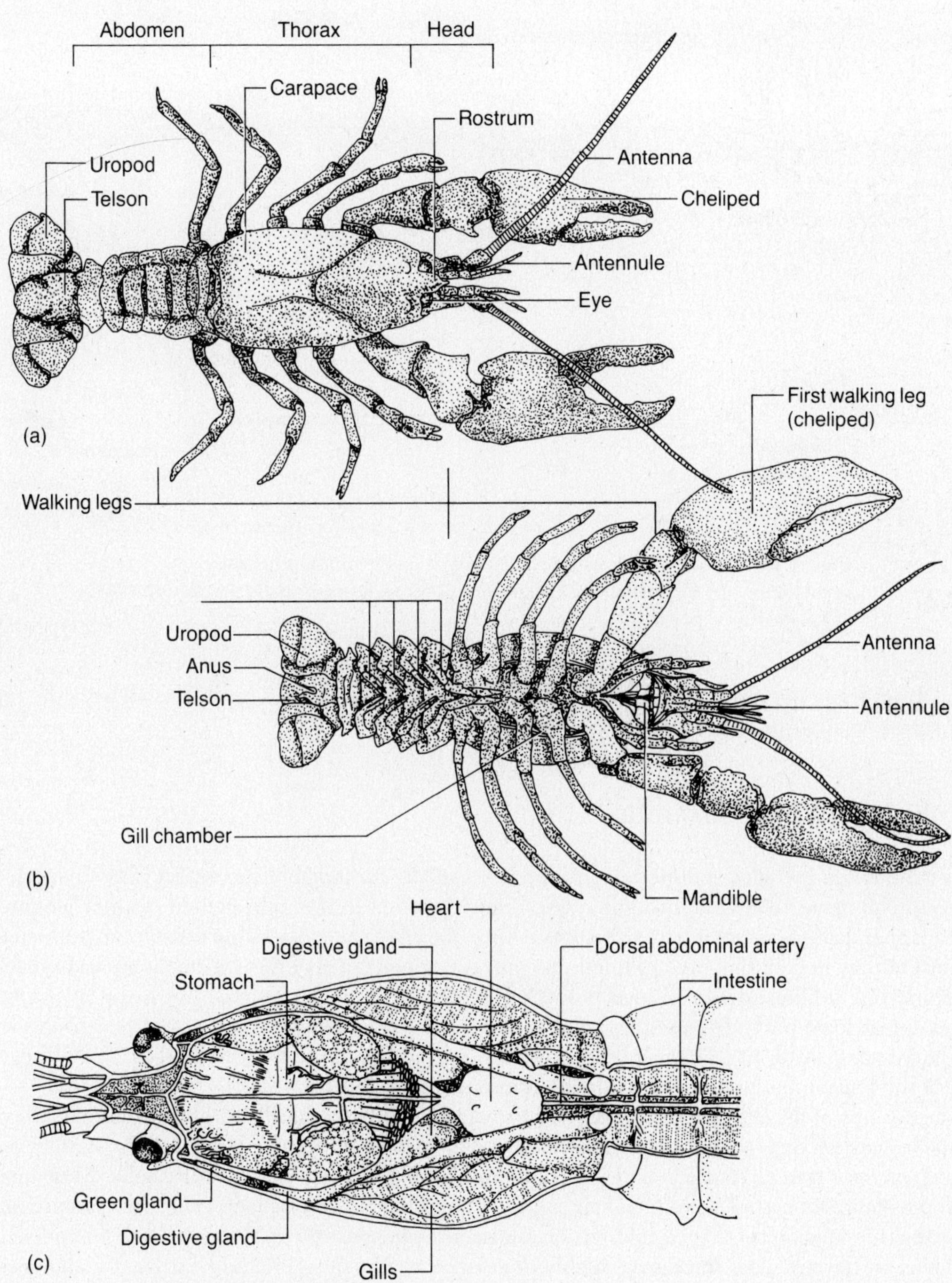

Figure 21-6 *Cambarus,* crayfish. (a) External anatomy, dorsal view. (b) External anatomy, ventral view. (c) Internal anatomy.

C. Crustacean Larvae

Many crustaceans go through one or more planktonic larval stages before assuming their adult forms and habits (which may be benthic or planktonic). The **nauplius** larva (Fig. 21-7a) is a stage shared by a broad range of crustaceans including some shrimps and crabs. Barnacles spend time in the plankton as a **cypris** larva (Fig. 21-7b) before settling down to a sedentary life on rocks or pilings. Crabs and lobsters pass through the **zoea** larval stage (Figs. 21-7c and d).

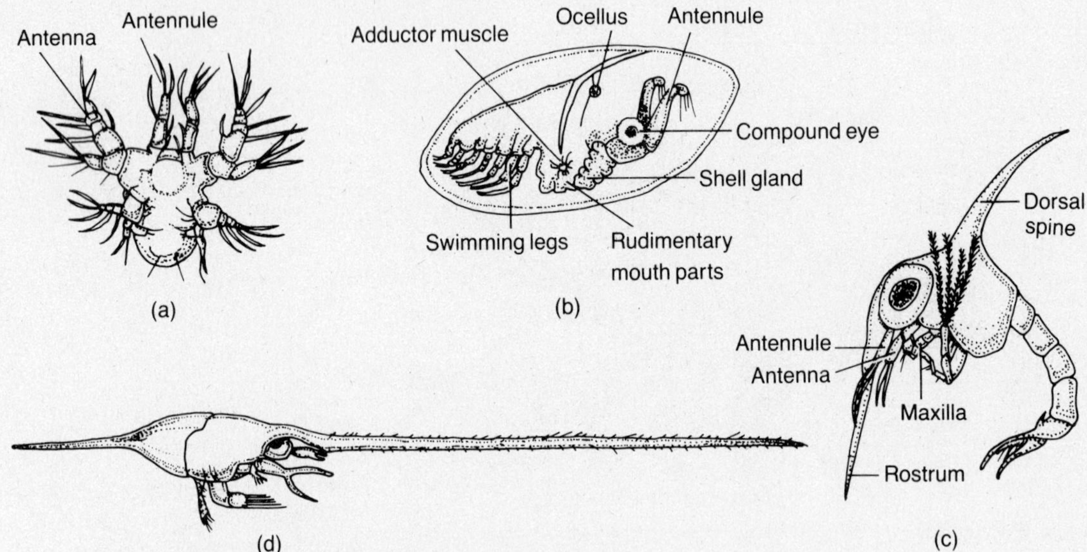

Figure 21-7 Crustacean larvae. (a) Nauplius larva common to many crustaceans. (b) Cypris larva of barnacles. (c) Zoea larva of crabs. (d) Zoea larva of lobsters.

- Observe any microscope slides of crustacean larvae on display and be able to identify the types shown in Figure 21-7.

D. Subphylum Uniramia

This subphylum includes centipedes, millipedes, and the remarkably successful Class Insecta, the insects. The name Uniramia (in Latin, "one branch") refers to the unbranched terminal segments of the appendages in members of this subphylum. You may remember that crustacean appendages are often branched and highly modified; in contrast, appendages of the Uniramia are unbranched.

Nearly one million species of insects live on Earth. Most are terrestrial, but many live in fresh water for at least part of their lives, and a few even live on the surface of the ocean or in the intertidal zone. And, of course, insects have conquered the air above the land as well—they are one of the few animal groups that contains numerous flying forms.

The success of insects can be attributed to several features. A hard, water-resistant cuticle prevents desiccation on land and helps maintain osmotic balance in aquatic habitats. A system of tubes called *tracheae* transports oxygen and carbon dioxide to and from metabolizing cells. Most insects undergo complete metamorphosis, changing form completely from larva to adult (for example, pupa to butterfly). Many insects have color vision (and can see in the ultraviolet range) to detect particular patterns on flowers. And some have highly developed senses of smell and hearing. Finally, insects also exhibit complex behaviors in feeding, reproduction, and fighting, and the highly ordered societies of social insects such as bees, wasps, and ants are well known.

- Use a stereoscopic microscope to examine the specimen of a common grasshopper, *Romalea* (Fig. 21-8). Like the crayfish, the grasshopper body is divided into head, thorax, and abdomen. The head bears two large **compound eyes** and three smaller **ocelli** near the center of the head. The compound eyes are composed of many light-detecting units, and thus the "image" they form is a composite of many points of light and dark, something like a coarse-grained newspaper photo. Resolution of images in the insect eye is much poorer than in vertebrates. Many insects have color vision and some can detect light in the ultraviolet region of the spectrum. These abilities are used to search for flowers with particular color patterns. Two sensory **antennae** emerge from the head. The chewing mouthparts and sensory palps are shown in Figure 21-8.

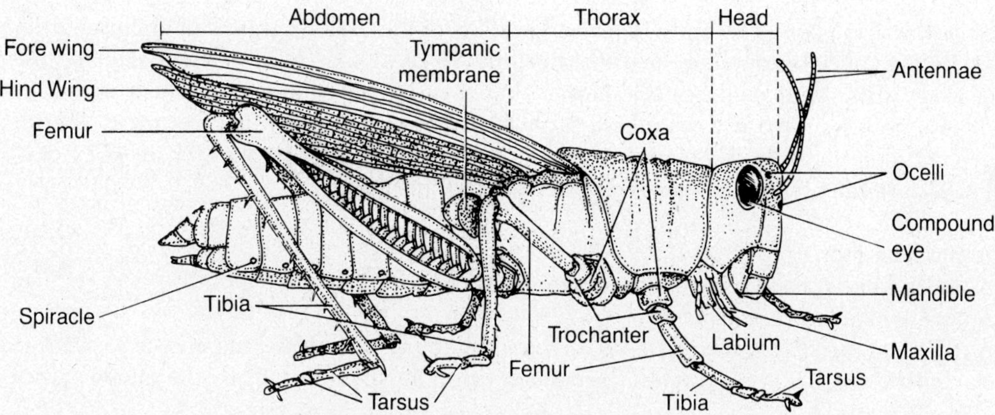

Figure 21-8 *Romalea*, grasshopper, external anatomy.

The thorax has three pairs of legs. The two forward pairs of legs are similar in structure to each other, and their parts are labeled in Figure 21-8. The hind legs, with their enlarged femurs, are modified for jumping, although the basic parts are the same as other arthropod legs. Spread the two pairs of wings attached to the dorsal surface of the thorax. Note that the fore wings are thicker and protective in function; the hind wings are thinner and used for flight. The abdomen is segmented externally (but not internally), and each segment has a spiracle near the ventral side. These open into the internal **tracheal system** of tubules that supply oxygen to all tissues of the body. On the sides of the first segment, near the base of the hind legs, are the **tympanic membranes**, sensitive sound detectors. In males, the posterior end of the abdomen is blunt. In the female, the posterior end of the abdomen is modified into an **ovipositor** for laying eggs.

E. Insect Metamorphosis

Most insects pass through larval stages that possess body plans that are radically different from the mature adult forms. This process is called *complete metamorphosis* and occurs in butterflies, beetles, and flies. Some insects (for example, grasshoppers) undergo incomplete metamorphosis, in which several juvenile stages occur, each one much like a miniature version of the adult.

- Examine any specimens of larval and adult forms your instructor may have on display.

EXERCISE 21-3 PHYLUM MOLLUSCA

Objectives To identify specimens of molluscs to the class to which each belongs and to identify the distinguishing characteristics of each class; to be familiar with the major organ systems possessed by molluscs and to understand how the four regions of the molluscan body are modified in each class.

The Mollusca (pronounced mow-LUS-cuh) represent a protostome line of evolution separate from annelids and arthropods—one in which segmentation was either lost through evolution or never evolved in the first place. The body types and ecology of the various groups of molluscs are quite diverse, from giant, jet-propelled, deep-ocean squid, to tiny clams in the intertidal zone, to large African land snails. Most molluscs are marine, but they are also common in fresh water and on land. Many molluscs have a trochophore larva like that of annelids; this feature is considered evidence that they shared a common ancestor.

The soft, unsegmented molluscan body has four distinct regions:

1. A muscular foot.
2. A visceral mass containing the internal organs.
3. A head with sensory organs.
4. A mantle of thickened, folded tissue surrounding the visceral mass; the mantle secretes material for the shell, if present, and is separated from the visceral mass by the mantle cavity.

The four major classes of molluscs display a diversity of variations on this basic four-part theme. These variations will be examined in sections on each of the four classes.

A. Class Polyplacophora

This group contains the chitons, not to be confused with the substance *chitin* found in the exoskeleton of arthropods. Chitons are slow-moving, snail-like creatures that inhabit the intertidal zone of oceans worldwide. They are considered relatively primitive in body form compared to other molluscs.

- Examine the chiton specimens provided by your instructor. Superficially, chitons appear to violate the "rule" of nonsegmented body form in molluscs because they possess a shell of eight armored **plates** (Fig. 21-9a). However, only the shell is segmented—the body is a single unit. Turn over the animal and locate the **mouth**, **head**, **mantle**, **foot**, **gills**, **anus**, and **mantle cavity** (Fig. 21-9b). By carefully pulling back the tissues around the mouth and examining the structure under the stereoscopic microscope, you may be able to see the feeding structure called the **radula**. This double row of teeth looks like a zipper. The chiton scrapes it back and forth across rocks to grind off bits of algae. Radulas are also found in gastropods.

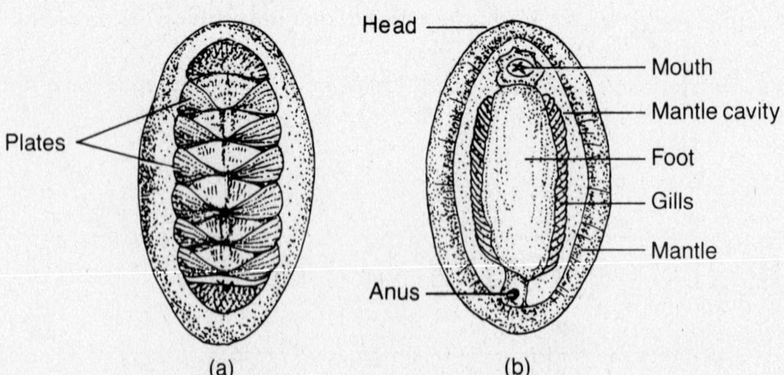

Figure 21-9 Chiton. (a) Dorsal view. (b) Ventral view.

B. Class Gastropoda

This large and diverse group comprises the snails, both aquatic and terrestrial, and their relatives such as abalone, conchs, and limpets. Most gastropods have a distinctive and often beautiful shell, although some gastropods, such as slugs and nudibranchs, lack a shell. Gastropods undergo a characteristic developmental process of **torsion** in the embryonic and larval stages. During torsion, the visceral mass is twisted 180° so that the anus and gills, which are located near the posterior end of the snail body, are brought forward to a position just over the head. This seemingly inconvenient arrangement does not appear to harm the animal; it may have evolved because it allowed the gastropod larval stage, known as the *veliger*, to more effectively withdraw exposed body parts into a tiny protective shell and away from predators.

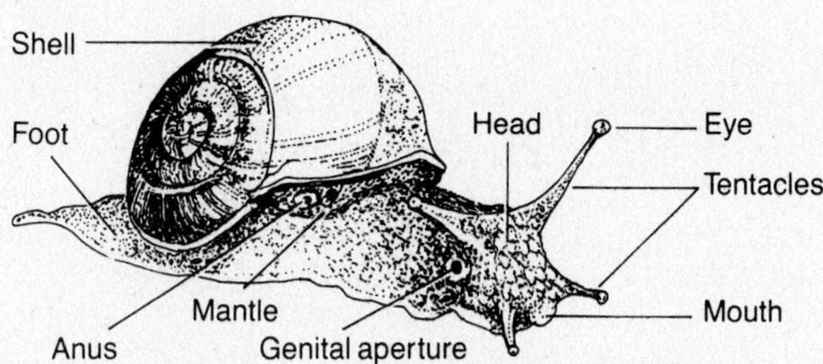

Figure 21-10 Gastropod (snail). External anatomy.

- Examine the gastropod specimen on display. Refer to Figure 21-10 and locate the basic body parts: head, foot, mantle, mantle cavity (not visible in the figure). Compare the location of the gills and anus relative to the head in the chiton with their arrangement in the gastropod, in order to see how the process of torsion has "rearranged" the location of these structures. Note also the protruding eyes and tentacles, and the genital aperture just behind one eye. The shell is typically coiled and encloses the visceral mass. The snail's foot protrudes through the **aperture** of the shell. Some snails have a circular plate, the **operculum**, on the posterior portion of the foot. When disturbed, the snail withdraws into the shell and the operculum neatly covers the aperture. In addition to protection, the operculum helps prevent water loss in some species.

C. Class Bivalvia

This class includes the oysters, clams, scallops, and mussels. Such animals have a shell consisting of two valves joined at a hinge. Bivalves live buried in mudflats, under rocks, and attached to pilings and other substrates. Most are marine but a number of clams inhabit freshwater rivers and streams. Clams are filter feeders, pumping enormous amounts of water through their body cavities by means of muscular contractions and powerful cilia. This pumping action also aerates the animal's gills.

- Examine the empty bivalve shells on display (Fig. 21-11a). Hold the shell with the bulbous projection, or **umbo**, uppermost and the inner surface facing you. The umbo is on the dorsal side of the shell, toward the anterior end. The lip of the shell is the ventral side. Note that a bivalve shell has anterior and posterior ends as well as left and right valves. The two valves join along the toothed **cardinal margin** of the shell and are held together by means of a hinge **ligament**. In most bivalves, the ligament is stretched when the shell is closed, so that the shell springs slightly open unless the muscles inside the shell hold it shut. **Muscle scars** mark the inner sites of attachment of muscles to the shell. The most prominent muscle scars are for the anterior and posterior **adductor muscles** (Fig. 21-11a). The strong adductor muscles clamp the valves together. The anterior and posterior **retractor muscles** move the foot in digging movements. The mantle secretes shell material along the ventral margin, and concentric growth rings are sometimes visible on the outer surface. The shell has three layers: a thin layer, the **periostracum**, composed of the same material found in the hinge ligament (this layer is often present only on newer shell material near the ventral lip); a middle **prismatic** layer made of calcium carbonate crystals; and the inner, glossy surface of **nacreous** material, or **mother-of-pearl**. Mother-of-pearl is laid down in layers by the entire mantle. The **pallial line** marks the

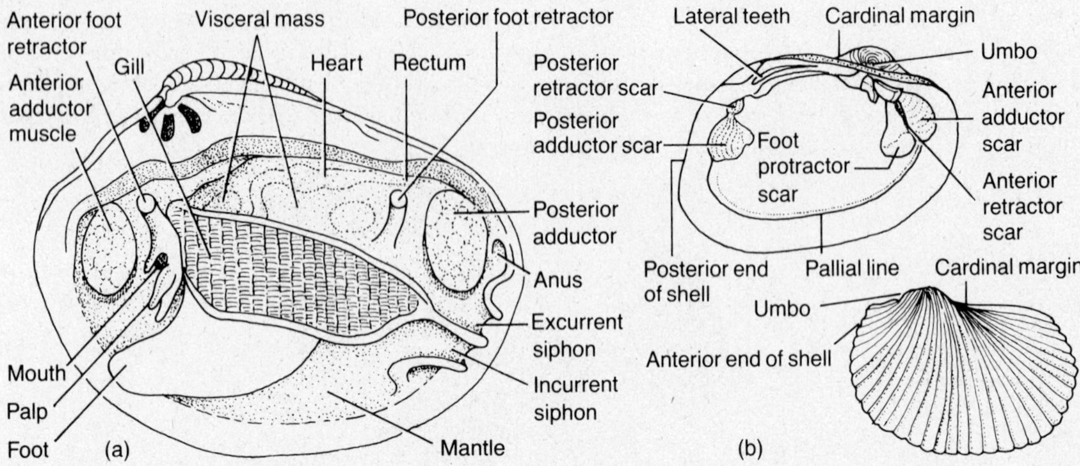

Figure 21-11 Bivalve. (a) Internal anatomy (b) Shell anatomy

former junction of the mantle with the shell. In some bivalves, sand or grit particles that get inside the pallial line serve as nuclei for pearl formation by the nacreous layer.

- Obtain a preserved specimen of the quahog, or edible clam, *Venus mercenaria*. To open it, slip a scalpel between the valves to cut the anterior and posterior adductor muscles. Estimate their location from your observations of the empty bivalve shells. Cut gently to avoid damaging other organs of the clam or your fingers. Once the clam is open, carefully cut away the outer layer of the mantle to expose the organs. Although the anatomy of the clam is very different from chitons or gastropods, the basic features of molluscan anatomy are present (Fig. 21-11b): muscular foot, mantle and mantle cavity, visceral mass with internal organs, and a "head" consisting of a mouth and labial palps. The foot, which can engorge with blood and change size and shape, extends outside the shell to dig or anchor the animal. The visceral mass contains the heart and digestive organs. Because clams are sedentary, except for some relatively slow digging movements, they must generate a substantial flow of water through the body to bring in food and oxygen and remove waste materials. Water flows in through the **incurrent siphon**, the current generated by the beating of cilia in the gill chamber. The labial palps sort larger particles of food, and cilia sweep smaller particles into the mouth. Oxygenated water flows over the large **gill**, or **ctenidium**, and then flows out the **excurrent siphon**. In some clams, the siphons are elongated and enclosed in a muscular sheath; when buried, these clams use the siphons as a snorkel to bring in clean water from the mud surface.

D. Class Cephalopoda

The members of this class are the most complex of the molluscs in both form and behavior. The squids, octopuses, chambered nautiluses, and cuttlefish are efficient ocean predators. The deep-sea nautiluses are the only members of the class to retain a large external shell, which is divided into gas-filled chambers that allow the animal to maintain buoyancy at different depths. In squids and cuttlefish the shell is reduced to an internal cuttlebone made of calcified chitin. Octopods lack any vestiges of a shell. Unlike other slow-moving or sedentary members of the phylum, cephalopods are excellent swimmers. They propel themselves by squirting jets of water from the mantle cavity. Cephalopods protect themselves by ejecting a cloud of ink, which obscures them from predators. Cephalopods have a well-developed nervous system and also possess a sophisticated eye that rivals that of vertebrates in visual acuity.

- Examine the external structure of the squid, *Loligo*, provided by your instructor (Fig. 21-12). In this organism, the muscular foot has been modified into specialized appendages bearing suckers. There are two long tentacles, which have flattened ends, and eight shorter arms. The two well-developed eyes lie on either side of the head, which is attached to the large, muscular

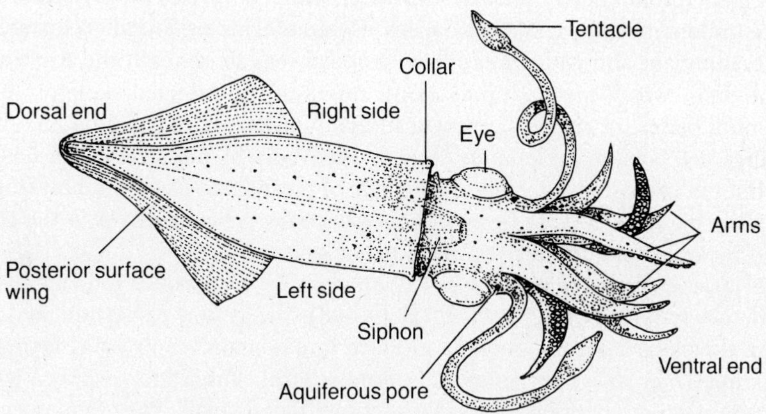

Figure 21-12 *Loligo*, external anatomy.

mantle. Jets of water are pumped out of the mantle cavity through the tubular **siphon** on the posterior surface of the animal. The pointed dorsal end of the squid bears wings that are used like the fins on a fish for maneuverability during swimming.

E. Molluscan Larvae

Many molluscs have a trochophore larva (Fig. 21-13a) similar to the one in annelids. This primitive larva is seen as evidence that the two phyla shared a common ancestor. Another larva, unique to mollusks, is the veliger, with ciliated lobes protruding from a larval gastropod (Fig. 21-13b) or bivalve (Fig. 21-13c) shell. Be able to identify these molluscan larval stages.

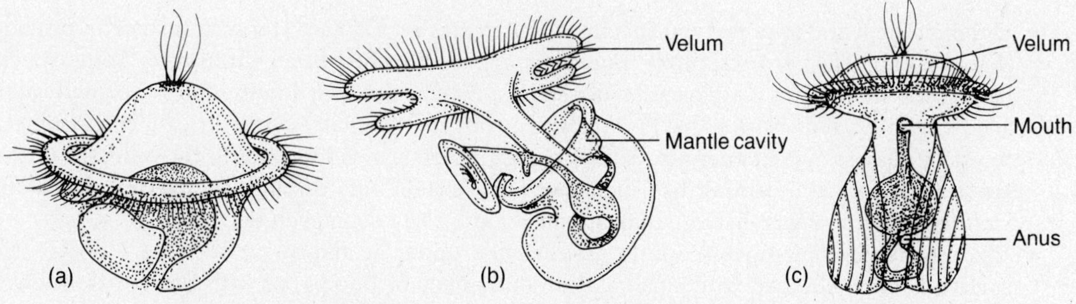

Figure 21-13 Molluscan larvae. (a) Trochophore. (b) Gastropod veliger. (c) Bivalve veliger.

Deuterostomes

EXERCISE 21-4 PHYLUM ECHINODERMATA

Objectives To identify specimens of echinoderms to their classes and to describe the distinguishing characteristics of each class; to describe the radial symmetry and the function of the water vascular system in echinoderms.

The Echinodermata (pronounced ee-KI-no-der-MAH-tuh) comprises the sea stars, brittle stars, sea cucumbers, sea urchins, sea lilies, and sea daisies. Echinoderms are found exclusively in the oceans, where they are abundant and widespread from tropical seas to beneath the Antarctic ice cap. The name of the phylum, which means "spiny skin," refers to the internal skeleton (**endoskeleton**) of calcium-containing plates, or ossicles, present in many members of the phylum.

Deuterostomes are coelomate animals, but in members of this group the coelom forms in a different way than in protostomes. Hollow pouches of mesoderm tissue bud off from the primitive gut; eventually the hollow spaces in these pouches become the coelom. As in the protostomes, the coelom is lined by a peritoneum derived from mesoderm.

All echinoderms are capable of movement, albeit slow, by means of an internal hydraulic network of tubes called the **water vascular system**, along with the action of certain muscles. The water vascular system develops from the coelom and also functions in respiration, feeding, and sensory perception. Echinoderm larvae are bilaterally symmetrical, but adults display a particular type of radial symmetry involving a pentamerous (five-sectioned) body plan. The circulatory system consists of a set of channels or sinuses. Excretory organs and a true heart are lacking. The nervous system of echinoderms is a simple set of nerve rings.

There are six classes of echinoderms: Asteroidea (sea stars), Ophiuroidea (brittle stars), Holothuroidea (sea cucumbers), Echinoidea (sea urchins and sand dollars), Crinoidea (sea lilies), and Concentricycloidea (sea daisies). You will examine specimens of the four most common classes. The Crinoidea are generally rare and found in deep water, and the Concentricycloidea have been discovered only recently.

A. Class Asteroidea

Asteroids, or **sea stars** (also called *starfish*), are perhaps the most conspicuous of echinoderms, being common on shorelines worldwide. They hold fast to rocks and pilings while they forage on clams, barnacles, and mussels.

- Examine the living or preserved specimen of *Asterias* or other sea star your instructor provides (Fig. 21-14a). Most sea stars have five arms or rays attached to a central disc. Some species have many more arms, and occasionally an arm may be missing due to injury. Normally a lost arm is regenerated. Notice that the sea star is not truly radially symmetrical. The symmetry sea stars possess is pentamerous, or five-parted. Each arm is identical to the others, but they are arranged on the central disc such that only certain cuts through the central disc would yield two mirror-image halves. Indicate on Figure 21-14a one such cut.
- Use the stereoscopic microscope to examine the upper or **aboral** surface (Fig. 21-14a). This surface is often covered with small, calcareous spines or bumps, or with fleshy extensions of

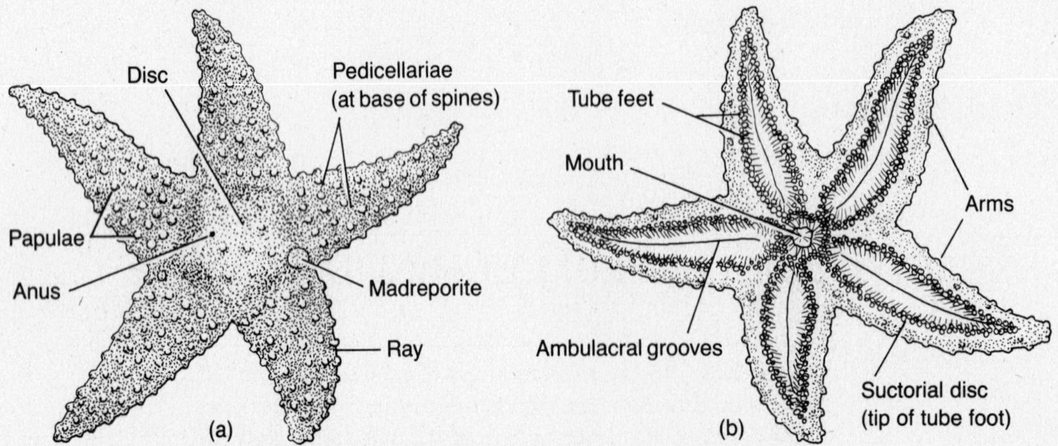

Figure 21-14 *Asterias,* sea star. (a) Aboral surface. (b) Oral surface.

the coelom termed **papulae**, which protrude through the plates of the endoskeleton. Pincerlike **pedicellariae**, derived from modified spines, are also found on the aboral surface, where they are positioned to pinch would-be predators. Near the edge of the central disc is the **madreporite**, a small, hard, circular plate that covers the opening into the water vascular system. Nearer the middle of the central disc is the anus. Now, turn over the animal and examine the **oral** surface (Fig. 21-14b). The mouth is located in the middle of the central disc, where the **ambulacral grooves** from the five arms come together. Lining the openings into the ambulacral grooves are many small spines, which can fold down to cover the groove. Within the grooves are hundreds of fleshy, tubular structures called **tube feet**. The external tip of each cylindrical tube foot is flattened into a **suctorial disc**, while the internal end is expanded **ampulla**, or **bulb**. Pairs of tube feet are arranged in a series along the radial canal of the water vascular system. A radial canal in each arm joins the ring canal in the central disc (see Fig. 25-36 in your text). The radial and ring canals and the tube feet are parts of a closed system of tubules. Movement of fluid in the water vascular system controls the movement of the tube feet. By moving fluid in and out of the tube feet, the sea star can attach the suctorial disk to surfaces.

- If your sea star is alive, turn it upside down in a dish of seawater and observe the movement of the tube feet under the stereoscopic microscope. Notice how undulating waves move up and down the rows of tube feet. Place a fingertip on the tube feet and allow them to attach. Pull your finger away gently—the tube feet can attach so tightly that they may tear off as you pull free. Although each tube foot is small, the combined force exerted by many tube feet is great. A sea star attached to the two shells of a bivalve can exert a sustained force for hours, until the bivalve tires and opens slightly. The sea star then everts its stomach into the shell, where digestion occurs. Allow the live sea star to right itself; describe how the animal accomplishes this movement and the role the tube feet play in the process.

B. Class Ophiuroidea

Ophiuroids, or **brittle stars**, are structurally similar to sea stars—they usually have five arms and a central disk, which is round or shaped like a pentagonal (Fig. 21-15a). The arms are set off sharply from the disk, however, and lack tube feet. The arms are also covered with armored scales; some brittle stars have many spines on their arms. Brittle stars live in mud and sand under rocks, where they scavenge for food particles.

- Use the stereoscopic microscope to examine the living or preserved ophiuroid specimen your instructor provides. Note the central disc, the five arms, and arm spines (if present) (Fig. 21-15a). On the oral surface, the mouth consists of five grooves bordered by **oral papillae**; between the grooves are five **jaws** (Fig. 21-15b). The specimen you observe may have spines or scales on the arms. These features vary greatly between species. If your specimen is alive, notice that brittle stars are much quicker and more active than sea stars. Turn the brittle star onto its aboral surface and observe the righting behavior. In the space below describe the process and compare it to the righting behavior of the asteroid described in the previous section.

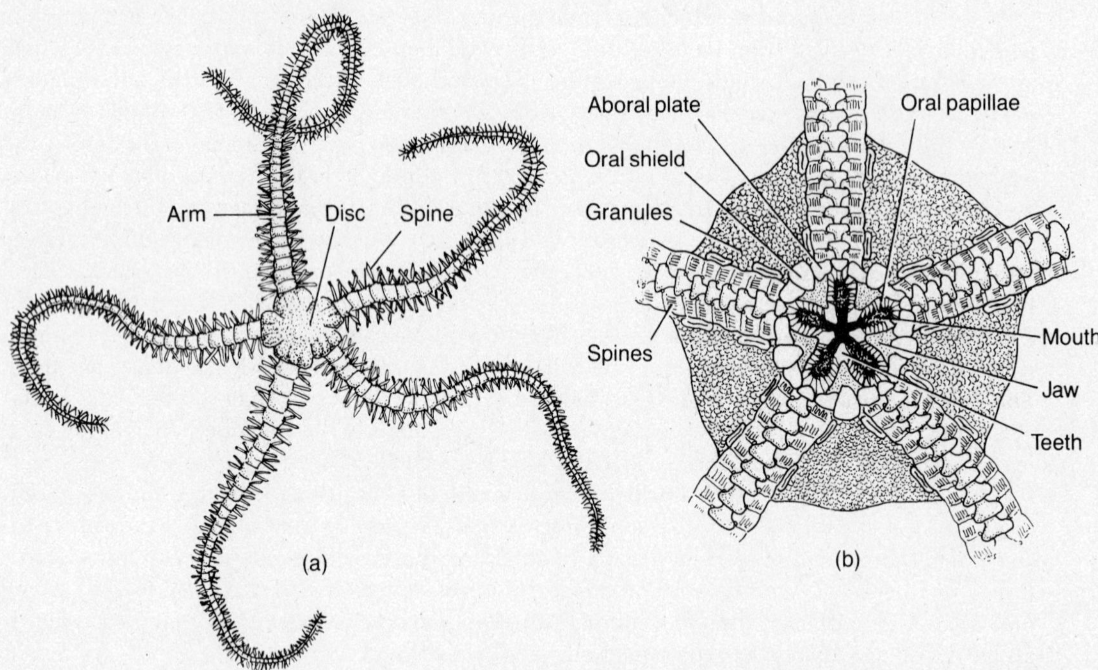

Figure 21-15 Ophiuroid, brittle star. (a) Aboral surface of spiny brittle star. (b) Oral surface of central disc of species with less conspicuous spines.

C. Class Holothuroidea

Holothurians, or **sea cucumbers**, are soft-bodied echinoderms, lacking the hard test or plates found in other members of the phylum. However, holothurians do have microscopic ossicles in their muscular body walls. Holothurians also have the pentamerous radial symmetry and water vascular system common to the phylum.

- Examine the holothurian specimen your instructor provides. Shaped like cucumbers or elongate sacs, holothurians are unappealing at first glance (Fig. 21-16). Close inspection, however, reveals a delicate system of **oral tentacles** at one end. The anus is at the opposite end of the body. Tube feet are arranged in five rows along the body, reflecting a radial pentamerous symmetry relative to the long axis of the body. Members of other echinoderm classes rest with the oral surface down, whereas holothurians usually lie on their sides, wedge themselves between rocks, or partially bury themselves in the substrate. The body wall is strongly muscled, making the animal much tougher than it appears. The body wall of sea cucumbers is eaten as a delicacy in China; however, the internal organs of some tropical species are poisonous. Rough handling of a live specimen may cause it to eviscerate—literally spilling its guts. The response is defensive, entangling a would-be predator in sticky viscera or providing a diversion while the sea cucumber escapes. The body wall can then regenerate the lost viscera.

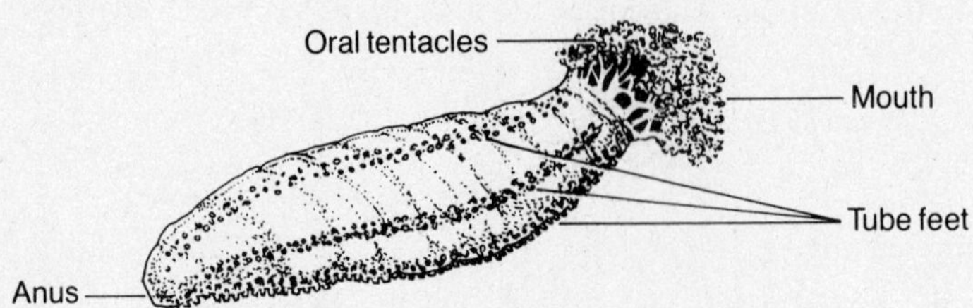

Figure 21-16 Holothurian, sea cucumber.

D. Class Echinoidea

Sea urchins and sand dollars have the most rigid endoskeletons of the echinoderms. Sea urchins have a globe-shaped central shell, or test, which bears many spines that can be moved to ward off predators. Some tropical species have poisonous spines that inflict a severe sting. Like sea stars, sea urchins move by means of tube feet in ambulacral grooves. Sand dollars are much like flattened sea urchins without long spines. All echinoids are marine, found in both shallow and deep water. Occasionally sea urchins form slow-moving herds that grazé en masse on underwater fields of algae.

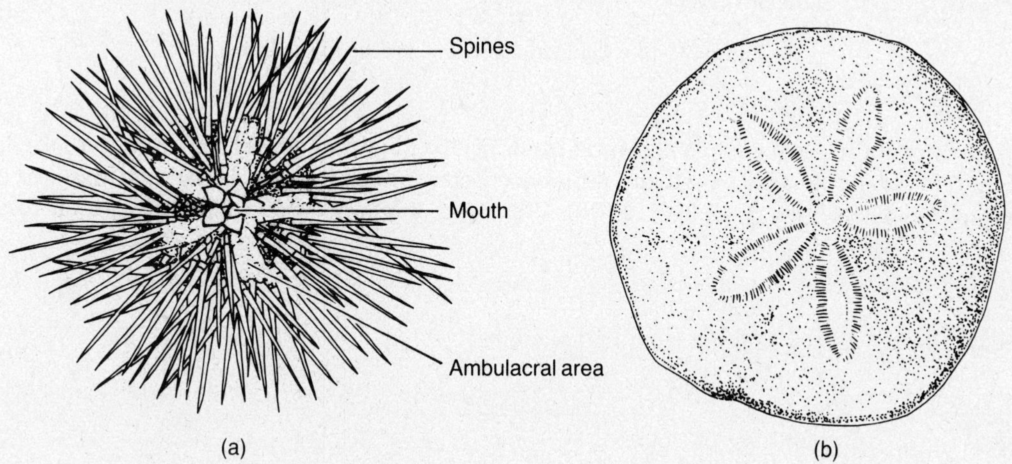

Figure 21-17 Echinoids. (a) Sea urchin, oral surface. (b) Sand dollar, aboral surface.

- Examine the specimen of a sea urchin provided by your instructor (Fig. 21-17a). The surface appendages, which were generally small in the asteroids and ophiuroids, are large and elaborate in members of this class. Pedicillariae are usually found in and among the long spines. Five ambulacral plates and associated tube feet are visible between spines. The anus is located at the center of the aboral surface. The mouth is at the center of the oral surface and is composed of a complex set of plates, which are actually the jaws of an even more complex internal set of plates termed *Aristotle's lantern.* The jaws are powerful grinding tools for scraping algae from rocks, boring into pilings and rocks. If you have a living sea urchin, gently probe between the spines with the eraser end of a pencil and try to touch the central test. How does the sea urchin respond?

  Is this an effective defense behavior?

- Examine the specimen of a sand dollar provided by your instructor (Fig. 21-17b). Although flattened, the sand dollar is basically similar in structure to the sea urchin. The aboral surface bears a five-rayed pattern of ambulacral plates, and five ambulacral grooves leading to the mouth are visible on the oral surface.

E. Echinoderm Larvae

Larvae of the main classes of echinoderms are shown in Figure 21-18. The dark lines in the figure show the location of bands of cilia that these free-living larvae use to swim. The larvae of the various

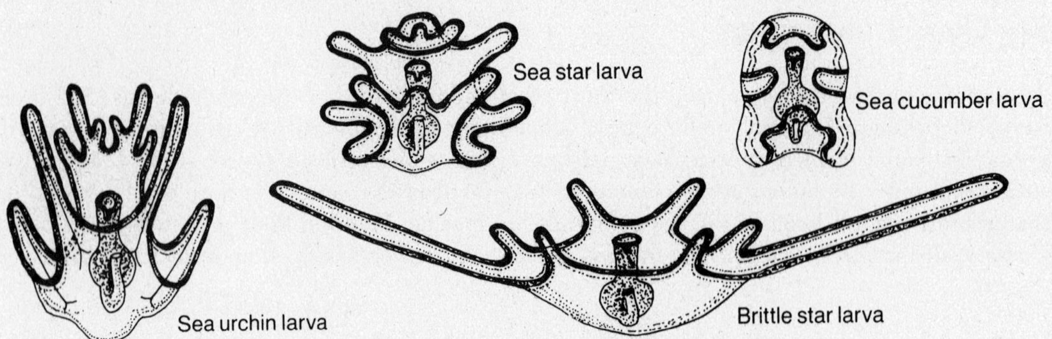

Figure 21-18 Echinoderm larvae for the four classes.

classes display a similar body plan (gut and bands of cilia), but they possess different sizes of ciliated lobes. You should be able to tell the difference between echinoderm larvae and those of other invertebrate phyla (Figs. 21-4, 21-7, 21-13). What kind of symmetry do echinoderm larvae display?

How is this symmetry different from that of adults?

Are there any vestiges of bilateral symmetry in the features of adult sea stars? (Hint: Look at the aboral surface of the central disc.)

The material in this chapter corresponds to Chapter 26 in your text.

22
KINGDOM ANIMALIA III. PHYLUM CHORDATA

The phylum Chordata includes those types of animals most familiar to us, as well as some that are more unusual. The more familiar chordates are those in the subphylum Vertebrata, which includes the fishes, amphibians, reptiles, birds, and mammals. Two smaller subphyla of invertebrate chordates are also known: the Urochordata (tunicates) and the Cephalochordata (lancelets). These subphyla include diminutive marine organisms that at first glance display little in common with vertebrates. However, the three subphyla share the following characteristics:

1. A notochord.
2. Gill slits (also called *pharyngeal slits*; not all function as gills).
3. A tail and muscle blocks.
4. A hollow nerve cord.

In some chordates, these features or their derivatives are present at all stages of development. In others, only embryonic stages exhibit some of the characteristics.

In the exercises for this chapter you will examine specimens of the three subphyla, including the major groups of vertebrates. Keep in mind the four shared characteristics of the Chordata as you examine each specimen.

EXERCISE 22-1 SUBPHYLUM UROCHORDATA

Objectives To identify in specimens of tunicates (sea squirts) the four basic characteristics shared by all chordates; to describe the general anatomy and habitats of adult and larval forms of tunicates.

Members of the subphylum Urochordata (pronounced YUR-oh-kor-DAH-tuh) are small marine organisms that live on rocks, pilings, or plants. Adults are usually **sessile**—they live permanently attached to the substrate—although some urochordates live in the open ocean. The specimens you will examine are in the Class Ascidiacea (from the Greek word *ascus*, meaning sac, also used in the name of the sac fungi, Ascomycetes). Ascideans are commonly called **tunicates** because of their leathery or fleshy, tuniclike covering. One group of bottom-dwelling tunicates are called **sea squirts** because they squirt streams of water through pores or tubes on the body. In general form they resemble sponges, but the internal anatomy of sea squirts is far more complex. Some sea squirts are **solitary**, growing alone, whereas others are **colonial** or **compound**, forming spreading sheets or crusts that contain many small individual animals (**zooids**).

- Examine the preserved specimens of tunicates your instructor provides. A typical solitary tunicate is *Molgula* (Fig. 22-1a). In the space that follows, make a sketch of the tunicate specimen you observe and label the structures written in boldface in the next paragraph.

The outer covering of tunicates is called the **tunic**, a tough or soft covering composed of a form of cellulose, which is also a basic structural component of plants. The base of the animal is cemented to the rock or piling upon which it grows by projections on the tunic. Cut through the tunic to expose the basketlike **pharynx** inside. The pharynx lies free inside the tunic except along one edge called the **endostyle**. The space between the pharynx and the tunic is the **atrium**. Cilia in the pharynx create a current of water, which flows in through the mouth of the **incurrent siphon**, past a mesh of **tentacles** into the pharynx, then out through a latticework of **pharyngeal slits** into the atrium. Streams of mucus produced by the endostyle collect food particles and carry them to the entrance to the gut at the base of the pharynx. The walls of the pharynx are highly vascularized

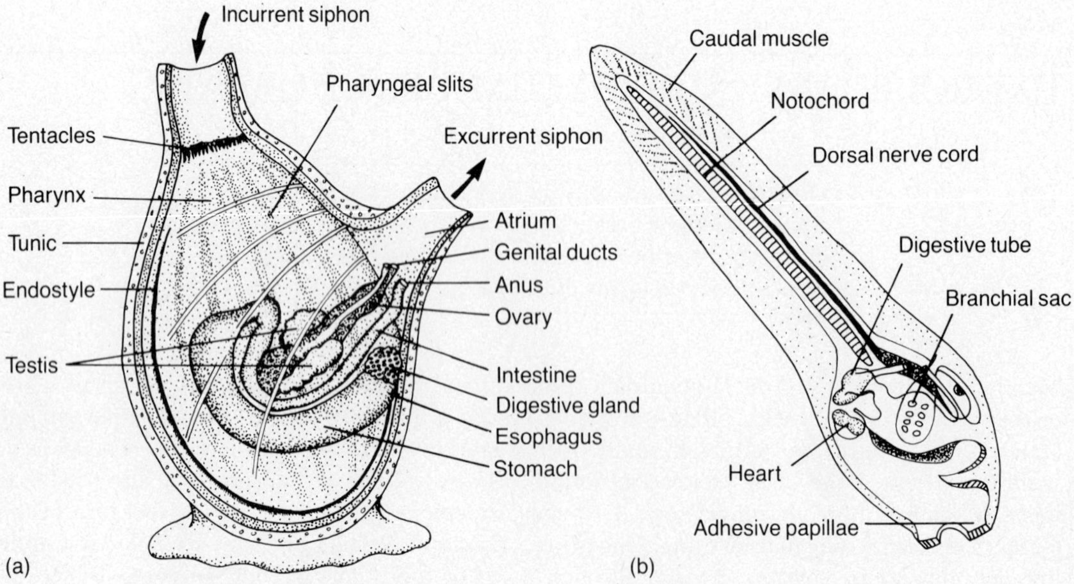

Figure 22-1 *Molgula,* a solitary tunicate. (a) Adult anatomy. (b) Tadpole larva.

and the blood is oxygenated as it flows through the pharyngeal slits. Water flows out of the atrium through the **excurrent siphon**.

- Observe the microscope slides of tunicate **tadpole larvae** and compare them to Figure 22-1b. Aside from the pharyngeal gill slits, the other chordate features are present only in the free-swimming tadpole larva, so-called because it resembles the tadpole larva of amphibians. The **notochord** runs down the center of the tail, and above it lies the hollow **dorsal nerve cord**. The **branchial sac** near the anterior end will develop into the pharynx of the adult. Note the reduced size of the digestive system. The tail is powered by muscle blocks. Before the larva metamorphoses to the adult form, it attaches to a hard substrate with its anterior **adhesive papillae**.

QUESTIONS

How would you classify urochordates if you knew nothing of their larval anatomy? (There is no simple correct answer to this question.)

Some biologists think that higher chordates evolved from a tunicate's tadpolelike larva that failed to metamorphose into a sessile invertebrate adult. Suggest one reason why this seems to be a reasonable hypothesis and one argument against it.

1.

2.

EXERCISE 22-2 SUBPHYLUM CEPHALOCHORDATA

Objectives To identify the chordate characteristics in specimens of adult lancelets and to describe the characteristic anatomy and habitat of lancelets.

The subphylum Cephalochordata (pronounced SEF-ah-lo-kor-DAH-tuh) includes the small, primitive, fishlike animals known as **lancelets**. You will observe specimens of *Branchiostoma* (sometimes called amphioxus, its former scientific name), which in adult form possesses the four chordate characteristics listed at the beginning of this chapter. *Branchiostoma* lives in marine habitats in shallow bays and inlets sheltered from heavy waves.

- Use the compound microscope to examine the whole mount specimens of *Branchiostoma* on microscope slides (Fig. 22-2). Keep in mind that this is the adult form and not a larval stage. The narrow, tapered shape gives the creature its common name, lancelet. Although the anterior end is obvious, a well-developed head is absent. A **buccal hood** and **buccal cirri** are clearly visible at the anterior end. The cirri function as a screen during feeding, when cilia on the **gill bars** create a flow of water into the **pharynx**; particles are trapped in mucus. The digestive tract is well-developed and includes a **liver** and **anus**. The **muscle blocks**, or *myotomes*, resemble fanlike chevrons. A **dorsal fin** extends the length of the body and is continuous with a **ventral fin** that extends about a third of the way up the body. A segmented **dorsal fin ray** lies at the base of the dorsal fin; below the fin ray is the hollow nerve cord and below that lies the notochord. The notochord and nerve cord may only be clearly visible on cross sections of *Branchiostoma*, which your instructor may provide.

QUESTIONS

The tadpole larva of urochordates is a temporary stage, whereas the lancelet is free-swimming throughout its life. Describe how this difference in life history might account for the differences in the following structures in these two creatures.

1. anterior end

2. gills/branchial sac

3. gut

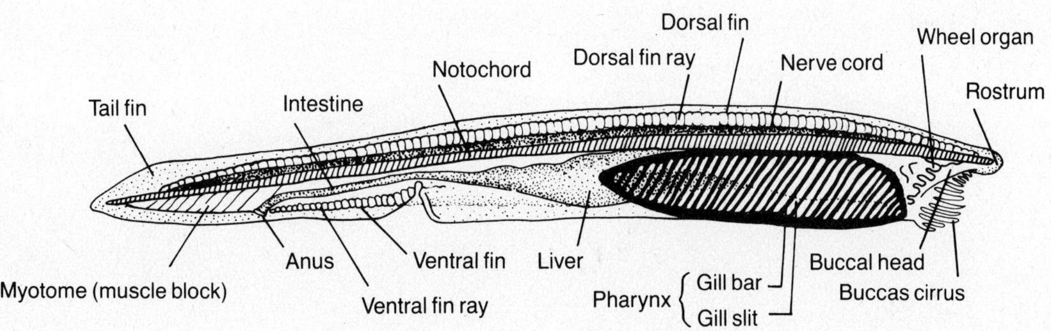

Figure 22-2 *Branchiostoma* (amphioxus).

EXERCISE 22-3 SUBPHYLUM VERTEBRATA

Objectives To describe the major groups of vertibrates in terms of their distinguishing characteristics, including skeletal systems, jaws, appendages, skin coverings, modes of embryonic development and nutrition, and type of thermoregulation; to trace the evolution of selected characteristics on a phylogeny of the vertebrates.

The vertebrates include a variety of organisms; no doubt you are already familiar with some of them. In the following activities you will observe some specimens of the major classes of vertebrates and identify their distinguishing characteristics. Because of the size and uncooperative behavior of many vertebrates, most or all of these specimens will be preserved so that you can observe them closely. However, your instructor may have some living vertebrates on display to enable you to observe their structures and behavior. You should familiarize yourself with the major features of external anatomy of members of each vertebrate class. You should also be aware of important adaptations of each class that may not be immediately observable (such as homeothermy in mammals). Try to identify those structures that are homologous (derived from the same ancestral structure) in different groups of vertebrates.

A. Jawless Fishes

Class Agnatha

- Examine the preserved specimens of a **sea lamprey** or **hagfish** provided by your instructor. Agnathans are the most primitive members of the vertebrates. Sea lampreys and hagfish (Fig. 22-3) are the only living members of this class, and they live by preying on living or dead fish. Instead of jaws, these fish have **circular mouths**. If specimens are available, sketch the mouths of the lamprey and hagfish next to Figure 22-3. You may observe several rows of teeth and a rasping tongue in the suction-cuplike mouths, which are used to attach and feed on the bodies of other fishes.

On top of the lamprey head is a single **nostril**, through which water can be pumped to the gills, while the lamprey's mouth is attached to a prey fish. Instead of elongated gill slits as in most jawed fishes, lampreys have a series of circular **gill pouches** behind each eye. The lamprey skeleton is made of **cartilage** and the skin lacks scales. Hagfish have the single nostril at the tip of the snout, and some species have only a single gill opening.

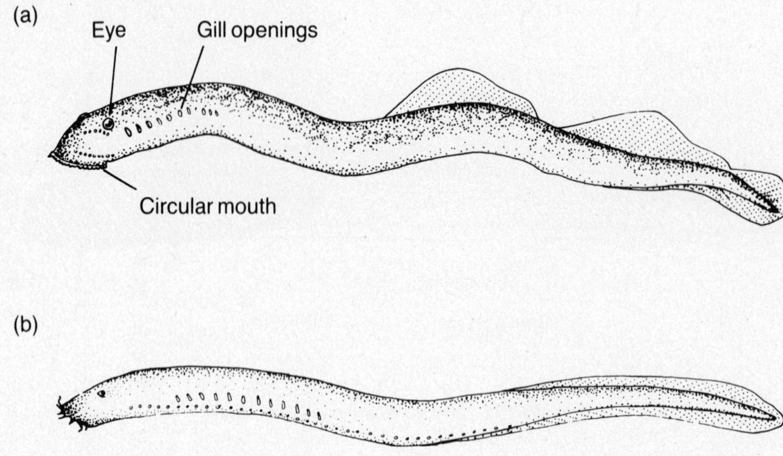

Figure 22-3 Jawless fishes (Class Agnatha). (a) Sea lamprey. (b) Hagfish.

B. Jawed Fishes

The jawed fishes exploited a new feeding mode and evolved a wide variety of body forms. Several extinct groups of jawed fishes are discussed in your textbook. Here you will examine specimens of the major living, or extant, groups.

Class Chondrichthyes: Cartilaginous Fishes

This class contains the **sharks**, **skates**, and **rays**. These fishes are considered primitive because of their nonbony **cartilaginous** skeletons. The use of the term *primitive* for these fishes accentuates its meaning in an evolutionary sense: Primitive means similar to ancestral types, not necessarily crude, inefficient, or unsuccessful. On the contrary, sharks are among the premier swimmers and predators of the sea, and the body forms of skates and rays are modified for living on the sea floor.

- Examine the specimen of a dogfish or other shark provided by your instructor. Locate the **dorsal fins**, **anal fin**, **pectoral fins**, **pelvic fins**, and large **caudal fin** (Fig. 22-4a). The caudal fin is heterocercal, having a longer dorsal lobe. As the shark swims with a graceful, sinuous motion, the upper lobe of the caudal fin provides a downward thrust, which is counteracted by the winglike pectoral and pelvic fins and the flattened head. The result is a net lift as the shark swims. In skates and rays, which spend much time resting on the bottom covered by sand, the pectoral fins have evolved into enlarged lateral wings, which are used in almost birdlike fashion to propel the animal. Most sharks are negatively buoyant and sink if they stop swimming. Note the **gill slits** on the shark. By swimming continuously, the shark forces oxygenated water into its mouth, over the gills, and out the gill slits. Sharks possess paired nostrils, in contrast to the single nostril of the Agnatha. Where are these nostrils located on the head of the shark?

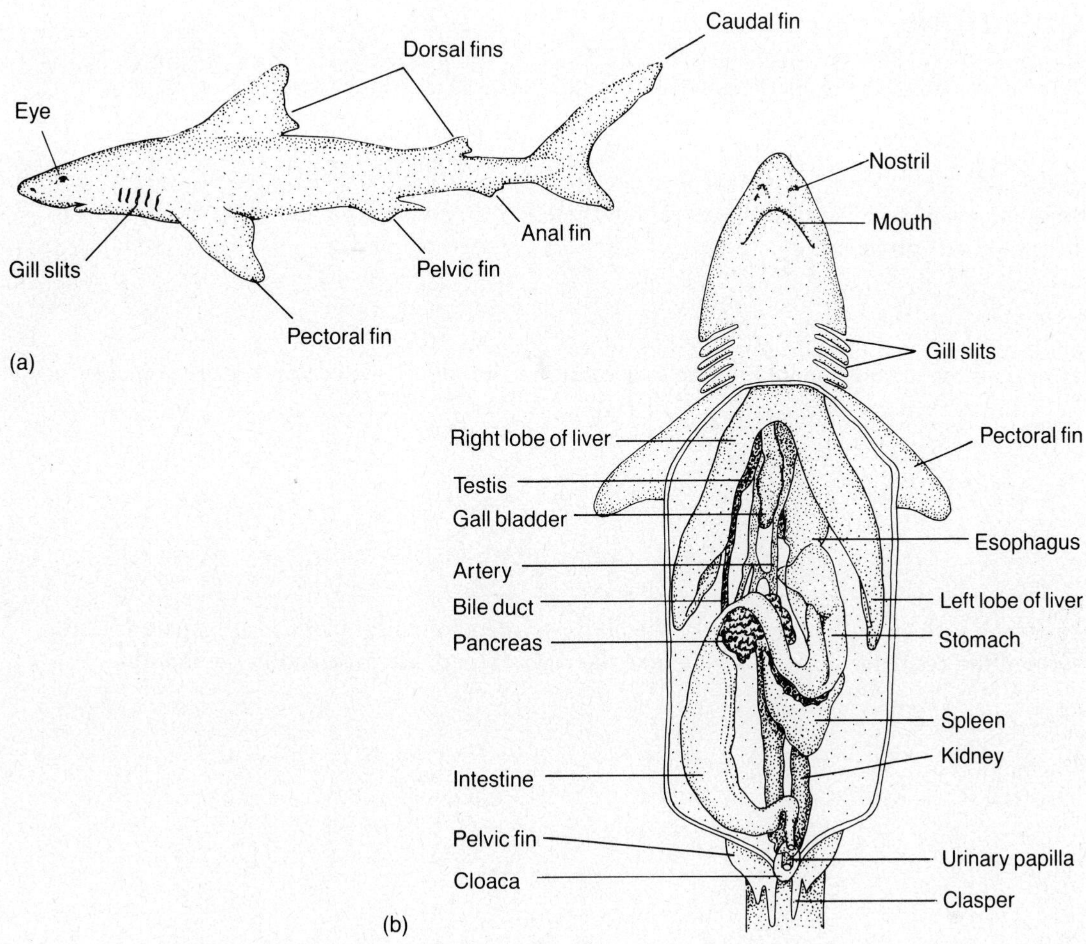

Figure 22-4 Shark (Class Chondrichthyes). (a) External anatomy. (b) Internal anatomy.

Shark scales are called **denticles** or **placoid scales** and are essentially tiny versions of their teeth. Observe a fin under high power with the stereoscopic microscope, or examine a prepared slide of a placoid scale under the compound microscope. Draw a picture of several scales.

QUESTIONS

Run your hand over the shark from snout to tail. What is the skin's texture?

Now run your hand over the shark's skin in the other direction, from tail to snout. What is its texture in this direction?

How does the arrangement of denticles account for the difference in skin texture you observed?

Now look at the mouth of the shark. Sketch the shape of a typical tooth and compare it to the form of the denticles. Also, describe how the rows of teeth are arranged in the mouth.

Sharks readily lose teeth during their violent feeding behavior. Suggest how the arrangement of its teeth might be advantageous to the animal.

- Your instructor may have a dissected shark on display. If so, examine the internal anatomy of the shark. The most conspicuous organ is the bilobed **liver**, which is rich with oil and partially counteracts the negative buoyancy of the body. Follow the **esophagus** to the **stomach**, **intestine**, and finally, to the **cloaca**. Fertilization in the Chondrichthyes is internal. Observe the pelvic fins of a male shark and note the specialized extensions called **claspers** that extend posteriorly. These claspers are used as intromittent organs and to anchor the male onto the female during copulation. Some species are **oviparous** (eggs hatch outside the female); some are **ovoviparous** (eggs hatch inside the female's body); and some are **viviparous** (young develop inside the mother's body and are born as free-swimming miniature adults). Internal fertilization and viviparity are considered relatively advanced traits in other groups (such as the mammals), in which they evolved independently.

Class Osteichthyes: Bony Fishes

This class includes the familiar types of fishes that are so dominant in fresh waters and oceans. Bony fishes are not only successful and abundant; they are amazingly diverse, including such types as tiny, bullet-shaped minnows; flattened sunfish; armored coelocanths; and giant sea bass. Of the four subclasses of bony fishes, two subclasses are common: the Sarcopterygii (primitive fleshy-finned fishes) and the Actinopterygii (spiny-finned fishes). The latter subclass includes the Teleostei, the group that comprises most living species of bony fishes. The fleshy-finned or lobe-finned fishes are not as abundant as spiny-finned fishes. Although you will probably not observe any in the laboratory, you should recognize that lobe-finned fishes are more primitive and more similar to the common ancestor of amphibians and fishes than are the spiny-finned fishes.

- Examine the preserved teleost specimen provided by your instructor (Fig. 22-5). The fins of teleosts are homologous with those of the sharks, skates, and rays, but their structure is quite different. Locate the first and second **dorsal fins**, **anal fin**, **caudal fin**, paired **pelvic fins**, and paired **pectoral fins**. These fins are composed of hard or soft **fin rays** covered by a flexible membrane. Describe how the structure of the teleost's fins is different from that of the shark's fins, and speculate on how this structural difference affects the maneuverability of the two types of fishes.

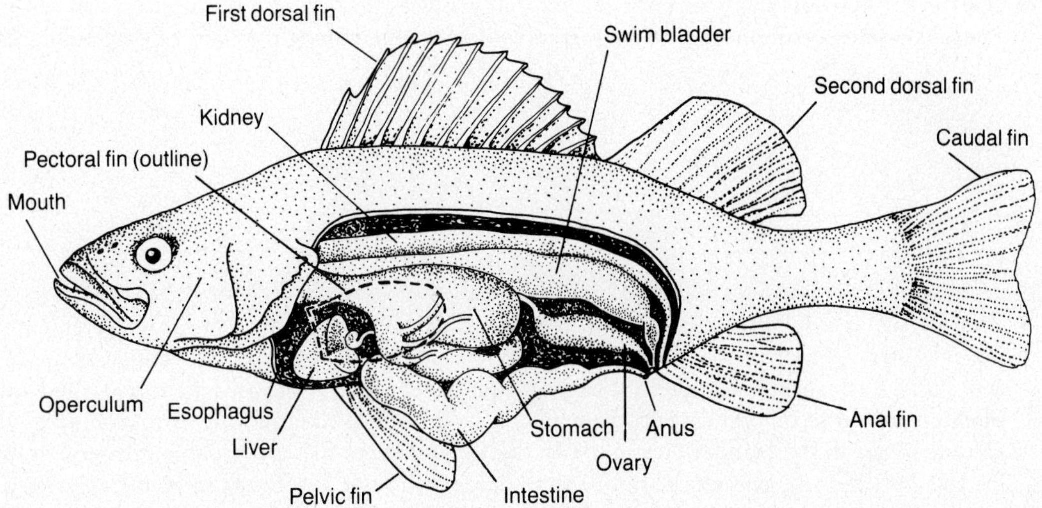

Figure 22-5 Typical teleost (Class Osteichthyes). External and internal anatomy.

- Pull off a scale or two from the bony fish and observe them under the stereoscopic microscope. Your instructor may also provide you with prepared slides of scales from a bony fish to observe under the compound microscope. Note that the scales are covered by a thin, transparent layer of skin. These **dermal scales**, though thin, are made of the same material as bone, and in fact, scales evolved from bonelike plates in ancient fishes. Both lobe-finned fishes and spiny-finned fishes have dermal scales. The scale may have **growth rings**, which represent periods of growth in the life of the fish. Make a sketch of a bony scale in the space that follows and compare it to the denticle of the shark.

- Pull open the **operculum** of the teleost and observe the **gill arches** inside. How does the gill covering (operculum) of teleosts differ from the gill opening in the shark you examined?

- The lateral line contains pressure sensors that are used to detect sounds and water motion. Speculate on the usefulness of having these sensors arrayed along the body of a schooling fish.

- Your instructor may have a dissected teleost on display. The internal organs (Fig. 22-5), including the liver, kidney, ovary, stomach, intestine, esophagus, and anus, are similar to those of the shark. A conspicuously different buoyancy organ is present, however. The gas-filled **swim bladder**, dorsal to the gut, is used to maintain near-neutral buoyancy at various depths. The volume of gas in the bladder changes with depth, and some fish are capable of compensating for this by diffusing gas into or out of the bladder through a network of blood vessels. The process is slow, however, and deep-sea fish brought to the surface in nets often have their swim bladders protruding from their mouths because of the rapid expansion of gas in the bladder.

800 225-

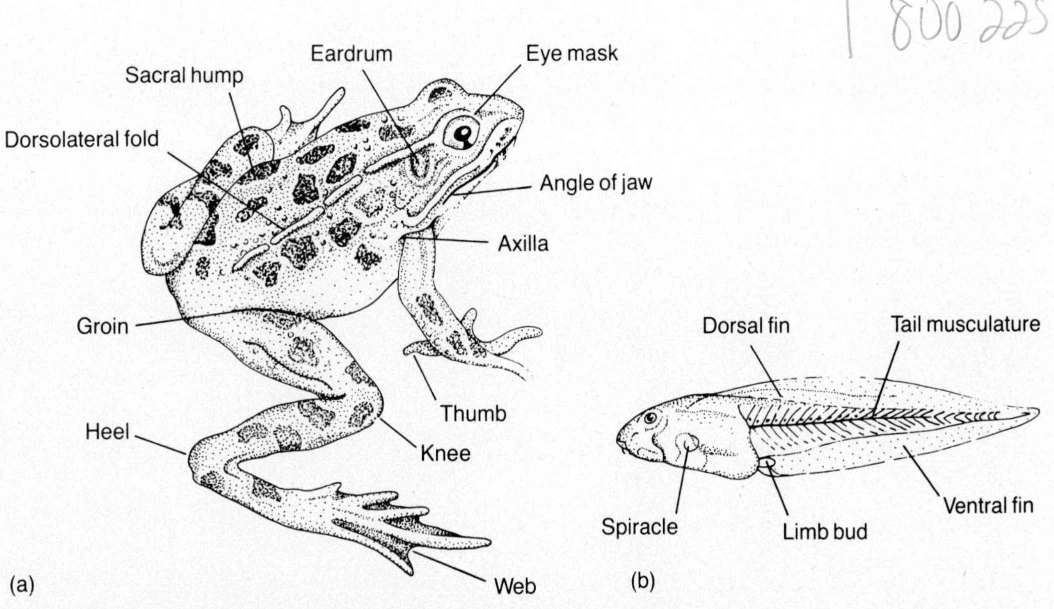

Figure 22-6 Frog (Class Amphibia, Order Anura). (a) External anatomy. (b) Tadpole larva.

C. The First Land Vertebrates

The primitive land vertebrates are clearly related to their aquatic relatives, although land vertebrates possess many specialized adaptations for a terrestrial existence. These adaptations, discussed in detail in your textbook, are:

1. A skeletal and muscular system to support the body and permit movement out of water.
2. Skin conducive to gas exchange.
3. Water-based reproduction.
4. Earlike structures for receiving airborne sound waves.

Some biologists consider the third feature a limitation as much as an adaptation because it restricts the mobility and habitats available to primitive land vertebrates.

Class Amphibia

Members of the class Amphibia possess the four characteristics outlined above. Thus, they are considered primitive and transitional in their ability to survive on land. Three orders of amphibians are recognized: Anura (frogs and toads), Urodela (salamanders), and Apoda (legless salamanders).

- Observe the specimen of the common laboratory frog provided by your instructor (Fig. 22-6a). Describe the features of the frog that correspond to the four adaptations listed above. (The third feature involves inferences about reproduction—your instructor may provide you with specimens of tadpoles for observation.)

1. Skeleton:

2. Skin:

3. Aquatic reproduction:

4. Earlike structures:

- Amphibians are the first four-footed (tetrapod) vertebrates you have encountered in this laboratory. Observe the forelimbs and hind limbs on the frog specimen (Fig. 22-6a). The forelimbs articulate with an internal set of bones called the *pectoral girdle*, and the hind limbs articulate with the set of bones called the *pelvic girdle*. What structures in the teleost are homologous with the forelimbs and hind limbs of tetrapods?

- The feet of anurans have developed digits, and the limbs are jointed in more complex ways than the homologous structures in fishes. If the specimen is a male, look at the inner margin of the inside digits (thumbs) on the forelegs. If the male frog is mature you may find the **nuptial pad**, a roughened pad used to grip the female during **amplexus** (mating embrace). Eggs are laid in a jellylike mass in ponds and hatch into tadpole larvae (Fig. 22-6b), which lead an aquatic existence before metamorphosing into land-adapted adults.

D. Advanced Land Vertebrates

The remaining three classes of vertebrates (Reptilia, Aves, and Mammalia) are more completely adapted to life on land. Their differing adaptations solve the same problems faced by amphibians: skeletal support, gas exchange involving lungs, an "aquatic" environment for early developmental stages, and development of sound-sensing organs (ears and internal attachments).

Class Reptilia

This class contains three orders, Squamata (lizards, snakes, iguanas, and legless lizards), Crocodilia (crocodilians), and Chelonia (turtles and tortoises). Fertilization is internal, and reptiles lay large **cleidoic** ("sealed off") eggs, which are covered by tough external shells and contain yolk for embryonic nutrition. The cleidoic egg allows the embryo to develop in a portable aquatic environment inside the egg. The reptilian egg, like that of birds (Fig. 13-16) has an amnion that surrounds the embryo.

- Your instructor may have specimens of preserved reptiles on display. Be able to describe any labeled structures on the display specimens and to compare them to similar structures on specimens of the other groups of land vertebrates.

The reptilian skin is covered with dry **epidermal scales** made of keratin (a fingernail-like substance composed of proteins and lipids). These scales are different from those of fishes, in which the scales are made of bony material.

- Pull off a small piece of reptilian skin and observe an epidermal scale under the stereoscopic microscope, or observe the prepared slide of a reptilian scale under the compound microscope. Sketch an epidermal scale in the space below, and describe how it differs from a scale of a spiny-finned fish.

Water loss in excretion by reptiles is minimized by an efficient kidney. Reptiles are **ectothermic** and do not control body temperature metabolically, although they have many behaviors (such as basking in the sun) that allow them to heat up or cool down as needed. The legless condition of snakes, as well as certain legless lizards, is considered to represent the evolutionary loss of appendages during their development from a tetrapod ancestor.

Class Aves

Birds range in size from hummingbirds to ostriches and giant condors (although the latter species is currently threatened with extinction). The two most obvious evolutionary developments in birds are feathers and the modification of their forelegs into wings for flight. The feathers covering the body contain keratin and are made of dead cells; they are considered homologous to the epidermal scales of the reptiles, from which birds diverged about 225 million years ago. Feathers function in both thermoregulation and in flight.

- Observe a feather provided by your instructor under the stereoscopic microscope. The **quill** is the basal part of the feather that inserts into the skin. The **shaft** is a light, hollow tube with **barbs** arranged in regular rows on either side. Small, hooklike **barbules** on the barbs interlock and hold the barbs in alignment.

Like mammals, birds are **homeothermic** and maintain a high internal body temperature. In addition to insulation from feathers, homeothermy requires the ingestion of large amounts of food (nectar or seeds) in some small-bodied species. Like reptiles, birds have internal fertilization and lay shelled, cleidoic eggs. Some birds have a **gizzard**, a muscular enlargement of the digestive tract, which contains gritty particles that aid in the breakdown of food items such as seeds. A gizzard is also found in the crocodiles and is considered evidence of an evolutionary link between birds and

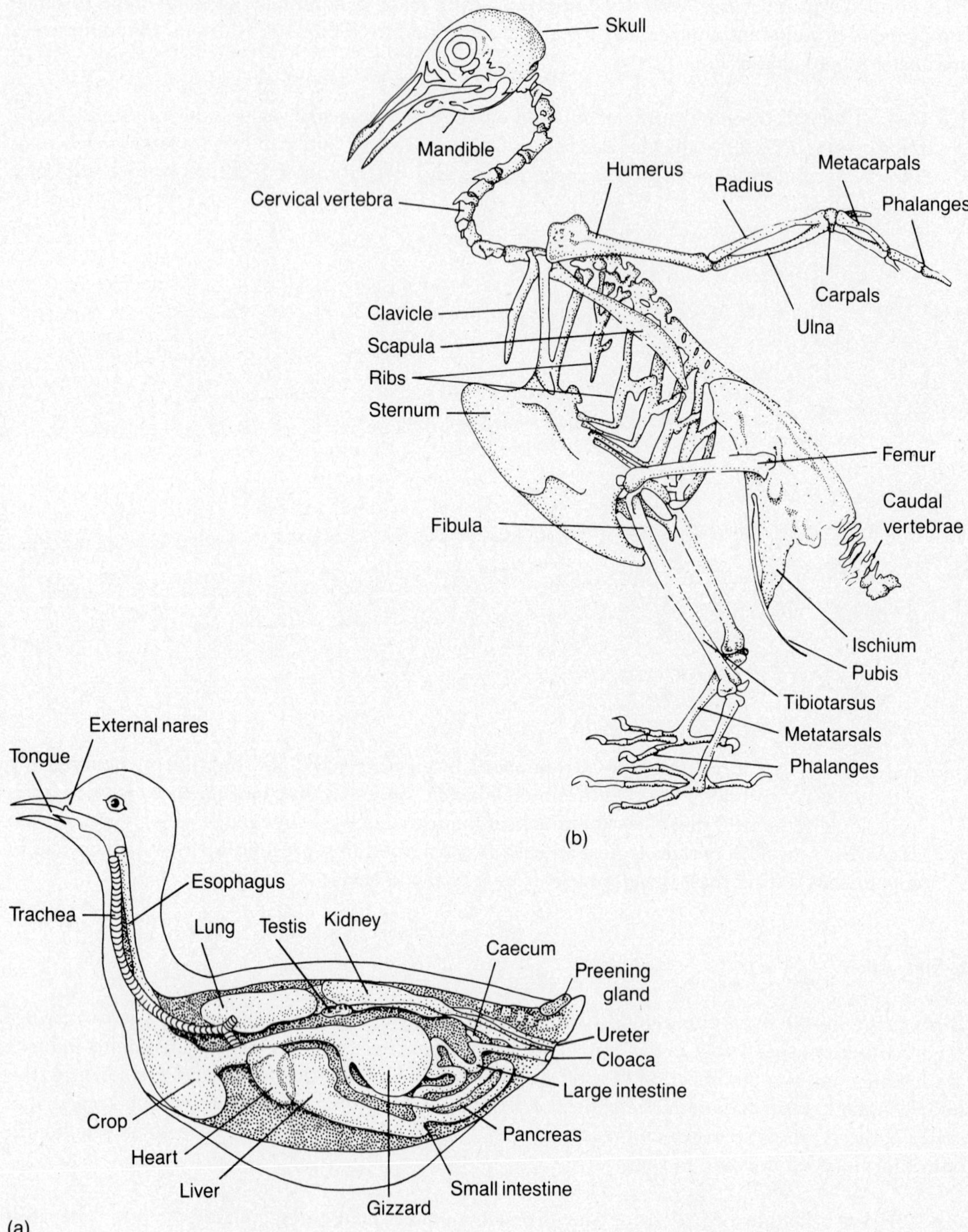

Figure 22-7 Anatomy of the pigeon. (a) Skeleton. (b) Internal anatomy.

these primitive reptiles. Birds do not produce dilute urine; instead their kidneys produce a pasty material (called *guano* in seabirds) containing uric acid.

- Examine the skeleton of a bird, if one is available, and notice the highly modified bones of the wings, as well as the flat and expanded **sternum** to which powerful flight muscles attach (Fig. 22-7a). If a chicken bone is provided by your instructor, cut it in half lengthwise. Describe the internal structure of the chicken leg and speculate on how this structure is adaptive to flying vertebrates. (Domestic chickens have little opportunity to fly, but they retain the basic birdlike bone structure.)

- Your instructor may also have a dissected bird specimen on display (Fig. 22-7b). If so, examine the specimen and be able to describe any labeled parts and to compare them to similar structures in dissected specimens of other vertebrate groups.

Class Mammalia

Mammals are unique in the living world in that they produce **milk** to suckle their young. The skin is covered more or less densely with **hair**, which also contains keratin and is homologous with the keratin-containing coverings of other vertebrate classes. Hair functions as insulation to help maintain body temperature; fat and blubber accomplish the same end in mammals such as whales and dolphins.

- Pull a hair from your head and examine it underneath the compound microscope, or examine the prepared slide of mammal hair. Each hair consists of a **root** (the part inserted into the skin) and a **shaft** (the part extending above the surface of the skin). In the space below, make a sketch of the hair.

Fertilization in mammals is internal, and the embryo develops internally for a period of time. The three groups of mammals (infraclasses) are distinguished partly on the basis of embryonic development: the Prototheria includes primitive types that lay eggs and have a reptilelike pelvic girdle; the Metatheria includes the marsupials of South America and Australia, whose young suckle and develop in a marsupial pouch for a period of time after birth; and the Eutheria includes the placental mammals, which have a prolonged period of internal development when the embryo is nourished by the mother via the placenta.

- Your instructor may have a dissected specimen of a mammal on display; however, you will do your own dissection of a fetal pig in Chapter 26 of this laboratory manual.

- Based on your observations of the display specimens of the major groups of land vertebrates, fill in Chart 22-1, comparing structures and adaptations in the three classes.

Chart 22-1 Comparison of adaptations in three vertebate classes.

Feature	Reptiles	Birds	Mammals*
Skin covering			
Type of appendages			
Site of fertilization			
Site of embryonic development			
Nutrition of embryo			
Type of thermoregulation			
Respiratory organ(s)			

*This refers to the Eutheria, the dominant mammals in North America; your specimen will probably be from this group.

E. Phylogeny of the Vertebrates

The evolutionary history of the vertebrates can be expressed by a **phylogeny**, or **cladogram**, which shows the nearness of relationship of the major groups and also can be used to display the evolution of various characters in the groups. As explained in Chapter 14 of this laboratory manual, one can construct such a phylogeny based on a chart of characteristics and character states of some of the major groups of vertebrates. The phylogeny represents a hypothesis of the path of evolution. As a hypothesis, it is subject to modification by new information or reinterpretation of existing data. In other words, like any other scientific hypothesis, a phylogeny is only as valid as the data on which it is based.

Ideally, a phylogeny should be constructed using as much information as possible. However, this can become a cumbersome task if many characteristics are included. In fact, a computer may be required to sort through the possibilities. Fortunately, one can construct a reasonable phylogeny of the major groups of vertebrates by considering only a few characteristics such as those in Table 22-1. Each characteristic has several possible character states.

Table 22-1 Character states of selected characteristics of major groups of vertebrates.

Characteristic	Possible character states
Amnion	absent; present
Appendages	fins; legs (or arms and legs); legs and wings
Body covering	smooth skin; dermal scales; epidermal scales; feathers; hair
Thermoregulation	ectothermic; homeothermic
Gizzard	absent; present

Complete the following chart of vertebrate characteristics based on your observations of specimens in this chapter and your reading in the textbook. One of the columns of character states is already filled in. One group, the lungfish, is a member of the group of primitive fleshy-finned bony fishes, the Sarcopterygii, in the Class Osteichthyes; the spiny-finned fishes are referred to as "ray-finned fishes" on the phylogeny diagrams.

Chart 22-2 Character states for selected characteristics in major groups of vertebrates.

Vertebrate groups (Common names)	Characteristic				
	Amnion	Appendages	Body covering	Thermoregulation	Gizzard
Lungfishes	absent				
Ray-finned fishes	absent				
Frogs	absent				
Salamanders	absent				
Turtles	present				
Crocodiles	present				
Snakes	present				
Lizards	present				
Birds	present				
Mammals	present				

One possible phylogeny of the vertebrates is shown in the first diagram of Figure 22-8. This phylogeny depicts the possible evolutionary relationships of fishes and land vertebrates, both of which are believed to have shared a common aquatic ancestor. The branches of the phylogeny are shown as bars, which can be shaded to indicate the evolution of character states in the groups at the ends of the branches. For example, in the first part of Figure 22-8, the branches are shaded to show the character states for "amnion." The branches shaded black indicate those vertebrate groups that have an amnion, either in the egg or in the developing body of the female. The unshaded branches indicate groups that lack an amnion. Notice that for the amnion, the phylogeny is the most parsimonious possible: The amnion evolved only once and was retained in all the descendant groups. Four additional blank phylogenies are shown in Figure 22-8.

- Trace the character states of the remaining four characters on these four phylogenies by shading or coloring the branches as shown in the phylogeny tracing the evolution of the amnion. If several groups share a common character state, fill in their branches with the same color. An evolutionary change from one character state to another should be represented by a color change at a branch point. You will need to use more than two colors for the characteristics "appendage type" and "body covering" because these characteristics have more than two character states.

QUESTIONS

Is the phylogeny also parsimonious for the other four characters?

Note that the phylogeny postulates that birds and crocodiles are more closely related than crocodiles and lizards. Is this surprising? Why?

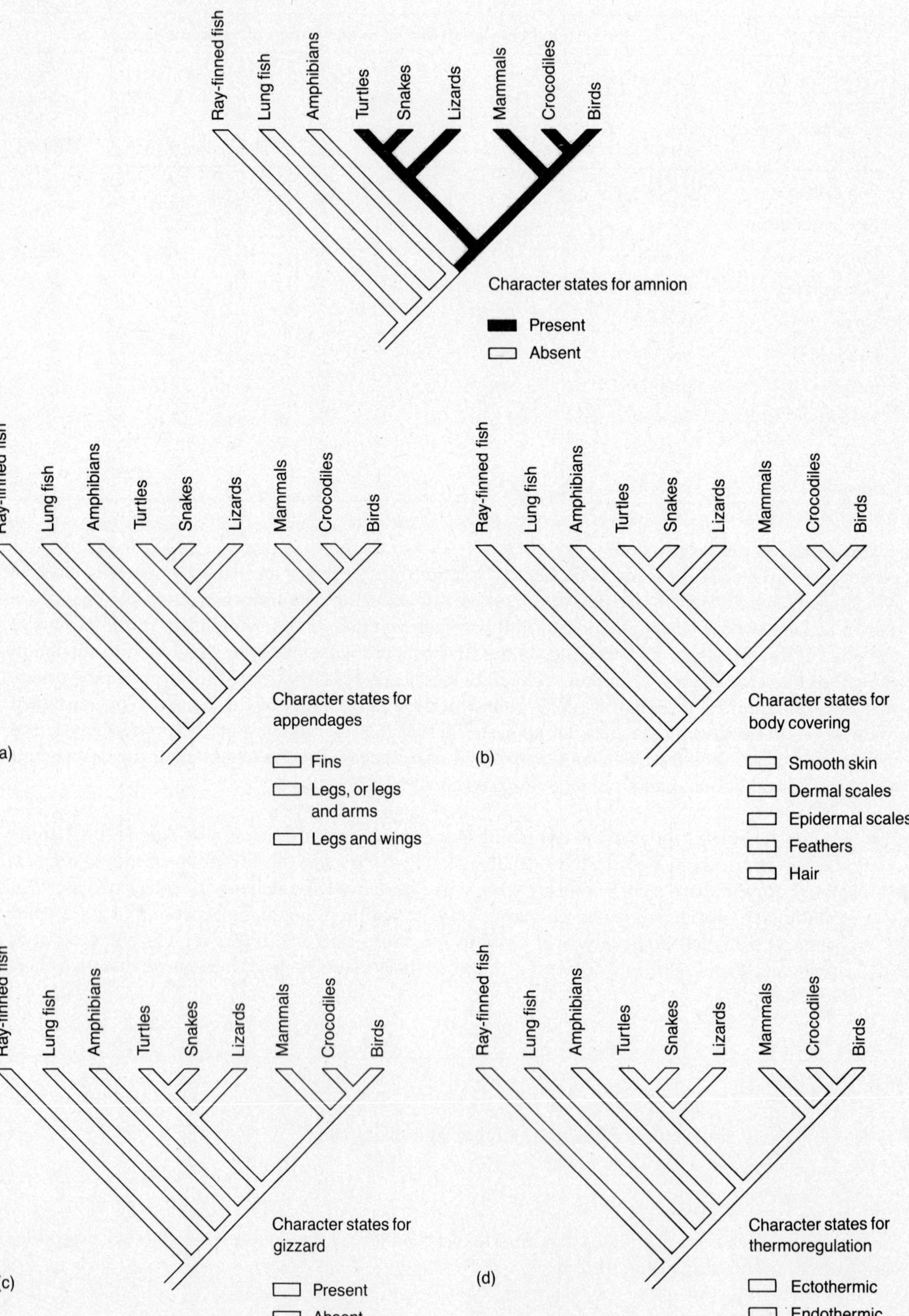

Figure 22-8 Phylogenies of the vertebrates. Dark bars in the first phylogeny trace the evolution of character states for the amnion.

Based on your tracing of the various characters on the phylogenies, what is the one feature that unites birds and crocodiles on the same branch?

Assuming for the moment that the relationship of birds to crocodiles on the phylogeny is correct, explain how this relationship between crocodiles and birds could have come about, given that birds, lizards, and crocodiles shared a common primitive reptilian ancestor several hundred million years ago.

Draw a branch for dinosaurs on one of the phylogenies (or draw a new phylogeny) that shows the evolutionary relationships of other vertebrates to the dinosaurs. Explain your reasoning for placing the dinosaurs at this point on the phylogeny.

Draw a branch for the Agnatha on one of the phylogenies (or draw a new phylogeny) that shows the evolutionary relationships of other vertebrates to the jawless fishes. What character state is unique to agnathans?

Explain your reasoning for placing the Agnatha at this point on the phylogeny.

The material in this chapter corresponds to Chapter 27 in your text.

23
PLANT ARCHITECTURE

Chapters 18 and 19 of this manual outlined the diversity of plants, from tiny unicellular algae to large flowering plants. Some aspects of flowering-plant structure were covered in these earlier chapters; however, in this chapter you will take a much closer look at the vegetative architecture of flowering plants. Plant growth and reproduction will be covered in Chapter 24.

It is easy to take for granted the remarkable architecture of these organisms, but perhaps after observing the details of their internal features (anatomy) and external structure (morphology) you will gain a new perspective on all plants. The focus will be on flowering seed plants, or angiosperms, but in this chapter and the next you will also observe the anatomy of selected gymnosperms. Two major groups of flowering plants, the monocots and dicots, were described in Chapter 19. Because these two groups differ in their morphology and anatomy, specimens from each group will be used in the exercises.

EXERCISE 23-1 ORGANIZATION OF THE VASCULAR PLANT BODY

Objectives To observe the general structure of the vegetative organs of the vascular plant body: the leaf, stem, and root; to identify the major external and internal features of vascular-plant structure, and to describe the continuity of these features between the three vegetative organs.

The vascular system of higher plants, like that of animals, consists of numerous interconnected parts. Certain tissue types are continuous from root to the tips of shoots and leaves. Figure 23-1 displays the major features of the vegetative organs of a generalized flowering plant. The illustration shows the internal connections of the tissue types. Take time to examine the illustration and gain an orientation to the whole plant body. In later exercises you will examine smaller details of leaf, stem, and root structure, and it will be important to relate those details to this diagram. The expression, "Don't lose sight of the forest for the trees," applies here on a different scale: Don't lose sight of the whole plant by focusing on the details of its anatomy.

A. External Features of the Stem

- Your instructor will provide you with several samples of plant stems. Be able to identify on the specimens those external features shown in Figure 23-1 and listed below. These features are listed as you would encounter them from the top to the bottom of the plant. In the space below, make a labeled sketch of each specimen.

Apex The growing tip of the plant is usually covered by bud scales, which enclose the growing tip of the plant and the primordial outgrowths that will become leaves. (These features will be examined microscopically in a later exercise in this chapter.)

Stem Primary organ of support of the plant.
Node The portion of stem where leaf arises.
Internode The portion of stem between nodes.

Leaf A flattened outgrowth of the stem, specialized for photosynthesis.
Petiole The stemlike, supporting structure of the leaf.
Blade The expanded, light-gathering portion of the leaf.

Axillary bud An embryonic shoot in the angle (**axil**) between the leaf petiole and the stem; the bud has the potential to become a branch.

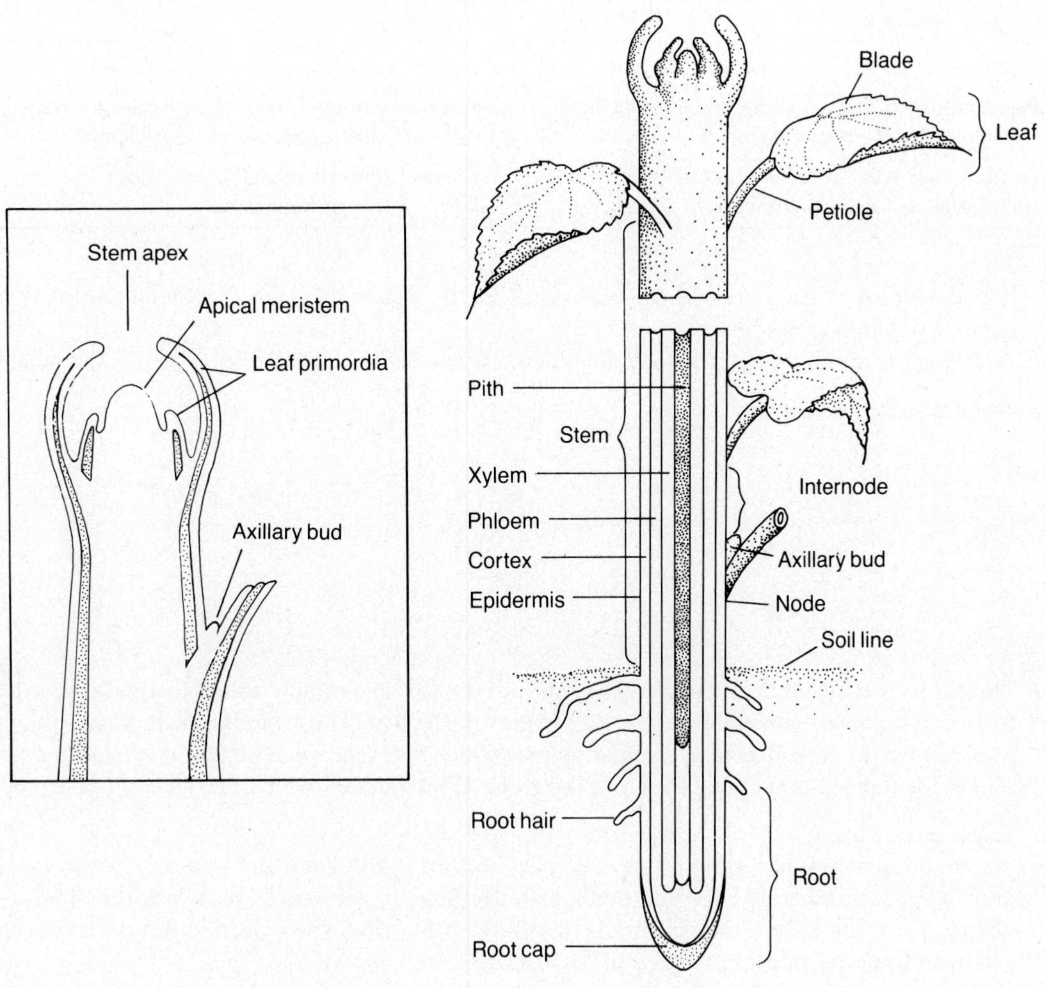

Figure 23-1 Diagrammatic representation of major external and internal features of a generalized vascular plant.

Root Organ of anchorage that absorbs water and nutrients from soil.

Root hairs Extensions of single epidermal cells where most absorption takes place.

Root cap Protective layers of cells at root tip that are sloughed off as the tip grows.

B. Internal Features of the Stem

The upper part of the stem below the apex (Fig. 23-1) consists of three **primary meristems**, or growing regions, which will differentiate into the mature primary tissues of the stem as shown in Table 23-1.

- Figure 23-1 shows the internal arrangement of the mature tissue types in the stem, leaf, and root. You will observe microscope slides of the cells that make up these tissues later in this exercise. For now, notice the relative placement of xylem and phloem in these three organ types and how this arrangement arises from the points of connection of the organs. You may

Table 23-1 Differentiation of primary meristems.

Primary Meristem	Becomes
Protoderm External meristem below apex	**Epidermis** Outer tissue layer in mature stem
Procambium Cylinder of meristem (or a ring of strands) inside the young stem	**Vascular tissues** Conducting tissues for water and nutrients (**xylem**) and food (**phloem**)
Ground meristem Meristem tissue in the young stem inside and outside of the procambium	**Cortex** (outside procambium) and **Pith** (inside procambium)

find it helpful to color-code the tissue types in the figure to make it easier to trace them between stem, leaf, and root.

- Describe the arrangement of xylem and phloem tissue in the stem. Which is nearer the outside of the plant? ____________

- The vascular tissue of the stem branches off into the leaf in a bundle called the **leaf trace**. The leaf trace branches into a smaller series of veins in the leaf. The strands of xylem and phloem remain next to each other in the leaf veins. Notice the relative positions of the xylem and phloem as the leaf branches away from the stem. Which of the two tissue types is uppermost?

  ____

- Water and nutrients absorbed by the root pass upward to the shoot and leaves, where they are used in photosynthesis. Food materials manufactured in the leaves pass into the stem and downward to the lower stem and roots. Indicate with arrows the direction of net flow in the xylem and phloem tissues pictured in Figure 23-1.

Now that you have a general orientation to the major plant organs, in the following exercises you will examine the structure of leaf, stem, and root in more detail.

EXERCISE 23-2 LEAVES

Objectives To describe characteristics of leaf structure, arrangement, shape, margins, and venation patterns; to describe tissues and structures that make up leaf anatomy, as well as the difference in arrangement of these tissues in monocots and dicots.

Leaves come in a wide variety of shapes, venation patterns, and arrangements on the stem. These characteristics affect the function of the leaf and are also important in the classification of plants.

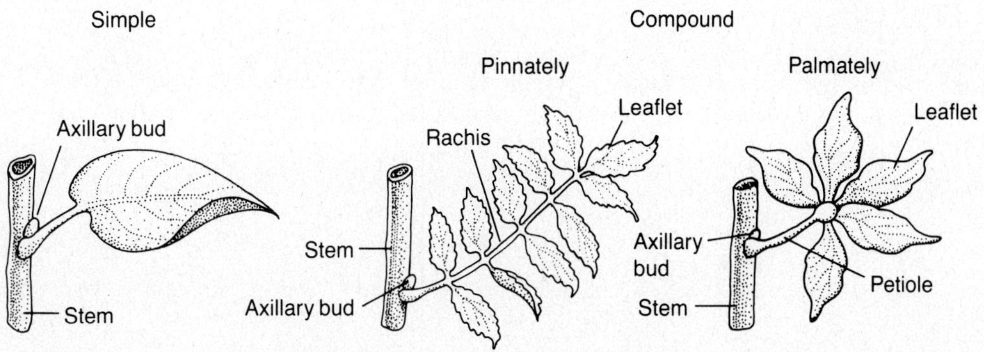

Figure 23-2 Simple and compound leaves.

A. Leaf Structure

Leaves may be simple or compound in structure. **Simple** leaves (Fig. 23-2) have a single blade. **Compound** leaves are divided into **leaflets** branching off a **rachis**, which is actually the midvein, modified into a petiolelike structure. Sometimes it is difficult to tell whether a leaf is simple or compound. This riddle can be solved by finding the axillary bud(s). A single leaf, whether simple or compound, has one or more axillary buds at its junction with the stem. Leaflets lack axillary buds at their junctions with the rachis. The most common types of compound leaves are shown in Figure 23-2. **Pinnately compound** leaves have pairs of leaflets arranged along the rachis like the rays of a feather. **Palmately compound** leaves have leaflets radiating from a central point like the arrangement of fingers on the palm of your hand.

B. Leaf Arrangement

Three basic patterns of leaf arrangement on a stem are shown in Figure 23-3. **Opposite** leaves branch off the stem opposite each other, one pair at each node. **Alternate** leaves branch off, one per node, on alternate sides of the stem. **Whorled** leaves are arranged in groups of three or more at each node.

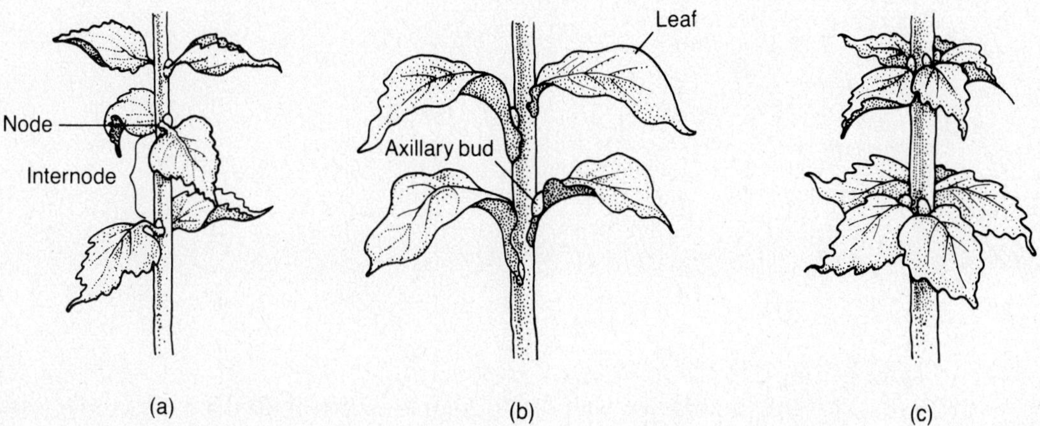

Figure 23-3 Leaf arrangements on the stem. (a) Opposite. (b) Alternate. (c) Whorled.

C. Leaf Characteristics

The diversity of leaf features is matched by the number of terms used to describe them. Some of the most common variations on leaf shape, margins (edges), and venation pattern are shown in Figure 23-4.

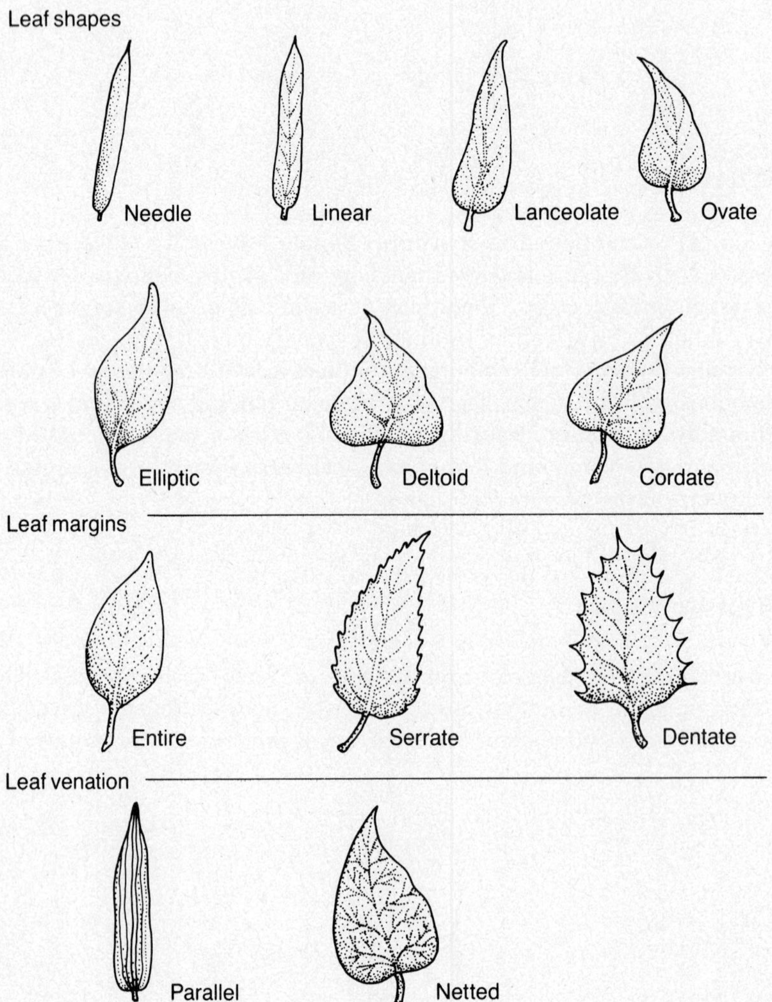

Figure 23-4 Common leaf shapes, margins, and venation patterns.

- Your instructor will provide you with leaves from a variety of plants. Characterize each leaf according to its simple or compound construction, arrangement on the stem, and shape, margin, and venation pattern. Leaf shapes do not always fit into one category, and leaves on the same plant may vary in shape and size. You may need to use several terms to describe their shape (e.g., lanceolate-ovate). Sketch each leaf and record your observations in Chart 23-1.

Chart 23-1 Leaf characteristics.

Plant name and leaf sketch	Simple or compound	Arrangement	Shape	Margin	Venation

Which of the specimens are monocots?

Which are dicots?

D. Leaf Anatomy

Leaves are light-collecting organs and the sites of photosynthesis, and their structure is well adapted for these functions. The leaf must balance the need for a large surface area that captures light and allows carbon dioxide to enter for photosynthesis with the need to prevent excessive water loss. Microscopic details of leaf anatomy reveal how this is accomplished.

- Your instructor will provide you with fresh leaves and a sharp razor blade to make thin cross sections. Cut the leaf transversely across the midvein, and slice off several thin slivers of leaf sections. Arrange them on a slide so that the cut surface faces up. Your instructor will also provide you with a vital stain (one that stains living tissues). Apply the stain to the leaf as directed by your instructor, and make a wet mount slide of the leaf sections. Observe them under the compound microscope. Make a composite sketch of the sections in the space provided. Return to the sketch and label the structures and tissues in it after you have examined the prepared slides of leaf sections.

- Your instructor will provide you with microscope slides of thin sections of leaves from a monocot (Fig. 23-5a) and a dicot (Fig. 23-5b). The leaf sections have been stained with various chemicals that are absorbed differently by cell walls of the different tissues. The color coding makes it easier to learn the cell and tissue types, but you should be able to recognize them regardless of the colors. Observe the leaf sections under the compound microscope and locate on each slide the structures written in boldface in the next paragraph.

A waxy **cuticle** covers the surface of the leaf and prevents water loss. Beneath the cuticle is a layer of cells, the **epidermis**, on both the upper and lower surfaces. Gas exchange occurs through openings termed **stomata** (singular **stoma**), each of which is bordered by two kidney-shaped **guard cells**. Between the upper and lower epidermis is a layer of mesophyll; **spongy parenchyma** cells are irregular in shape, whereas **palisade parenchyma** cells are columnar and arranged side by side in a regular array. **Vascular bundles**, or **veins**, consist of the two basic tissues, xylem and phloem.

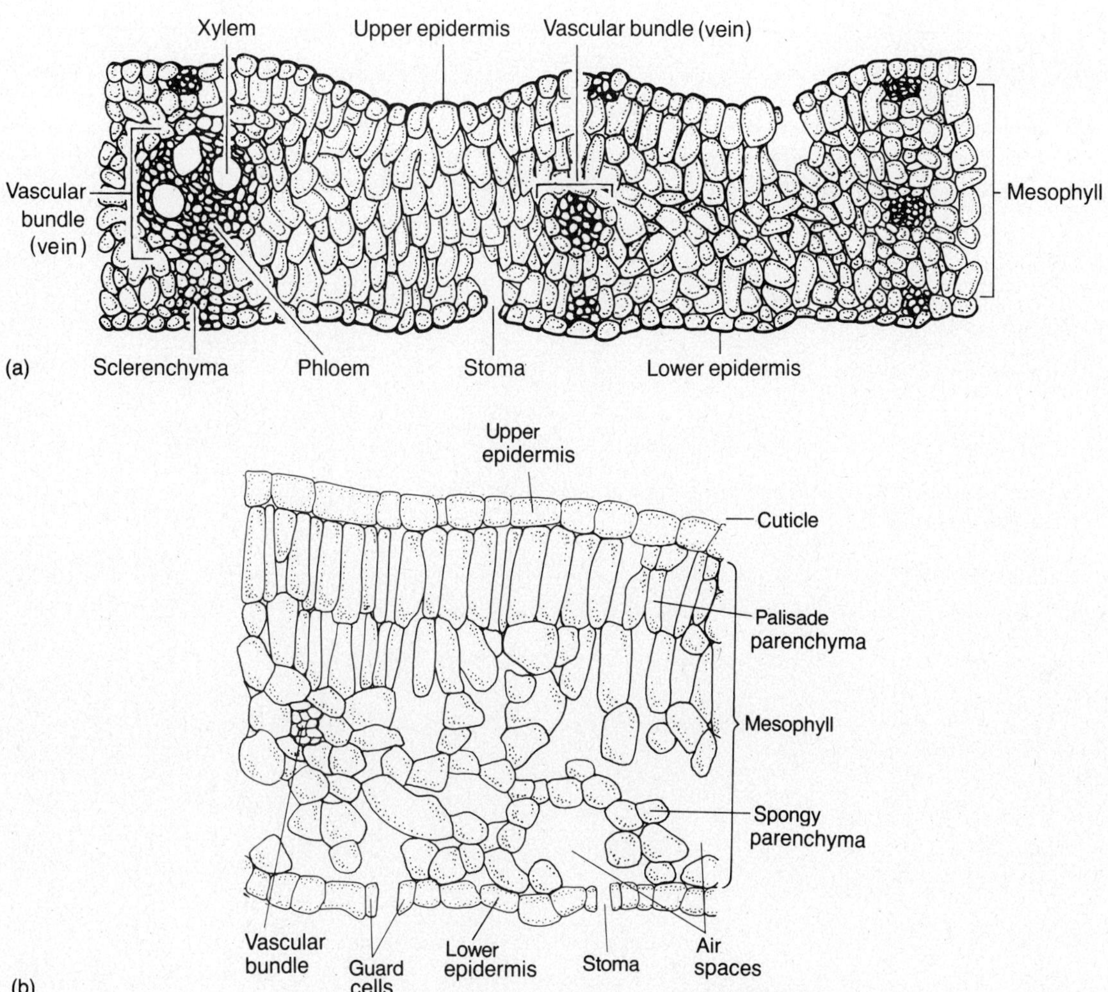

Figure 23-5 Leaf cross sections. (a) Monocot. (b) Dicot.

- Label the sketch of your hand-prepared leaf sections. In Chart 23-2 note any differences in the structures, if any, between dicot and monocot leaves.

Chart 23-2 Comparison of leaf anatomy in monocots and dicots.

Structure	Monocots	Dicots
Epidermis		
Cuticle		
Stomata		
Guard cells		
Palisade mesophyll		
Spongy mesophyll		
Veins		
Xylem		
Phloem		

QUESTIONS

Which vascular tissue (xylem or phloem) is nearer the upper surface of the leaf? ____________
How do the relative positions of the xylem and phloem in the leaf relate to the concept of the leaf as a lateral outgrowth of the stem?

Is your hand-prepared leaf section from a monocot or dicot? ____________
How can you tell?

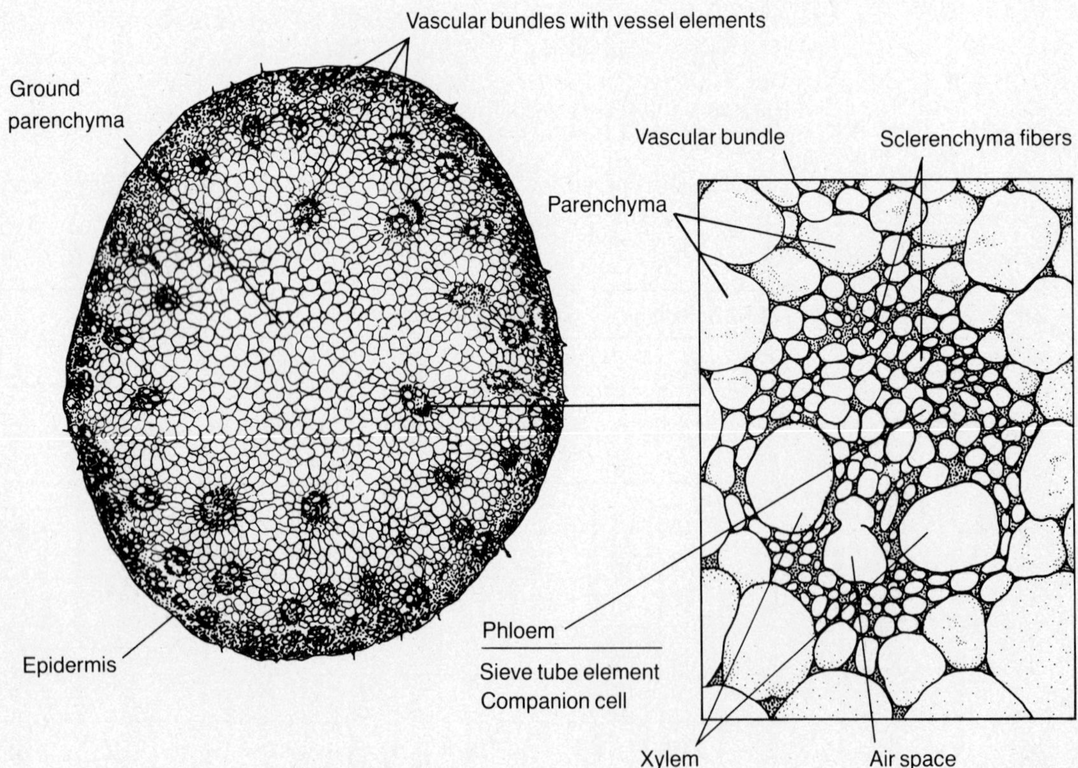

Figure 23-6 Typical monocot stem (cross section).

EXERCISE 23-3 STEMS

Objectives To observe the cellular components and arrangement of tissues that make up the stem in herbaceous vascular plants; to name the cell types in stem tissues, and to describe the differences in arrangement of tissues in monocot and dicot stems.

The basic external and internal features of stems were covered in Exercise 23-1. In this exercise, you will take a closer look at the tissues and cell types in stems by observing thin sections of herbaceous plants. The structure of these green, nonwoody stems is called **primary growth** because the tissues are derived from the primary meristems. Woody stems display an interesting modification of growth and differentiation, called *secondary growth* (derived from secondary meristems, which are separate from the primary ones); you will observe secondary growth in more detail in Chapter 24.

- Take one of the green-stem specimens provided for Exercise 23-1 and cut it cleanly between two nodes, perpendicular to the long axis of growth. Slice off a section thin enough to be translucent to light, and place it on a slide. Your instructor will provide you with a vital stain and instructions on how to apply it to the stem section. Place a cover slip over the stained stem section, and observe it under the compound microscope. Make a sketch of the section, showing any discernible tissues in the roughly circular section.

- Your instructor will provide you with a prepared slide of a longitudinal section through the apex of a young stem. Locate the apical meristem and leaf primordia (Fig. 23-1). Although the cells near the apex appear somewhat homogeneous, you should be able to locate the general regions of the protoderm, ground meristem, and procambium. Cells are more clearly differentiated further down the stem into the primary meristems, which you will examine later in cross sections.
- Your instructor will provide you with stained thin sections of stems from a typical monocot and a typical dicot. Examine the thin sections under the compound microscope and locate the structures written in boldface in the next paragraphs.

In the monocot stem (Fig. 23-6), an outer epidermis covers the surface of the stem. Inside, vascular bundles are scattered in a tissue called **ground parenchyma**, where thin-walled parenchyma cells function in food storage. Air spaces may also be present in the ground parenchyma. Each vascular bundle contains xylem tissue toward the inner margin and phloem tissue toward the outer margin. Large **vessel elements** in the xylem tissue sometimes give the appearance of a large pair of eyes in a "face" formed by the vascular bundle. Also present on the outer edges of the bundles are **fibers**, composed of nonliving **sclerenchyma** cells, whose thickened, lignified walls give structural rigidity to the stem. The phloem tissue is composed of relatively thin-walled **sieve tube elements**, interspersed with **companion cells**. The sieve tube elements lack nuclei, and are believed to rely on the nucleated companion cells for essential macromolecules.

The dicot stem (Fig. 23-7) also is covered by epidermis and contains vascular bundles, but its anatomy displays some distinct differences with that of monocot stems. Beneath the epidermis are several layers of **collenchyma** cells, with thickened walls that add support to the stem. The vascular bundles, instead of being scattered in a ground parenchyma, are arranged in a ring near the periphery of the stem. A **bundle cap** of thick-walled sclerenchyma cells may be present on the outer margin of each vascular bundle. The familiar phloem and xylem tissues are present, and they are separated by a thin zone of cells called the **vascular cambium**. The vascular cambium is a meristematic region, which in some plants gives rise to secondary growth (see Chapter 24). The region of parenchyma cells in the center of the dicot stem is called the **pith**.

- Despite the different arrangement of vascular bundles, there is a consistent arrangement of the xylem tissue relative to the phloem tissue within the bundles. Describe this arrangement.

- Return to your drawing of the section from the stem specimen, and label the regions that were discernible.

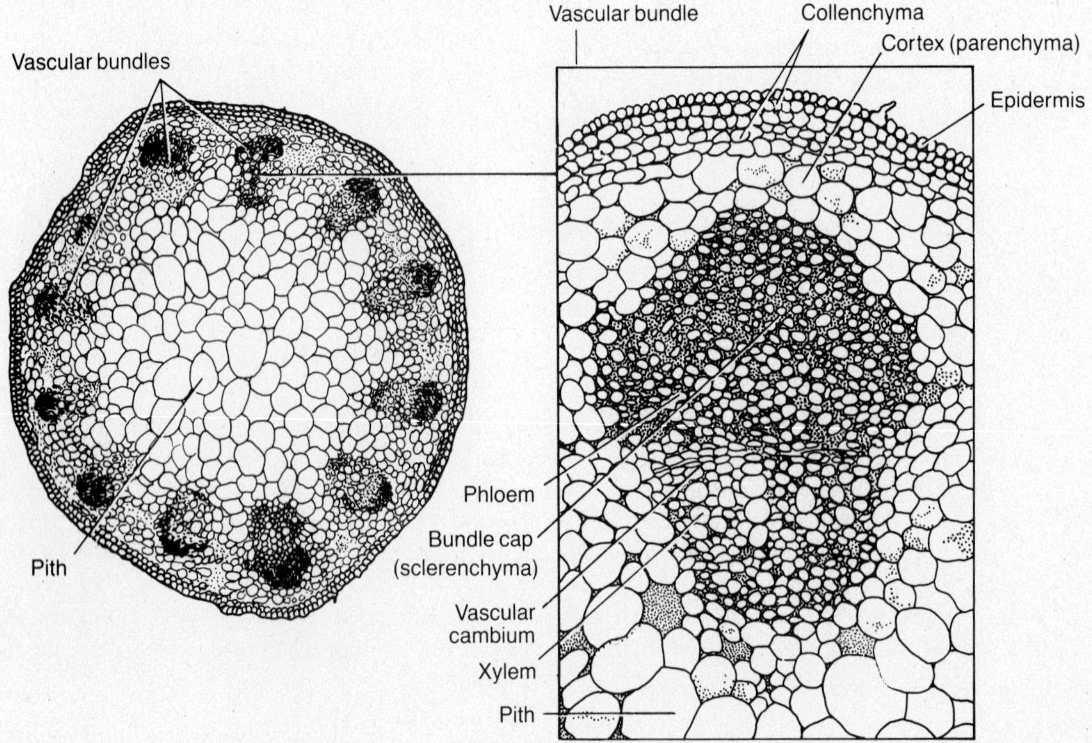

Figure 23-7 Typical dicot stem (cross section).

Indicate in Chart 23-3 the differences in stem anatomy, if any, between monocots and dicots.

Chart 23-3 Comparison of stem anatomy in monocots and dicots.

Tissue or cell type	Monocots	Dicots
Epidermis		
Collenchyma		
Parenchyma		
Pith		
Vascular bundles		
Xylem		
Phloem		
Vascular cambium		
Sclerenchyma		

EXERCISE 23-4 ROOTS

Objectives To observe the cellular components and arrangement of tissues in roots; to name the cell types of root tissues, and to describe the differences in arrangement of tissues in monocot and dicot roots.

Roots serve as anchors and absorb water and nutrients for transport to the upper portions of the plant (stem and leaves). They contain the same basic tissues as stems and leaves, but in a different arrangement. Certain tissue types (such as endodermis) are unique to the root. Also, the epidermis of roots is quite different from that of leaves and stems, a feature that makes sense in light of the root's function.

- Your instructor will provide you with fresh roots. Use a razor blade to make several thin sections of roots that are about 5 mm in diameter. Place the root sections on a microscope slide and apply a vital stain as directed by your instructor. Make a wet mount slide of the root sections and observe them under the compound microscope. Make a composite sketch of the root sections in the space provided.

- Your instructor will provide you with microscope slides of thin sections of a typical monocot and a typical dicot root. You should be able to locate the structures written in boldface in the following paragraphs.

In the monocot root (Fig. 23-8), an epidermis again covers the surface of the organ, as it did in the leaf and stem. However, there is no cuticle on the outer surface of the epidermis; a water-

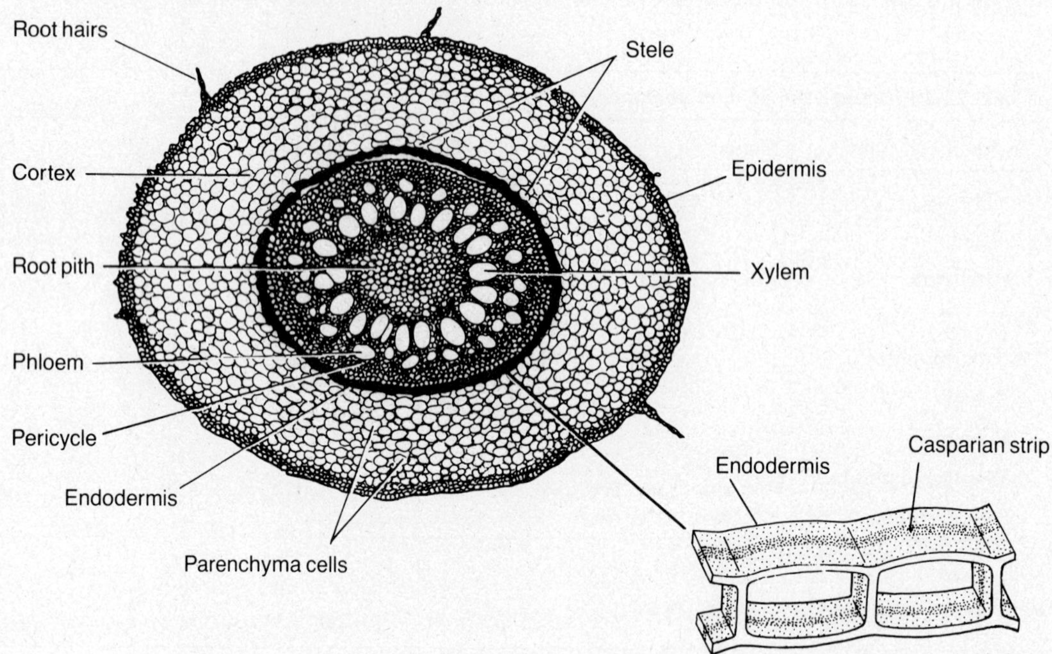

Figure 23-8 Monocot root (cross section). Inset of Casparian strip on endodermal cells.

resistant cuticle would interfere with the absorptive function of the root. Some cells of the epidermis produce elongated, thin extensions called **root hairs** (which may not be visible on your specimen), which are the sites of water and nutrient absorption. At the center of the root is a **stele**, which contains the vascular tissues that are connected to the tissues of the vascular bundles in leaves and stems. The xylem and phloem tissues are arranged in alternate bundles around a central **root pith**. Between the stele and the epidermis is a **cortex** of parenchyma cells, which store starch. Water absorbed by the root hairs passes through the cortex to the stele. The stele is surrounded by a layer of cells called the **endodermis**, which is sometimes darkly stained in root cross sections (Fig. 23-8). Some of the walls of endodermal cells are impregnated with a **Casparian strip** containing **suberin**, a substance impermeable to water. The inset in Figure 23-8 shows how the Casparian strip lines the top, bottom, and two of the sides of each cell in the endodermis. The cell wall facing the stele and the opposite wall, facing the cortex, lack the strips and are permeable to water. Thus, water and materials passing into or out of the root pass through the cytoplasm of the endodermal cells.

Just inside the endodermis is a zone of cells called the **pericycle**, which surrounds the xylem and phloem in the stele. These cells are sometimes difficult to distinguish. However, the pericycle is easy to locate on a cross section showing the origin of a **lateral root**. The lateral root extends from the pericycle through the endodermis, cortex, and epidermis. Find a cross section with a lateral root emerging from the pericycle and sketch it in the space below.

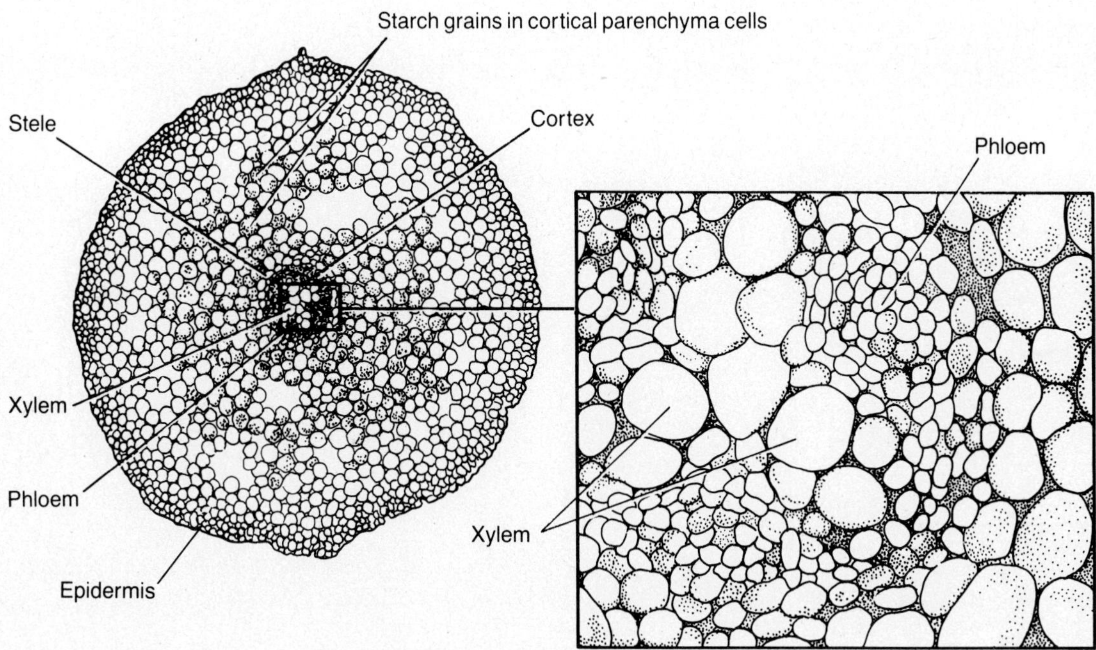

Figure 23-9 Dicot root (cross section).

The dicot root (Fig. 23-9), like the monocot root, has a starch-containing cortex and a central stele. However, xylem and phloem tissues are arranged differently in the dicot stele than in the monocot stele. In dicot roots, the xylem forms an "X" or star shape in cross section. Phloem tissue is arranged in bundles between the arms of the xylem tissue.

- Complete Chart 23-4 by describing the differences in anatomy, if any, between dicot and monocot roots.

Chart 23-4 Comparison of root anatomy in monocots and dicots.

Structure	Monocots	Dicots
Epidermis		
Cortex		
Stele		
Vascular tissues		
Xylem		
Phloem		

- Return to your drawing of the section from the root specimen, and label the structures and tissues that were discernible.

The material in this chapter corresponds to Chapter 28 in your text.

24
PLANT GROWTH AND REPRODUCTION

In this chapter you will observe a variety of macroscopic and microscopic structures that flowering plants employ in reproduction. Angiosperm reproduction was first introduced in Chapter 19, which outlined the structure of flowers and fruits and the differences between monocots and dicots. In this chapter's exercises, the hidden microscopic details of sexual reproduction are discussed, along with more common modes of vegetative (asexual) reproduction. You will also take a closer look at secondary growth of woody plants, the process that produces the tremendous girth of trees.

EXERCISE 24-1 VEGETATIVE REPRODUCTION

Objectives To observe structures of vegetative reproduction in flowering plants; to describe common vegetative reproductive structures of plants; and to describe possible conditions under which these vegetative reproductive structures might be advantageous for plants.

Vegetative reproduction is widespread in the plant kingdom. In fact, some plant species are entirely asexual—they propagate solely by vegetative means. This type of reproduction yields offspring that are genetically identical to the "parent." However, some genetic variation still occurs, because nonlethal somatic mutations (mutations in nonsex cells) are passed on when cells divide. Thus, a mutation in an axillary bud may result in a branch that differs from the rest of the tree on which it grows. The mutation may also produce differences in flowers on that branch and thereby affect the sexual process. But this kind of genetic variation is very different from the recombination of entire sets of genomes in sexual reproduction.

Vegetative reproduction in plants is possible because of the **totipotent** nature of meristematic cells in the growing regions of root and shoot tips. That is, each cell is capable of reproducing the entire plant. But the totipotent cells cannot accomplish this feat alone. Vegetative reproductive structures often include modified leaves, stems, and roots that store food, which maintains vegetative propagules and supports their germination.

Chart 24-1 lists the common types of vegetative structures found in plants. It also provides an illustration of each type as well as a description of the plant organ (stem, root, or leaf) that is modified to produce each type.

Chart 24-1 Common vegetative structures in plants.

Structure	Example	Lab specimens
Rhizome an underground stem with nodes.	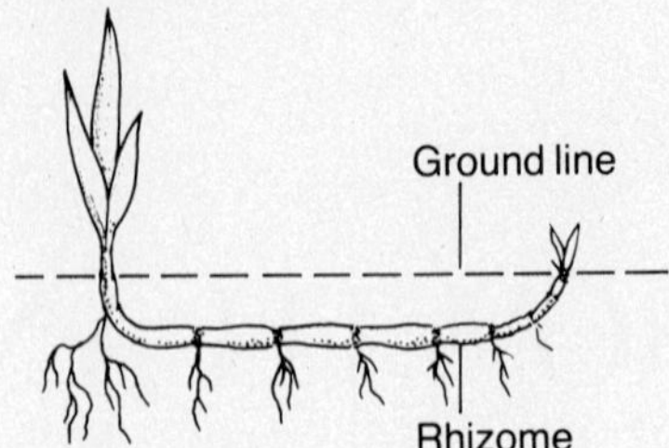	
Stolon or runner a branch of an aerial stem that touches the ground and takes root at the nodes or apex.	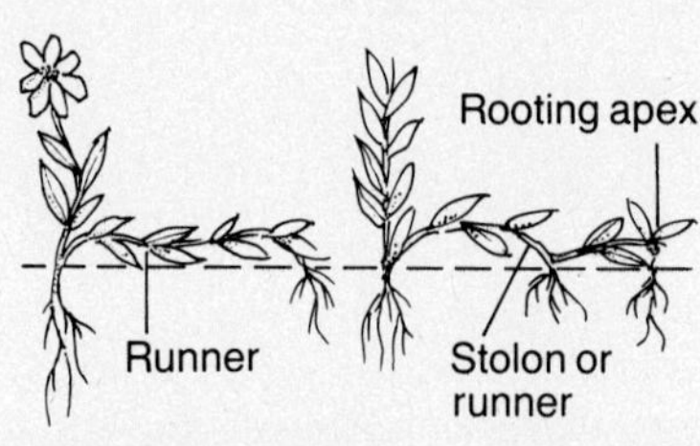	
Corm a solid underground stem with fleshy storage tissue.	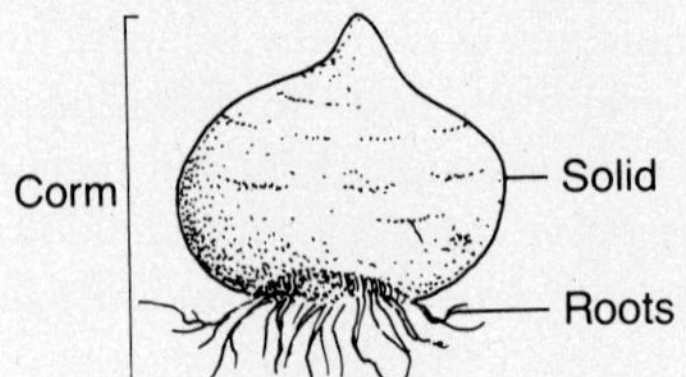	
Bulb an underground leaf bud with fleshy scales (storage leaves).	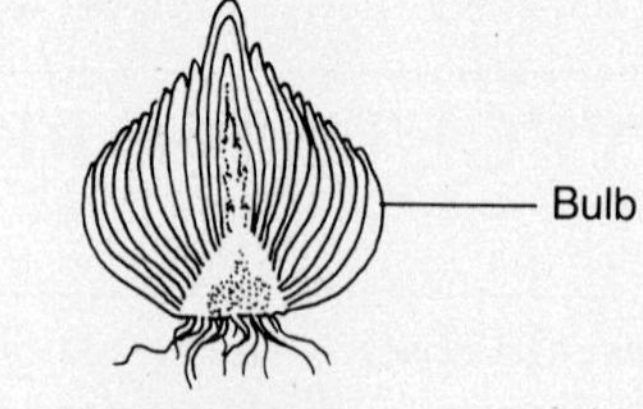	
Tuber a stem, usually underground, that has many buds ("eyes") and is thickened with storage tissue.	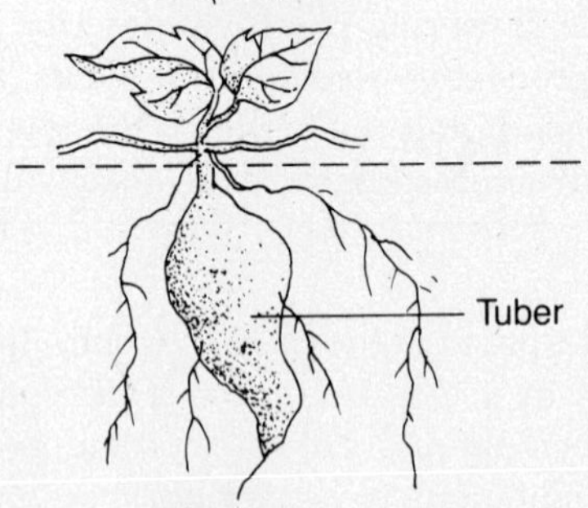	
Storage root a root thickened with storage tissue.	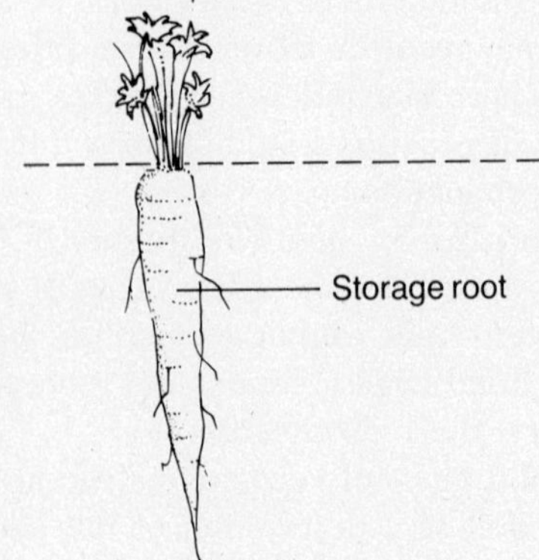	

- Your instructor will provide you with pieces or portions of plants representing each type of vegetative structure. Categorize each plant part according to the type of structure it represents. Then list the specimens in the appropriate boxes on the right hand side of the chart, and include a sketch of each one.
- Your textbook suggests that vegetative reproduction is an efficient means of propagating genetically identical offspring into nearby areas. Some of the structures in the foregoing chart contain large amounts of storage tissue, whereas others do not. Suggest a set of environmental conditions in which each type of structure would be advantageous.

rhizome:

stolon or runner:

corm:

bulb:

tuber:

storage root:

- Corn, one of the staples of agriculture in the United States, is an annual—it must be replanted each year. Scientists believe that the ancestor of corn was a perennial (resprouted each year from a perennial root system). What advantage might be gained if researchers were to breed a perennial variety of corn?

EXERCISE 24-2 SEXUAL REPRODUCTION

Objectives To observe the microscopic structures involved in pollen and egg production in angiosperms; to describe the events leading to the production of male and female gametophyte stages in angiosperms, and to describe the process of double fertilization, which is unique to angiosperms.

Although sexual reproduction in flowering plants appears superficially similar to the process in animals, the sex life of plants is markedly different from animals in many respects. Flowers were first mentioned in Chapter 19 of this manual, where you dissected specimens of several types. In this exercise you will observe cross sections of parts of the flower at various stages of egg and pollen production. Keep in mind that angiosperms have an alternation of generations (sporophyte and gametophyte generations) as do many algae and lower plants, such as ferns and mosses. In angiosperms, the gametophyte is reduced to just a few cells, which are completely contained inside the sporophyte (except while the male gametophyte, the pollen grain, is in transit to the stigma of the flower). The extreme reduction in size of the gametophyte in angiosperms is considered the end result of an evolutionary trend toward decreasing gametophyte size in vascular plants in general. Keep this trend in mind as you view the detailed structures of male and female gamete production.

A. Flower Anatomy

- Figure 24-1 reviews the anatomy of a typical flower. Imagine this flower at the unopened **bud** stage of its development. Your instructor will provide you with a microscope slide of a cross section of a bud; one is illustrated in Figure 24-2. Observe the slide under the compound

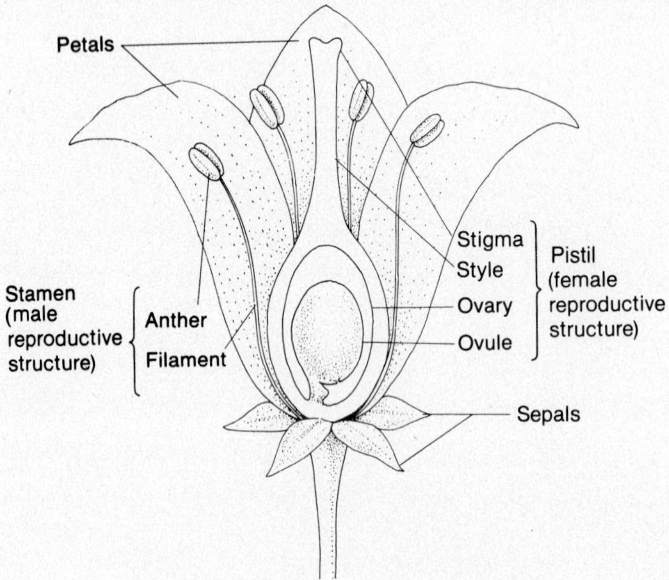

Figure 24-1 Anatomy of a typical flower.

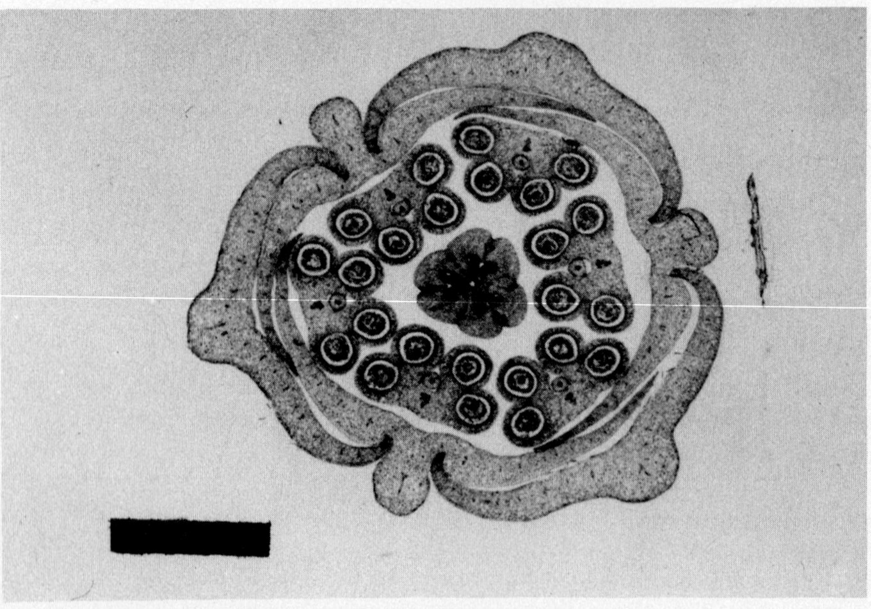

Figure 24-2 Cross section of flower bud showing immature ovary and stamens.

microscope and locate the structures labeled in Figure 24-2. The **ovary** and **stamens** contain the immature stages of egg and pollen, respectively. In many cases, the unopened bud is enclosed by the immature **sepals** and **petals**, which are collectively termed the **perianth**.

B. Pollen Development

- Observe the cross section of the flower bud once again (Fig. 24-2). Pollen grains develop through the process of **microsporogenesis** and **microgametogenesis**, shown in Figure 24-3. Inside the stamen are **microspore mother cells**, each of which will divide twice in meiosis (microsporogenesis) to produce a **tetrad** of haploid **microspores**. If cross sections of later stages

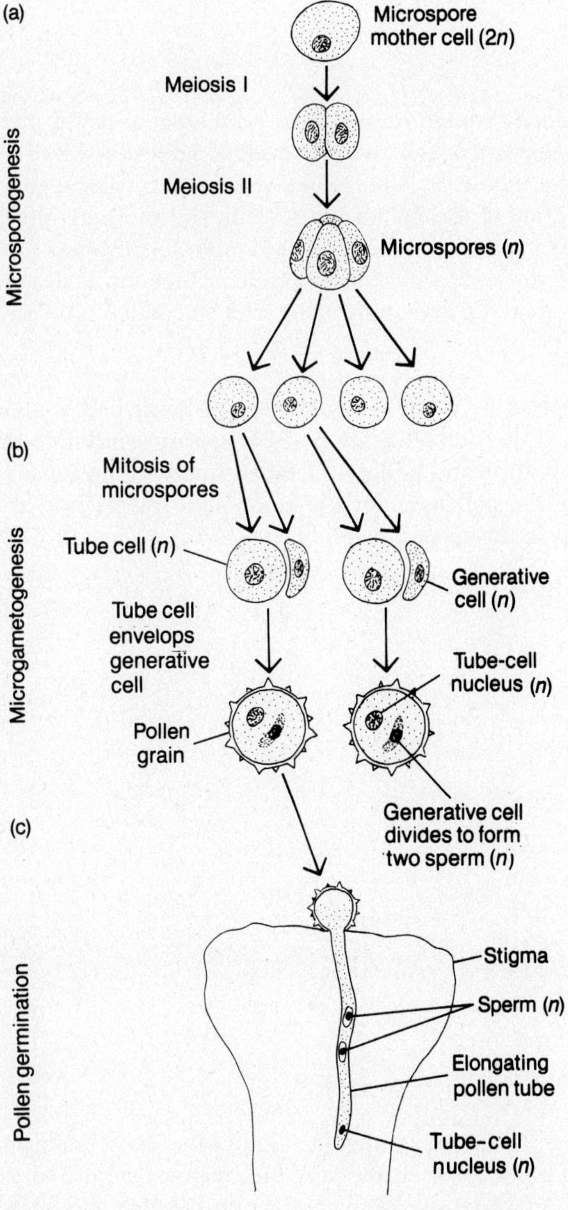

Figure 24-3 Pollen production and germination in a flowering plant.

of stamen development are available, observe them under the compound microscope and sketch a tetrad in the space provided.

A microspore divides once through mitosis (microgametogenesis) to produce a two-celled **pollen grain** (a **tube cell** and a **generative cell**), which develops a thickened wall (Fig. 24-3). The generative cell is actually inside the tube cell. After pollen reaches the stigma, the tube nucleus directs the germination and elongation of the **pollen tube**, while the generative cell divides to produce two **sperm** (Fig. 24-3). These sperm will function in double fertilization, to be described later. Your instructor may provide you with slides of longitudinal sections of ovaries containing germinated pollen grains. The germinated pollen grain along with the pollen tube constitutes the mature **male gametophyte**.

- If stamens from a plant are available, gently scrape some pollen grains from the stamen onto a clean microscope slide. Add a half drop of 1% sucrose solution to the slide and place a cover slip over the sucrose drop and pollen. (Distilled water would cause the pollen grains to swell or burst.) Observe the pollen under the compound microscope at high power and make a sketch of the grains in the space provided.

Pollen sketch. Plant species: ______________

- Your instructor may provide you with pollen grains that have been germinated on sucrose-agar plates. The pollen tubes grow on the agar in a manner similar to the way they grow on the stigma of a flower. Observe the plates under the stereoscopic microscope and sketch a germinated pollen grain in the space provided. Applying a drop of aceto carmine stain to the pollen tube stains the nuclei a dark purple. Stain several pollen tubes and observe them under the stereoscopic or compound microscope (place a cover slip over the agar surface for the latter), and indicate the location of the nuclei on your sketch.

C. Egg Production

Eggs are produced through a series of divisions analogous to the processes of pollen production. Inside the **ovule**, which in turn is inside the **ovary** (Fig. 24-1), a **megaspore mother cell** divides

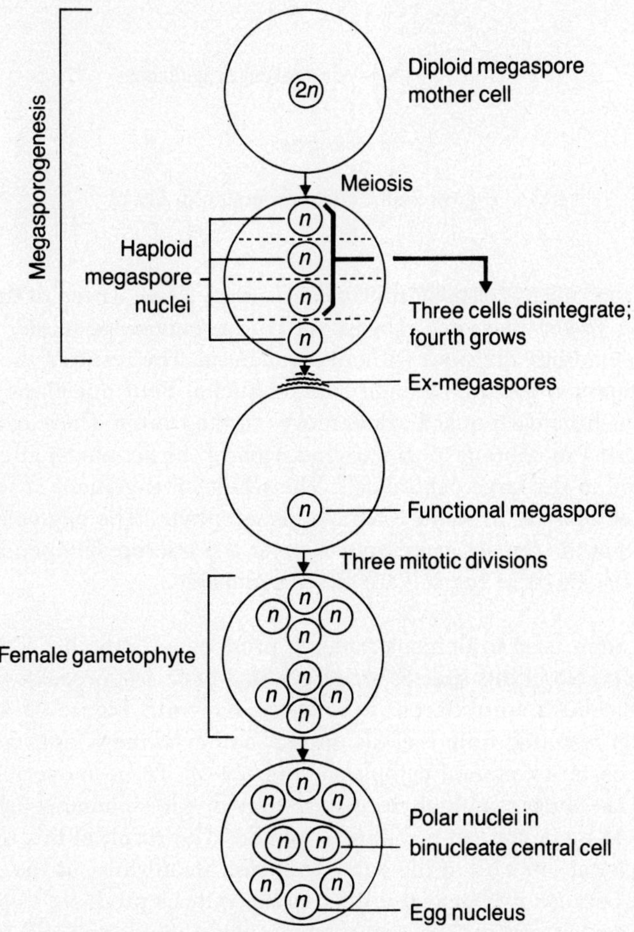

Figure 24-4 Egg production in a flowering plant.

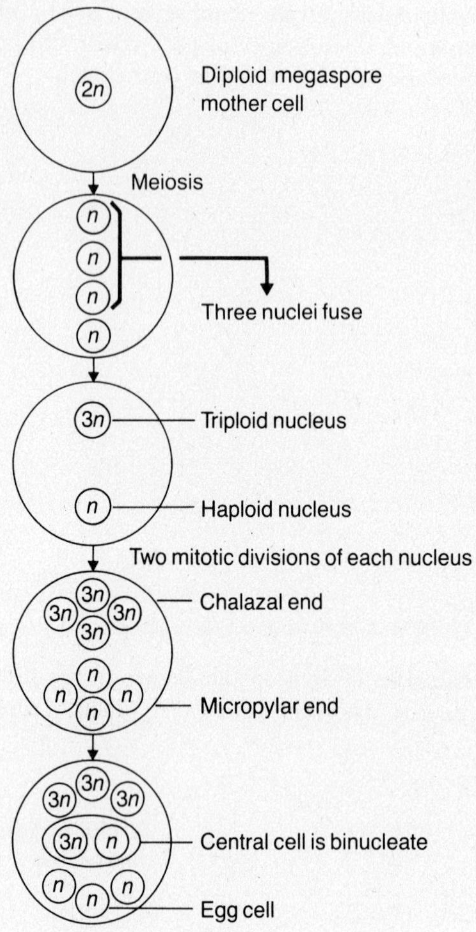

Figure 24-5 Egg production in lily.

twice meiotically in the process of **megasporogenesis** (Fig. 24-4). Three of the four resulting cells degenerate, leaving a single functional **megaspore**. In **megagametogenesis**, the functional megaspore undergoes three mitotic divisions without cytokinesis. The result of these divisions is a large cell (the **megagametophyte**) containing eight haploid nuclei. Four nuclei move to each end of the large cell; one nucleus from each quartet then moves to the center. These center nuclei are called the **polar nuclei**. Plasma membranes form around each of the six nuclei at either end. The polar nuclei remain unfused in the large central cell. The whole arrangement of seven cells constitutes the mature megagametophyte, or mature female gametophyte. The **egg cell** is the middle of the three cells at the end of the female gametophyte, near the **micropyle** (opening) in the ovule (Fig. 24-1). The two cells flanking the egg cell are called **synergids**.

- The plant most often used to demonstrate egg production is the lily (genus *Lilium*), because the relevant structures in this species are large. However, the processes of megasporogenesis and megagametogenesis are different from those shown in Figure 24-4. In the lily, all four megaspore nuclei resulting from meiosis persist, and cytokinesis does not occur. As a result, the four nuclei lie in a common cytoplasm (Fig. 24-5). Three move to one end (called the **chalazal end**) of the megagametophyte, where they divide simultaneously, and their chromosomes assemble at metaphase at a common spindle. The result of this unusual mitosis is two triploid ($3n$) nuclei at one end of the egg apparatus. Meanwhile, at the other end (called the **micropylar end** because it is near the micropyle), mitosis produces two haploid ($1n$) nuclei. Next, the cells at each end of the female gametophyte divide to yield four triploid nuclei at one end and four haploid nuclei at the other. A nucleus from each end moves to the center, and the pair form a binucleate central cell. Superficially, the mature female gametophyte appears similar to the one depicted in Figure 24-4. In the lily, however, one of the bipolar nuclei in the central cell is haploid while the other is triploid. The cells at the chalazal end are triploid, and the egg cell and synergids at the micropylar end are haploid.

- Your instructor will provide you with microscope slides of various stages of egg production in the lily. Complete Chart 24-2 by drawing a sketch of each stage listed, and indicate in your sketch the state of each nucleus. Also, refer to Figure 24-5, and label the structures noted in boldface in the chart.

Chart 24-2 Egg production in the lily.

Stage	Drawing
Megaspore mother cells prior to meiosis	
Four nuclei in common cytoplasm, produced by two meiotic divisions	
Mitosis of haploid nucleus at **micropylar end** and **common spindle** of three haploid nuclei at **chalazal end**	

Continued on p. 326.

Chart 24-2 (continued) Egg production in the lily.

Stage	Drawing
Four-nucleate stage, with pair of **haploid nuclei** at micropylar end and pair of **3*n* nuclei** at chalazal end	
Final division of nuclei, showing pair of **spindles** at each end	
Mature female gametophyte with three **haploid nuclei**, including the **egg**, at micropylar end, three **triploid nuclei** at chalazal end, and one binucleate **central nucleus** ($n + 3n$)	

D. Double Fertilization

- Observe the prepared microscope slide showing fertilization in the lily. The pollen tube enters the ovule through the micropyle and carries the two sperm nuclei into the female gametophyte. One nucleus unites with the egg and one unites with the polar nuclei. Compare the fertilization slide to the slides you observed of the female gametophyte alone, and identify the sperm nuclei. Draw the sperm nuclei on your illustration of the mature female gametophyte in 24-2, and indicate with arrows those nuclei with which the sperm cells fuse.

- The fusion of egg and one sperm nucleus produces a diploid ($2n$) zygote. The other sperm nucleus combines with the polar nuclei to form the **primary endosperm nucleus**, which divides many times to produce endosperm tissue. In the usual case of haploid nuclei, the endosperm is triploid ($3n$); in the lily the central nucleus is tetraploid ($4n$), so the endosperm is pentaploid ($5n$). What role will the endosperm play in the developing embryo?

E. Embryo Development

- After fertilization, the zygote undergoes a series of cell divisions to produce an embryo inside the seed (mature ovule). Embryonic development varies between species, but a weed called *Capsella bursa-pastoris* (whose common name is "shepherd's purse") is a typical dicot with a large, easily visible embryo. Your instructor will provide you with microscope slides of two stages of its embryo development. Make sketches of both stages in Chart 24-3 and label those structures written in boldface.

Chart 24-3 Embryo development in the weed *Capsella*.

Stage	Drawing
Early embryo showing **suspensor** (column of cells connecting **embryo** to **ovule wall**).	
Mature embryo showing **radicle** (embryonic root), **cotyledons** (pair of embryonic leaves), and **plumule** (apical meristem).	

- Your instructor will provide you with a corn grain (corn fruit). Working carefully, use a razor blade to cut the grain in half as shown in Figure 24-6a. The outer covering of the corn grain is the matured ovary wall (Fig. 24-6b). Most of the grain is endosperm. The embryo is a relatively small structure at one end of the grain. It consists of a radicle and plumule, which is covered by the **coleoptile**. Corn is a monocot and has one cotyledon or embryonic leaf (also called a scutellum).

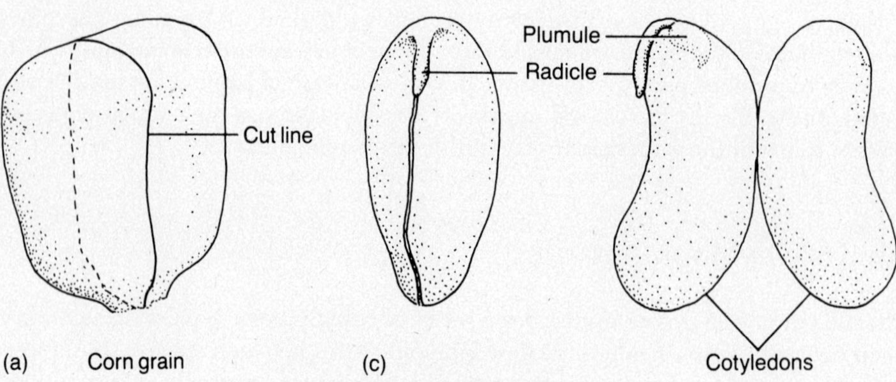

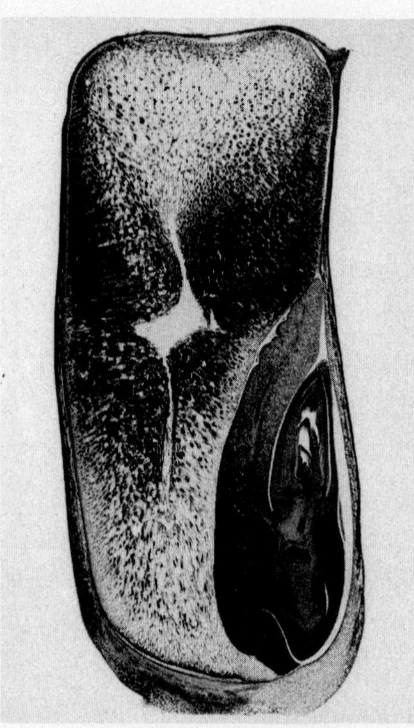

Figure 24-6 Embryos in corn grain (monocot) and bean seed (dicot). (a) Method of cutting grain. (b) Internal structures of corn grain. (c) Structures in the bean seed.

- If Lugol's solution (iodine) is available, place a drop on the cut surface of the corn grain. After a few seconds, wipe off the excess fluid with a paper towel and examine the cut surface of the grain under the stereoscopic microscope. What color is the endosperm? ______________ What does the color change tell you about the composition of the endosperm tissue? (Hint: see Chapter 4.)

What tissue do you suppose makes up the white tasty part of popcorn?

- Your instructor will provide you with a garden bean or other dicot seed. Split it open and locate the structures shown in Figure 24-6c. Notice that there is no endosperm in the bean seed. What has happened to it?

F. Seedlings

- Your instructor will provide you with young seedlings of corn and bean plants. These are illustrated in Figure 24-7 and discussed in your textbook. Find the structures on the monocot and dicot labeled in Figure 24-7. Complete Chart 24-4, which compares germination and

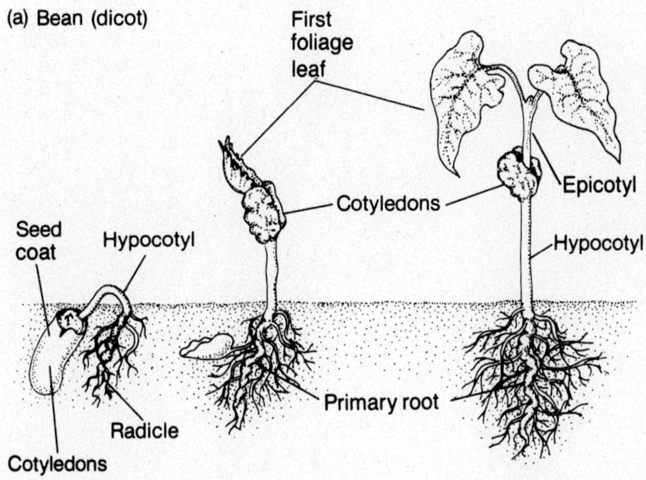

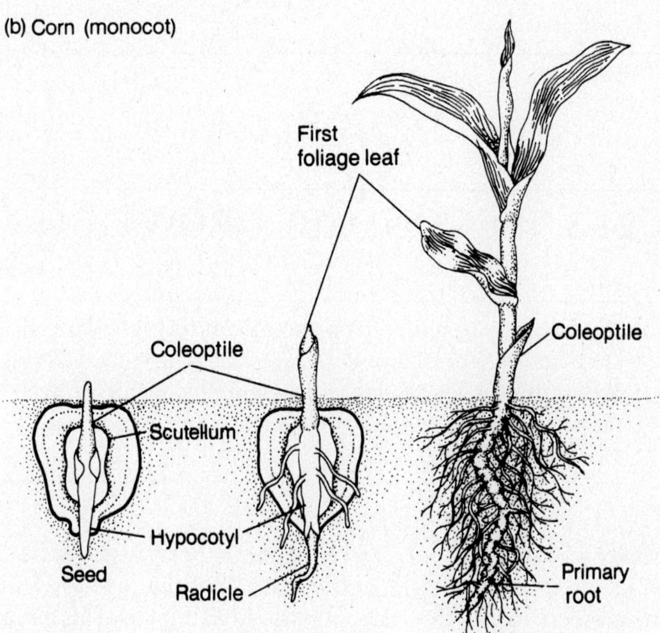

Figure 24-7 Young seedlings of corn (a) and bean (b).

seedling growth in corn (monocot) and bean (dicot). In the spaces on the right, describe the structure or process named and note any differences between monocots and dicots. If a structure is absent in either monocots or dicots, indicate this in the chart.

Chart 24-4 Comparison of germination and seedling growth in corn and bean plants.

	Description in	
Structure or process	Monocot (corn)	Dicot (bean)
Radicle		
Hypocotyl		
Epicotyl		
Cotyledon(s) or scutellum		
First foliage leaf		
Coleoptile		

EXERCISE 24-3 SECONDARY GROWTH OF STEMS

Objectives To understand the role of the vascular cambium and cork cambium in the secondary growth of stems; to describe how secondary xylem and phloem are derived, the structure of annual growth rings and bark, and the structure and origin of cork.

Some plants, especially woody types, increase in diameter as well as height during their lifetimes. The apical meristem adds cells and height to the plant, and the primary tissues are derived from this primary meristem (see Chapter 23). The increase in diameter of stems and branches is due to the process called **secondary growth**, so named because it follows primary growth and adds tissues to those structures derived from primary growth. Secondary growth is accomplished by the production of new cells and tissues by **secondary**, or **lateral**, meristems. These secondary meristems consist of two cylinders of growing tissue in the stem called the **vascular cambium** and the **cork cambium**. In this exercise, you will observe these two secondary meristems and their products.

A. Macroscopic Anatomy of Stem Sections

- Your instructor will provide you with sawed chunks of a woody stem. Even without a microscope you can see the arrangement of xylem and phloem and infer the position of the vascular and cork cambiums. Figure 24-8a shows a section from a typical woody stem. The vascular cambium is a continuous cylinder of cells on the border between the bark and wood. (The vascular cambium will probably not be visible in a wood chunk.) The vascular cambium gives rise to two tissues, xylem and phloem. Because they arise from the vascular cambium instead of from primary growth near the apex, they are called **secondary xylem** and **secondary phloem**.

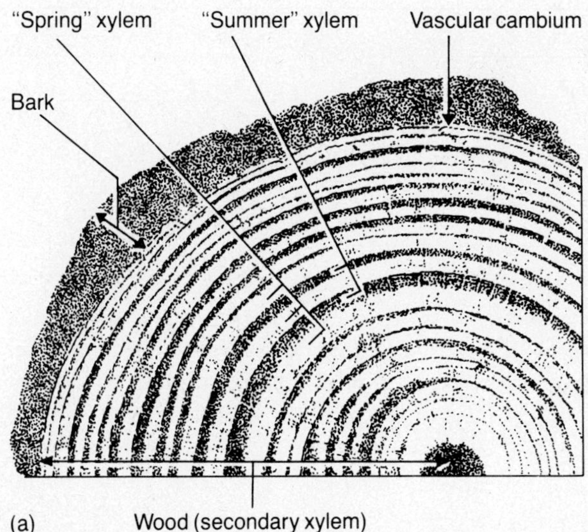

Figure 24-8 Macroscopic woody stem anatomy. (a) Section of a woody stem. (b) Section showing heartwood and sapwood.

Secondary xylem cells are located on the inner border of the vascular cambium (Fig. 24-8a). The **wood** of the stem consists of this secondary xylem. You are probably familiar with **tree rings**. Each ring consists of xylem cells laid down in spring and summer. The spring cells were laid down when water was more abundant; they appear lighter because they are larger and less dense. The outer portion of each ring consists of summer xylem cells, which were produced when less water was available; they are smaller and denser and appear dark. Vascular rays are thin strands of parenchyma cells in the wood that transport water and nutrients laterally in the stem.

- Observe the width of the tree rings in your specimen under the stereoscopic microscope. Use a ruler or stage micrometer to measure the width of the ten outermost rings. Record the data in the following Chart 24-5.

Chart 24-5 Tree ring data.

Width of 10 outermost rings (in mm—use significant digits rule).

_______ _______ _______ _______ _______ _______ _______ _______ _______ _______

Mean width = ____________ Minimum width = ____________ Maximum width = ________

What might account for the variation in width of the rings?

Suggest how measuring widths of tree rings in a several-thousand-year-old bristlecone pine tree might provide information about prehistoric weather conditions.

- Observe the dark and light colored regions of wood that may be present in the stem (Fig. 24-8b). These are larger regions than the rings of dark and light cells in the rings. The dark, inner region is older, nonfunctional secondary xylem called **heartwood**. The lighter, outer region is living, functioning secondary xylem called **sapwood** (with flowing sap).
- Observe the bark on the outer surface of the stem (Fig. 24-8a). The bark consists of all the tissue outside the vascular cambium, including secondary phloem and other tissues to be examined microscopically later.

Microscopic Anatomy of Secondary Growth

- Observe the microscope slides of thin sections through a young woody stem (Fig. 24-9). Near the periphery of the stem, find the vascular cambium, a single layer of cells that borders the secondary xylem on the inside and secondary phloem on the outside. When the vascular cambium differentiates from the procambium in the young stem, it lies between the primary xylem and primary phloem. Later, as layers of secondary xylem and secondary phloem are produced by the cambium, the primary xylem and phloem grow farther apart and are compressed into thin layers of cells (Fig. 24-9). **Phloem rays** are present in the phloem; they transport photosynthetic products vertically in the stem.

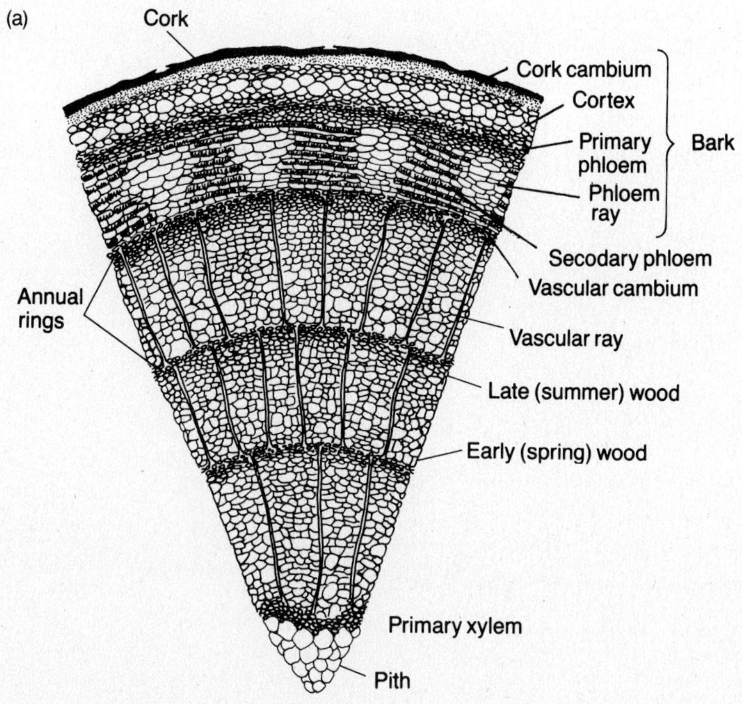

Figure 24-9 Microscopic woody stem anatomy.

Outside the vascular cambium, the bark contains a number of tissues in addition to primary and secondary phloem. Outside the phloem is a layer of parenchyma cells called the **cortex**. Outside the cortex is another single layer of cells that makes up the secondary meristem called **cork cambium**. The cork cambium produces cells on its outer margin that make up the **cork**, a water-impermeable layer of dead cells containing suberin. As the diameter of the stem grows, the cork splits apart at areas called **lenticels**. These splits function in gas exchange between the inner layers of cells and the environment. Lenticels are analogous to what structures in leaves and young stems? ______________

- Scientists who study tree rings bore into a tree trunk with a hollow metal cylinder a little wider than a soda straw and remove a long, thin cylinder of wood for study. Explain why this procedure would cause little, if any, harm to a tree, whereas cutting only a few centimeters into the tree *all the way around the trunk* would kill the plant.

- Most monocots have no secondary growth, although some monocots such as palm trees have a woody internal stem structure. Explain why even woody monocots lack the rings found in many dicot trees and gymnosperms.

The material in this chapter corresponds to Chapters 29–30 in your text.

25 WATER MOVEMENT AND HORMONES IN PLANTS

Chapters 23 and 24 considered the vegetative and reproductive structures of plants. You observed prepared microscope slides and specimens of plants, in which given features were "frozen" in place to make them readily observable. In this chapter, you will carry out exercises that familiarize you with some of the important and easily observed functions of the various plant parts. Specifically, you will perform experiments that demonstrate the movement of water in plants and the effects of certain hormones and a special pigment on plant growth and seed germination.

EXERCISE 25-1 WATER MOVEMENT

Objectives To demonstrate the principles of water movement by observing guttation, capillary action, and transpiration; to describe the events observed in the context of the underlying theories of root-pressure, capillary-action, and transpiration-pull.

Anyone who has ever nurtured a house plant or outdoor garden realizes the importance of soil water in maintaining the plant's health. Water enters the roots, and conducting tissues carry it to the upper portions of the plant. This movement of fluid involves several processes: *guttation, capillary action*, and *transpiration*. The first two processes are effective in small plants; the third (transpiration) accounts for most of the water movement in large plants such as trees.

Guttation

One force that moves water upward in a plant is root pressure. Roots actively take up mineral ions, which increase the concentration of solutes within the xylem of the root. According to the root-pressure theory, the increase in solute concentration causes water to diffuse into the root by osmosis through the endodermis and into the root xylem. Because the solute concentration is actively maintained in the xylem, water is continually forced into the cells and pushes the water already present inside the cells in the only direction possible: up. Eventually, water is exuded from leaves and forms small droplets at tiny openings called **hydathodes** (which are distinct from stomata). This process is called **guttation**.

- Observe the plants under the bell jar set up by your instructor. Where have the droplets formed on the leaves? ______________
- Sketch a leaf to show the location of the droplets.

Guttation occurs during periods when the rate of water absorption of the roots exceeds transpiration and water use by the plant. The morning dew on grass is due in part to guttation caused by root pressure.

- Suggest one or more reasons why this dew accumulates in the early morning rather than some other time of the day.

- Observe a well-watered plant that has not been kept under a bell jar. Speculate on why the droplets are absent from the leaves.

Capillary Action

Guttation can account for some but not all of the water movement in small plants. Another force involved is **capillary action**, the tendency of water to move upward in a small, thin tube. In plants, capillary action causes water to move upward in the elongated, thin cells of the xylem. Capillary action occurs because of the *cohesion* of water molecules to each other and the *adhesion* of water to the sides of the tubes. One can mimic the capillary action of xylem cells with thin glass capillary pipettes. (You may remember that you used capillary pipettes in the chromatography experiments of Chapter 9.) Your instructor will provide you with surgical pipettes similar to the one shown in Figure 25-1. Pipettes of various diameters can be made by heating up a portion of a pipette and pulling gently at both ends.

- Grasp the wide end of the pipette between two fingers and hold the other end with forceps. Hold a portion of the pipette over a Bunsen burner's pilot light (or low flame) for several seconds until you can just barely feel the glass begin to soften. Then, in one smooth movement, move the pipette out of the flame and pull gently at both ends. The heated, softened glass will stretch into a thin tube. The longer you draw out the tube, the thinner its diameter will become.

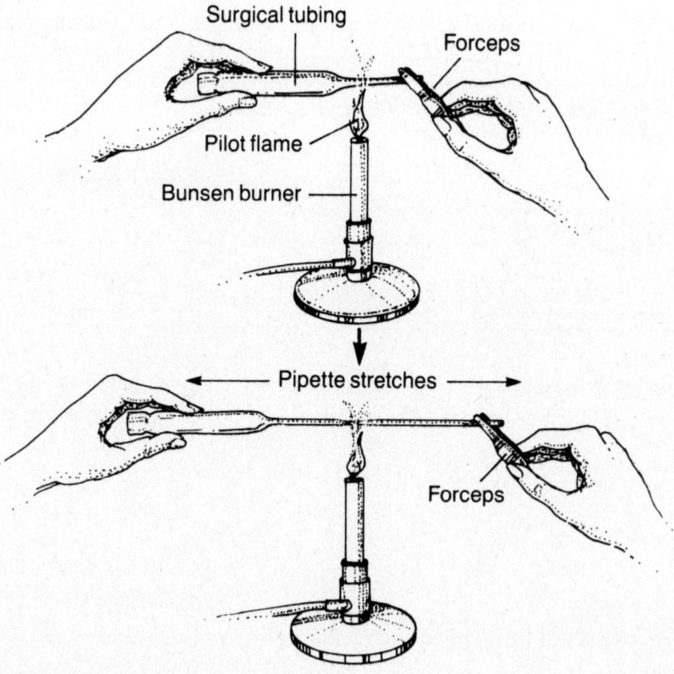

Figure 25-1 Technique for making pipettes of different diameters.

After stretching the heated tube, allow it to cool for 10 to 15 seconds. Use a small file to nick each end of a thin, relatively uniform portion of the tube. Wrap the tube loosely in a paper towel, and hold it over a designated waste container. Carefully break the tube at each nick by breaking it away from your body. The resulting tube should be at least three centimeters long and have a smooth opening at both ends. Discard the glass pieces in a safe designated container. Make three pipettes of distinctly different diameters. The narrowest should be slightly wider than the capillary tubes, and the widest should be no larger than three millimeters in diameter. Arrange the three tubes plus a capillary pipette in order of increasing diameter, and number them 1 (narrowest) to 4 (widest). Place a ruler or stage micrometer on the stage of a stereoscopic microscope and estimate the inner diameter of each tube (use the significant digits rule). Record the inner diameters in Chart 25-1.

- Dip one end of pipette #1 (capillary pipette) about 1–2 mm into the beaker of colored water provided by your instructor. What happens to the water? How far (in mm) does the fluid move into the pipette? Record the measurement in Chart 25-1.

- Pull the pipette out of the water. Does the level of fluid in the pipette change?

- Put the pipette back in the water. Does the water level remain the same?

- Repeat the procedure with the other two pipettes. Record your measurements in Chart 25-1.

Chart 25-1 Capillary action in pipettes of different diameters.

Pipette #	1	2	3	4
Estimated inner diameter	________	________	________	________
Distance moved by water (mm)	________	________	________	________

- Explain the difference in water movement in the pipettes in terms of the principles of cohesion of water molecules to each other and the adhesion of water to the glass sides of the tubes.

- Explain how this experiment suggests why the xylem cells of even very large trees are very small in diameter.

Transpiration

Neither guttation nor capillary action can account for the tremendous distances water moves in the stems of large plants such as redwood and eucalyptus trees. In fact, exactly how such movement occurs in large plants is not known. One possibility for which there is considerable evidence is the **transpiration-pull** theory (or **cohesion-adhesion-tension** theory). Instead of water being pushed upward by root pressure or drawn upward by the relatively weak force of capillary action, the transpiration-pull theory postulates that water is *pulled* upward in a continuous column of fluid. The pulling force is generated by evaporation of water through the stomata of leaves (transpiration). The process is roughly analogous to drinking through a straw: Sucking fluid out the top of the straw pulls more fluid into the bottom opening. The upward pull of fluid against the downward tug of gravity can only occur as long as the column of fluid is intact—as you know if you have ever accidentally pulled the bottom of a straw out of a drink. The reason that a continuous column of water can be maintained in plant xylem vessels is that water molecules have a strong tendency to cohere or "stick together." If the hydrogen bonds responsible for the cohesion of water molecules were significantly weaker, the long columns of water in xylem vessels would break apart. (Or more accurately, very tall plants might never have evolved.)

- You will measure transpiration rate using a device called a **potometer**, shown in Figure 25-2. Setting up the potometer requires several steps. Work in pairs or small groups.

1. Fill a shallow, flat pan half full with water. Submerge a glass pipette (1-ml size) in the pan along with a short piece of rubber tubing. Make sure no air bubbles remain in either item. Insert the tapered end of the pipette into the rubber tubing.
2. Take an intact green plant (such as geranium) having two or three leaves, and hold the stem under the water. With the cut end submerged, slice the stem cleanly with a razor blade.
3. Without removing the stem from the water, insert the cut end of the stem into the free end of the rubber tubing.

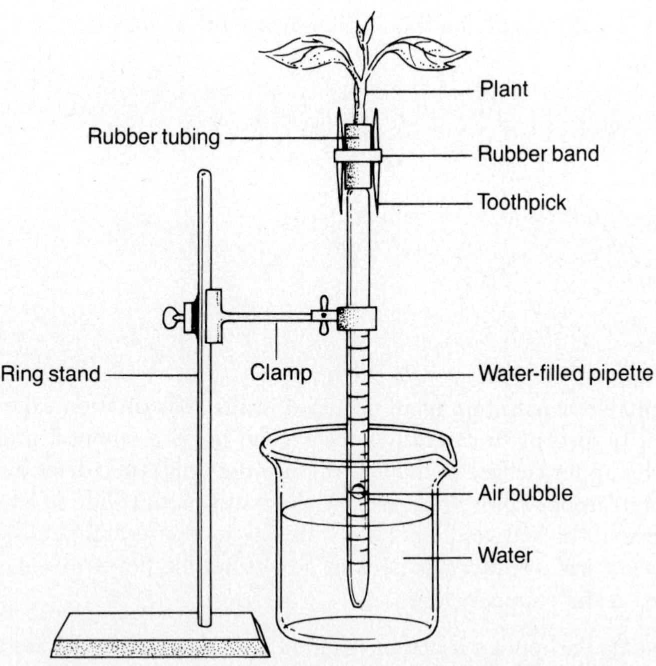

Figure 25-2 Potometer used to measure transpiration rate.

4. Place your finger over the free end of the pipette and pull the apparatus out of the water. Wiggle your finger until a small bubble enters the pipette. Now, submerge the free end of the pipette in a beaker of water and clamp the pipette in an upright position onto a ring stand. Reinforce the rubber tubing and plant stem with toothpicks or other rigid sticks held on the pipette with a rubber band. *Do not let the free pipette end emerge from the water.*

- Let the apparatus equilibrate for a few minutes, then record a starting time in the chart below. Keep track of bubble movement for 10 or 15 minutes or until it moves a little less than a third of the way along the pipette. In Chart 25-2, record the time interval and the distance the bubble moves (measured in fractions of a milliliter on the pipette—use the significant digits rule). The "distance" moved translates to the volume of water transpired by the plant.
- Next, before the bubble moves appreciably, rub petroleum jelly on the *upper* surface of the leaves, and measure transpiration over a time interval similar to that used earlier.
- Finally, rub petroleum jelly on the lower surface as well, and measure the transpiration rate again for an equal time period.
- Calculate the transpiration rate (ml/minute) for each of the three treatments and record the values in Chart 25-2.

Note: If the bubble moves too far toward the plant, you may have to take the tubing off the plant and reassemble the potometer with the bubble near the tip of the pipette.

Chart 25-2 Transpiration rate in a plant under several conditions.

Treatment	Distance moved by bubble (volume displaced, ml)	Time interval	Transpiration rate (ml/minute)
Normal plant	________	________	________
Jelly on upper leaf surface	________	________	________
Jelly on both leaf surfaces	________	________	________

What was the effect of putting jelly on the upper surface of the leaves?

What was the effect of putting jelly on both surfaces?

- Take a leaf from a demonstration plant not used in the transpiration experiment and break off a small piece. Use forceps to carefully peel a small portion (about 5 mm in diameter) of the epidermis on the upper surface of the leaf. Before the epidermis dries out, make a wet mount slide, and label it "upper epidermal peel." Make a wet mount slide of an epidermal peel from the lower surface of the leaf, and label the slide "lower epidermal peel." Count the number of stomata visible on each epidermal peel in two different fields of view at low power (10X objective). Record the counts below.

  Number of stomata on upper surface in two fields of view __________ __________

  Number of stomata on lower surface in two fields of view __________ __________

Do these counts suggest to you an explanation of the results of the potometer experiment? Explain.

- Your instructor may have on display an experiment to demonstrate whether water flow occurs through the xylem or phloem. The experiment consists of two jars, each containing a submerged stem (Fig. 25-3). Both stems have been cut and the bark has been removed. Petroleum jelly has been applied as a water-tight seal to different portions of the stems. In one jar, the petroleum jelly has been applied to cover the tip of the cut stem. In the other jar, petroleum jelly has been applied to cover the cut surface of the bark. Recalling the tissue types that make up the bark and those that make up the central stem (Chapter 23), name the tissues that are sealed by the petroleum jelly covering in each of the two jars.

  Jar 1:

  Jar 2:

Initially, the two jars contained the same amount of water (marked by a line on jar). By the time you observe them, one will have lost more water through transpiration than the other. Which jar has lost more water? How do you interpret this result in terms of the flow of water through the tissues of the stem?

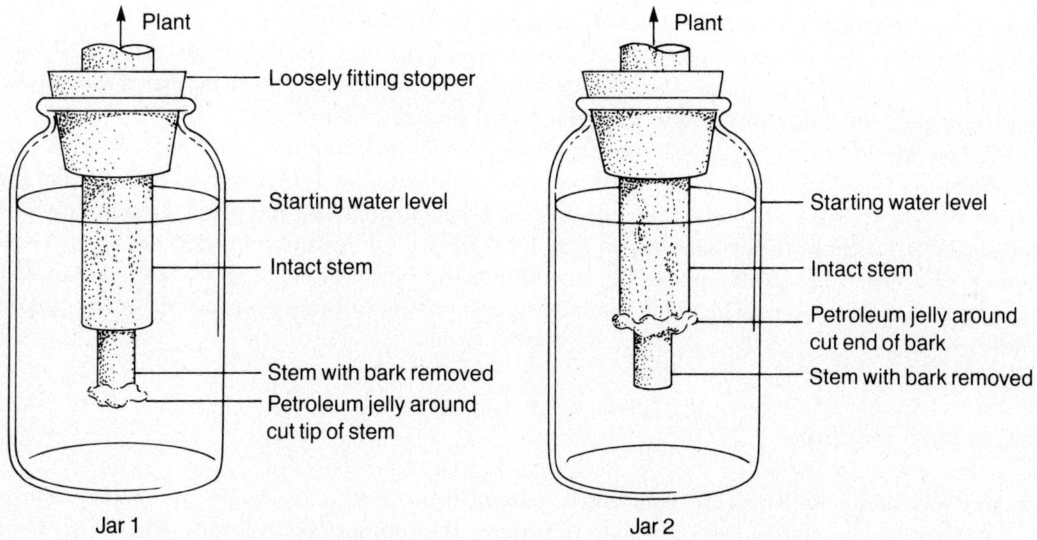

Figure 25-3 Experiment to determine flow of water through xylem or phloem.

- If time permits, your instructor may have you perform additional experiments on the effects of certain environmental factors. You should be able to design an experiment to test the effect of one of the following factors on transpiration: (1) temperature, (2) wind, (3) light and dark, or sun and shade.

EXERCISE 25-2 HORMONES

Objectives To observe the effect of selected hormones on plants and seeds; to describe the effect of auxins on root initiation and petiole abscission, the effect of gibberellins on stem elongation in dwarf plants, and the reversible effect of red and far-red light on lettuce germination.

Plants exhibit many responses to their environment, from the simple (stems grow up, roots grow down) to the complex (flowering). Many of these responses are controlled by **hormones**. Hormones are substances produced in small quantities by one part of the plant that are transported to and produce a response in another part of the plant. By definition, hormones are substances manufactured by the plant that (1) are extractable from plant tissue, (2) work in very low concentrations, and (3) have the same biological effect on all members of a plant species. Scientists have extracted many types of hormones from plants and have synthesized some of them. You will observe the effects of certain hormones on some important plant responses.

A. Auxins

Auxins are plant hormones that affect a variety of responses involving cell elongation and plant movements, from **phototropism** (bending of stems toward light) to **gravitropism** (bending of roots toward the direction of pull of gravity) to **apical dominance** (suppression of growth of side branches).

These effects result from an expansion of particular cells that are affected by the auxin. Auxin's effect is indirect: The hormone promotes the release of hydrogen ions from the cell, which lowers cellular pH and thereby increases the activity of enzymes that loosen the structure of the cell wall. Once loosened, the cell wall expands due to internal turgor pressure.

In these experiments you will observe the effect of auxin on bending of seedlings, root initiation, and abscission of petioles. The auxin used will be indoleacetic acid (IAA) mixed with lanolin. This mixture makes a paste that can be applied directly to specific parts of the plant. Depending on the time available for these experiments, you may work in pairs or groups. You may set up the experiment in the initial laboratory period and complete the observations a week later. Some of the treated plants or controls may be made available as demonstrations that your instructor has prepared in advance.

Bending of Seedlings

- Your instructor will provide you with a pair of bean seedlings. Apply the auxin paste to a seedling on one side of the internode just above the topmost set of leaves (Fig. 25-4). On the other seedling, apply auxin to one side of the internode just below the lowermost set of leaves. Label each seedling with tape on the pot. Your instructor will provide you with two kinds of controls. Based on your understanding of the scientific method, describe how these controls should be treated. Check with your instructor to see if your descriptions are correct, and perform the appropriate treatments.

  Control 1:

  Control 2:

  After one week, describe in Chart 25-3 the appearance of the treated seedlings and the controls.

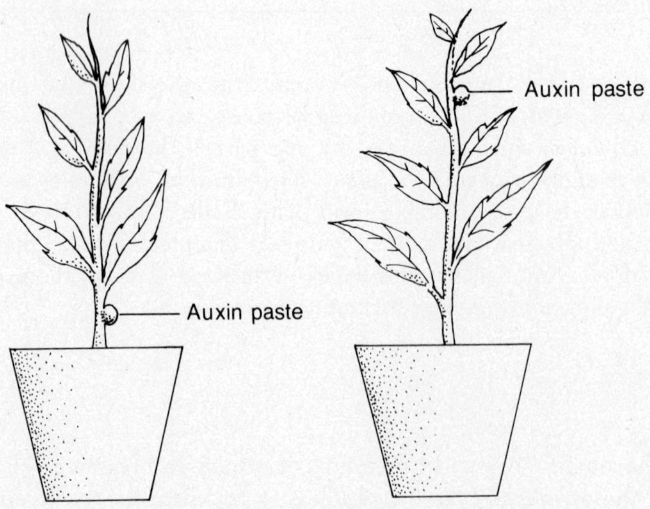

Figure 25-4 Sites of application of auxin paste.

Chart 25-3 Auxin effect on bending of seedlings.

Treatment	Appearance after one week
Auxin near top	
Auxin near base	
Control 1	
Control 2	

What was the general effect of auxin on the bean seedling stems?

Explain this effect in terms of the differential elongation of certain cells on the plant.

What effect did location of application of auxin have on the response of the seedling?

Root Initiation

At some time you may have established cuttings of plants by planting cut stem sections into soil. The stems form **adventitious roots** on the subterranean stem sections. This experiment uses this technique to demonstrate the effect of auxin on adventitious root development in cuttings.

- Your instructor will provide you with individual seedlings in pots or a tray of seedlings that the class will share. Cut off two seedlings just above the soil level and sterilize the cut ends in a

5% Clorox solution for two minutes. While sterilizing the cuttings, prepare tags for the plants. One tag should read "treated," followed by your initials or some other identifying code. The other tag should read "control" and have the same code. After sterilization, coat the bottom 2–3 cm of one cut stem (treated) with auxin paste. Coat the bottom of the other stem (control) with paste lacking the auxin. Now, place the treated and control stems in separate trays of soil or potting material. The entire class will use these two trays, so be sure that all the plants treated with auxin are placed in one tray and all the controls are in another. After one week, uproot the seedlings and compare the root development on the treated and control stems. Devise a means of quantifying the difference in root development between the two. For example, count root numbers and/or length. Your instructor may have the class discuss the method to be used and choose one by consensus. In Chart 25-4, indicate the quantitative difference in root development between treated and control plants.

Chart 25-4 Auxin effects on root development.

	Description of root development	Quantification method and measurements
Treated		
Control		

What effect did auxin have on adventitious root development in the seedlings?

The development of roots from stem cells demonstrates what general quality of plant cells?

Leaf Abscission

This experiment demonstrates the inhibitory effect of auxin on the process of **leaf abscission**, the normal separation of the leaf petiole from the stem. In some plants, when auxin levels decline in the leaf blade, a special zone of cells called the **abscission layer** forms at the junction of the petiole and stem. In this experiment you will artificially control auxin levels in petioles of leaves whose blades have been removed.

- You will use three bean seedlings. On one seedling, cut the blade from a leaf, leaving as much of the petiole intact as possible. Rub auxin paste on the cut end. The other two seedlings will serve as controls. Describe how the two controls should be treated to control for the two factors of auxin paste application and deblading.

Control 1:

Control 2:

- Check with your instructor to see if your descriptions of the controls are correct.
- Observe the seedlings after one week. Record your observations in Chart 25-5.

Chart 25-5 Effect of auxin on leaf abscission.

Seedling	Appearance
Treated	
Control 1	
Control 2	

Describe the effect of auxin on leaf abscission.

Why didn't you simply apply auxin paste to the intact blade as one treatment? Would this be a worthwhile experiment?

In some plants, the presence of the hormone abscissic acid or ethylene gas (produced by ripening fruit) induces leaf abscission. Describe an experiment to test the effect of abscissic acid or ethylene gas on leaf abscission in bean seedlings.

B. Gibberellins

Gibberellins are plant growth promoters. Over 70 different types of gibberellins are known. In this experiment you will observe the effect of a gibberellin on stem elongation in dwarf and tall varieties of pea plants. The gibberellin you will use is gibberellic acid, the most common type. Because of the number of plants used in the experiments, you will work in groups.

- Your instructor will provide you with two dwarf pea seedlings and two tall pea seedlings. Attach a tag bearing your group's initials or some other identifying code to each of the four plants. Count the number of internodes on the stem of each seedling. Assign a number to each internode (number 1 at the bottom) and measure their lengths. You may wish to tie a numbered tag around each internode. Record the data in Chart 25-6.

Chart 25-6 Effect of gibberellic acid on stem elongation in dwarf and tall pea seedlings.

Treated dwarf seedling

Internode #	Length (cm) at start	Length (cm) after one week	Length (cm) after two weeks

Control dwarf seedling

Internode #	Length (cm) at start	Length (cm) after one week	Length (cm) after two weeks

- Next, use a pipette to apply one milliliter of gibberellic acid solution to a leaf near the top of one dwarf seedling. The gibberellic acid is dissolved in an ethanol solution; apply one milliliter of the solution without gibberellic acid to a young leaf of the second dwarf seedling as a control. Mark the tags "treated" or "control" as appropriate. Apply gibberellic acid or ethanol solution to the two tall pea seedlings and mark them appropriately.
- After one week, repeat the internode counts and measurements on the seedlings. Record the data in Chart 25-6. Reapply the gibberellic acid or ethanol solutions to the plants.
- After one more week, repeat the internode counts and measurements (two weeks after initial measurements and treatments). Record the data in Chart 25-6.
- After the second week of measurements, graph your data on Figure 25-5. In each graph, draw a segmented vertical line to represent the plant. Draw each segment to scale to represent the length of the internodes on the plant. Mark each node with a dot between segments. Connect the dots for each node on the three vertical lines to graphically display changes in internode length.

Chart 25-6 (continued) Effect of gibberellic acid on stem elongation in dwarf and tall pea seedlings.

Treated tall seedling

Internode #	Length (cm) at start	Length (cm) after one week	Length (cm) after two weeks

Control tall seedling

Internode #	Length (cm) at start	Length (cm) after one week	Length (cm) after two weeks

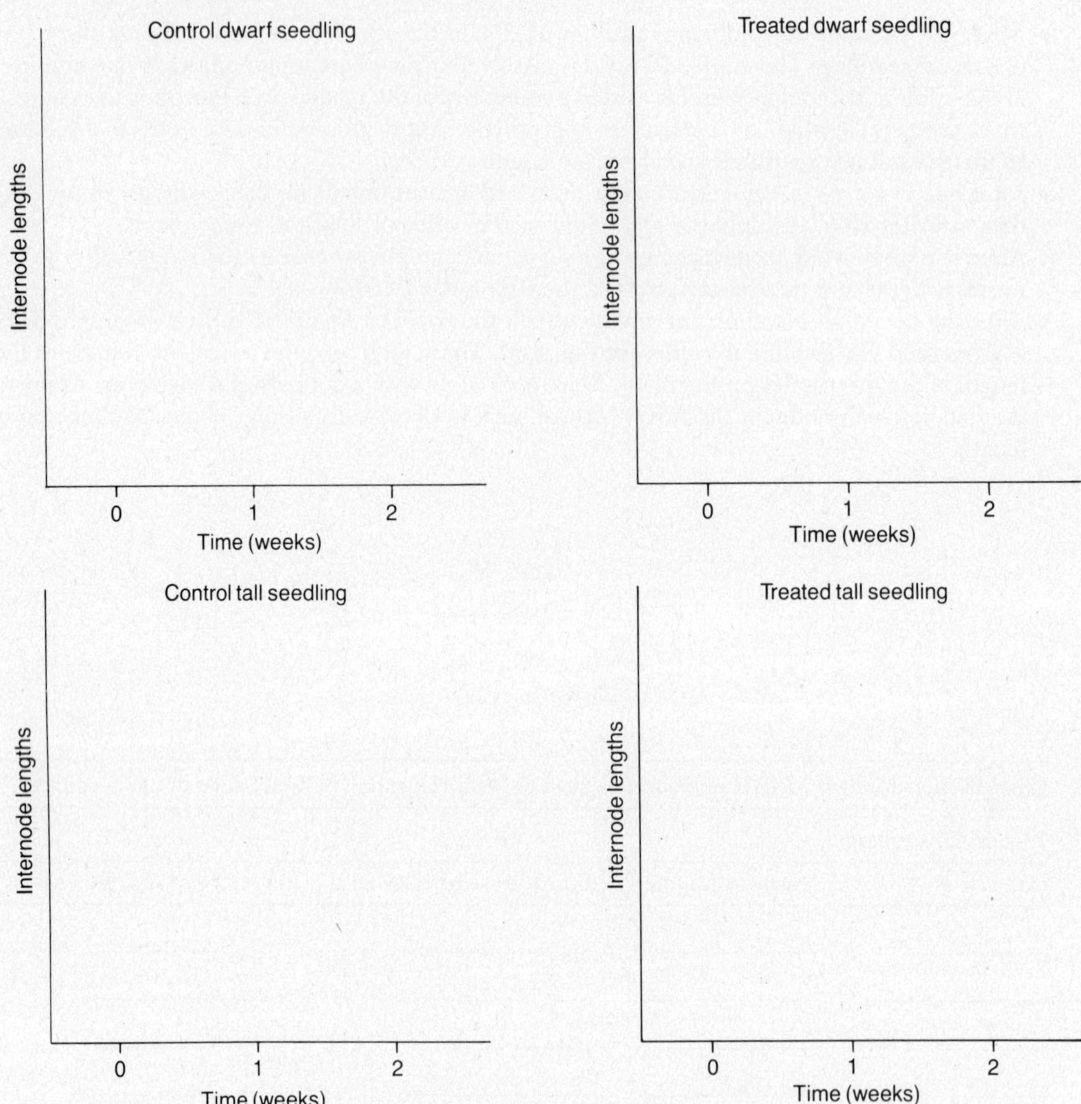

Figure 25-5 Gibberellic acid effects on stem elongation in dwarf and tall pea seedlings.

In one or two sentences, describe the effect of gibberellic acid on internode elongation in the dwarf pea seedlings.

Was the effect of the gibberellic acid the same for all internodes? Describe any differences in the effect on the internodes.

Was the effect of gibberellic acid the same during both weeks? Describe any change in effect over time.

In one or two sentences, describe the effect of gibberellic acid on internode elongation in the tall pea seedlings.

What do you infer about natural levels of gibberellic acid in the dwarf pea and tall pea seedlings?

EXERCISE 25-3 LIGHT EFFECTS ON FLOWERING AND SEED GERMINATION

Objectives To observe the effects of photoperiod on flowering of several types of plants and the effects of red and far-red illumination on the germination of lettuce seeds; to describe the role of the phytochrome pigment system in each experiment.

Many plants flower in response to environmental cues. Two such cues are the length of light or dark periods and the exposure to certain wavelengths of light. These two cues actually involve the same **phytochrome pigment system**. Phytochrome is a pigment consisting of a protein component and a light-absorbing pigment molecule.

Early in this century, scientists discovered that flowering plants could be categorized into three groups according to the effect of **photoperiod** on flowering. These groups are:

Short-day plants flower after growing under a light regime of short light periods (or more accurately, long dark periods, or nights).

Long-day plants flower when grown under conditions of long light periods (or short dark periods).

Day-neutral plants flower in response to cues other than length of light or dark period.

Photoperiodism involves the phytochrome pigment system. Phytochrome occurs in two conformations: phytochrome red (P_r) and phytochrome far-red (P_{fr}). These forms are interconvertible by exposure to different wavelengths of light. P_r absorbs red light (about 660 nm), and the light energy converts the pigment-protein complex into the P_{fr} form. P_{fr} absorbs far-red light (about 730 nm) and is converted back into P_r. During the day, sunlight converts most of the P_r to P_{fr} because sunlight is more energetic in the red part of the spectrum. P_{fr} is the active form of phytochrome in that it causes the production of a variety of enzymes that induce flowering. During the night, P_{fr} is gradually converted back to the P_r form. This dark conversion takes only about three hours in both short-day and long-day plants, a fact that indicates that phytochrome alone does not account for the difference in photoperiod between the two types of plants. Some other factor, such as an internal biological clock, is also hypothesized to be involved.

In the following experiments you will observe the effect of photoperiod on the flowering of several types of plants and the effect of red and far-red light on the germination response of lettuce seeds.

Photoperiod

Because this experiment involves growing plants under different light regimes for several weeks, your instructor will provide you with the end result: plants of various species that have been grown under short- and long-day conditions. These conditions are shown below.

8 hours 16 hours
Short-day conditions

16 hours 8 hours
Long-day conditions

Short-day light conditions are written as $8:\overline{16}$; long-day light conditions are written as $16:\overline{8}$.

- Complete Chart 25-7 and categorize the plants as short-day, long-day, or day-neutral.

Chart 25-7 Photoperiod and flowering in selected plants.

Plant species	Photoperiod ($8:\overline{16}$ or $16:\overline{8}$)	Flowers (present or absent)	Type of plant (short-day, long-day, or day-neutral)

Seed Germination

Some seeds must be exposed to specific environmental conditions before they germinate. Often the conditions can be ascribed to survival value: Certain seeds germinate only after exposure to freezing temperatures, cueing them to the passage of winter. In other seeds, the phytochrome pigment system plays a role. This experiment shows the effect of red and far-red illumination on lettuce seed germination and also demonstrates the interconversion of P_r and P_{fr} forms of phytochrome.

- Work in pairs or small groups, as instructed. You will need five petri dishes, each containing a filter paper disk that has been soaked in nutrient medium and sterilized. In each dish place 50 lettuce seeds that have been surface sterilized by soaking in 5% Clorox solution for 15 minutes. Spread the seeds evenly over the filter paper.
- Separately wrap two of the dishes in red cellophane. Separately wrap two of the remaining dishes first in a layer of red cellophane, then with a layer of blue cellophane on the outside. Apply a strip of masking tape across the folds of the cellophane on the *bottom* of each dish. Leave the remaining dish unwrapped as a control. Write the following numbers on the tape on each dish. Number the red dishes 1 and 2; number the two red/blue dishes 3 and 4; number the unwrapped control dish 5. The red cellophane acts as a filter to let in only red light; the red and blue cellophane layers let in only far-red light.
- Place the five dishes in a dark drawer or cupboard. Allow the seeds to sit overnight, during which time they will imbibe water and prepare for germination. (Your instructor may provide you with seeds that have already been sitting overnight in unwrapped petri dishes, which you will then wrap.)
- Take the dishes out of darkness and place them under fluorescent growth lights for five minutes. Place one red dish (1), one far-red dish (3), and the control dish (5) back in the dark. Remove the outer covering of blue cellophane from dish 4 and wrap it around dish 2. Expose these two dishes to an additional five minutes of fluorescent light, then place them back in the dark. The dishes have now been exposed to different regimes of red and far-red light as shown in Chart 25-8.
- After one week, remove the dishes from the dark and count the number of germinated seeds—you may want to sort the germinated and ungerminated seeds onto different sides of the dish first and then count them. Fill in the data in the chart, and calculate the percentage of seeds that germinated in each plate.

Chart 25-8 Effect of red and far-red illumination on germination of lettuce seeds.

Light treatment	Number of seeds germinated	Percent germinated
1. Red	______________	______________
2. Red, far-red	______________	______________
3. Far-red	______________	______________
4. Far-red, red	______________	______________
5. Control	______________	______________

- Describe the effect the illumination periods have on the P_r and P_{fr} forms of phytochrome in the seeds.

Dish 1:

Dish 2:

Dish 3:

Dish 4:

Dish 5:

Based on what you know of the conversion of the red and far-red forms of phytochrome, interpret the results in terms of the effect of phytochrome on seed germination.

What do the results of the control dish tell you in this experiment?

The material in this chapter corresponds to parts of Chapters 25–35 and Chapter 40 in your text.

26

VERTEBRATE ANATOMY

Although Chapter 22 considered the diversity of vertebrates, it did not give much detail on the anatomy of vertebrate animals. That was because the best way to learn vertebrate anatomy is through dissection of a representative organism, such as the fetal pig. Careful exploration of structures, coupled with reference to illustrations, provides an excellent opportunity to learn the spatial arrangement of an animal's working parts.

You will work in groups of two or three students to dissect a fetal pig during the course of several laboratory sessions. For this activity, the usual format of this manual will be modified. Instead of exercises, this chapter is divided into sections corresponding to organ systems or regions of the body to be dissected.

Objectives To identify the anatomical structures discussed and illustrated in the manual and, based on the comments here and in your textbook, to describe the functions of these structures.

In addition to developing your dissection skills, you will need to memorize a fair amount of material. Although the number of features you will observe may seem daunting at first, you will find that learning through dissection is easier and more effective than simply staring at diagrams. Therefore, make sure you take part in the dissection. After completing a portion of the procedure, review the material by pointing out the structures you have observed, and give your lab partners a mini-lecture on the dissected pig. By presenting your observations to your partners and discussing their presentations you will gain a thorough understanding of the fetal pig's anatomy.

Humans are vertebrates and share many of the anatomical features you will study in these exercises. Thus, certain structures will be discussed in terms of their location or function in humans as well as in pigs. In particular, muscles whose location and form are visible on the surface of the human skin will be mentioned. These muscles can usually be located on one's own body or on the body of a nonbashful volunteer.

Dissection Techniques

Your instructor will provide you with tips on handling and dissecting the pig—how to rinse it of excess preservative and store it in a plastic bag between laboratory periods. Few tools are required for dissection. You will need only a **scalpel**, **scissors**, 1–2 **dissecting needles**, and a **blunt probe**. In addition, keep in mind the following rules of thumb:

1. Be extremely careful in handling dissection tools, some of which are exceptionally sharp.
2. Always cut *away* from your fingers and body. Cut gently—never use so much force that a slip would damage the pig or your fingers.
3. Use the scalpel as little as possible and only on tissue that requires cutting. In fact, few tissues besides the skin and certain muscles require cutting. A blunt probe is usually sufficient to tease apart tissues as you follow nerves and blood vessels within muscles and organs.
4. Treat your fetal pig with respect. It is all too easy to make a mess of dissection, which simply makes learning difficult and upsets your laboratory partners.
5. You can protect your hands from irritation caused by the preservative (usually a mixture containing formalin) in the fetal pig's tissues by wearing surgical gloves or rubbing a lanolin-based lotion on your hands prior to working. The hand lotion will also help cut down on the pig's unappealing odor, which tends to linger with you after laboratory.

SECTION 1 EXTERNAL ANATOMY

After obtaining your fetal pig and rinsing it of excess preservative, place it in the dissection pan, and cover it with a moist paper towel. Whenever you pause in the dissection, keep the pig covered with the towel to prevent it from drying out. Between laboratory periods, store the pig in a plastic bag in a cupboard or drawer as directed by your instructor.

- Orient yourself to the anatomical planes and directions of the pig's torso by referring to Figure 26-1. The terms in this figure will be used throughout the chapter to describe the relative placement of various structures. The back is the **dorsal** surface, whereas the belly is the **ventral** surface. The head is at the **cranial** or **anterior** end; the tail is at the **caudal** or **posterior** end.

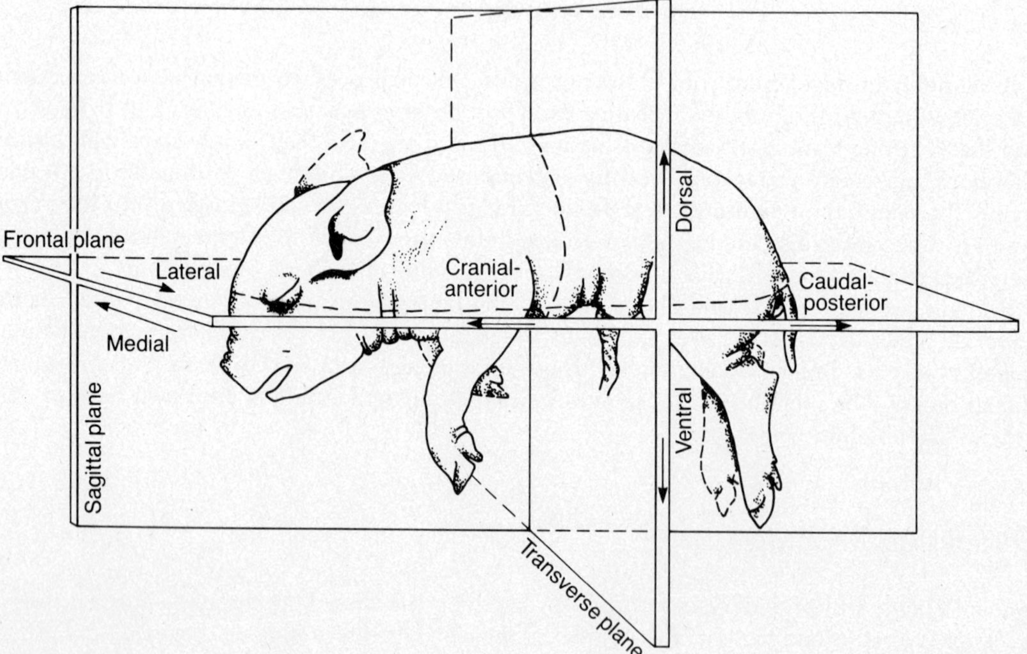

Figure 26-1 Anatomical directions and planes in the pig.

Nerve signals from the cerebrum pass through the thalamus to the cerebellum and motor nuclei in the medulla, where they play a role in equilibrium and motor responses.

- Your instructor may provide you with a sheep brain, which is large enough to identify some of the **cranial nerves**. These nerves are numbered with Roman numerals I to XII. Their names and functions are listed in Table 26-1. Notice that some of them contain sensory neurons, some contain motor neurons, and some contain both.* The cranial nerves are shown in Figure 26-22c, but be aware that some of the cranial nerves are difficult to see, even on a large brain.

SECTION 9 SENSE ORGANS

- Your instructor will have on display various models or specimens of the eye and ear. Examine these materials and be able to identify the structures shown in Figures 26-23 and 26-24.

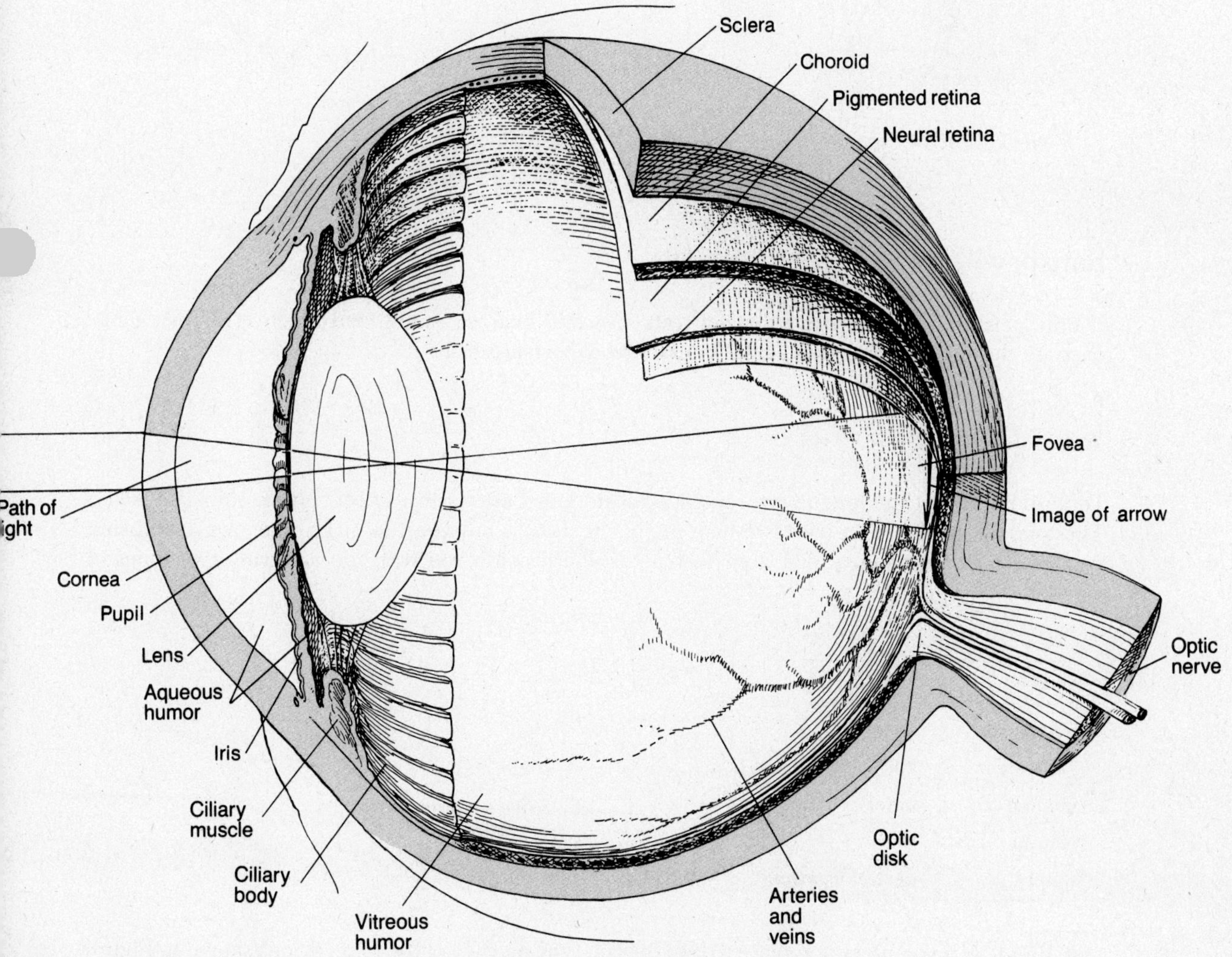

Figure 26-23 Anatomy of the eye.

*An aid to remembering the names of these nerves is the mnemonic device "**O**n **O**ld **O**lympus' **T**owering **T**ops, **A** **F**inn and **G**reek **V**iewed **S**ome **H**ops." The first letters of the words match the first letters of the nerves, I–XII.

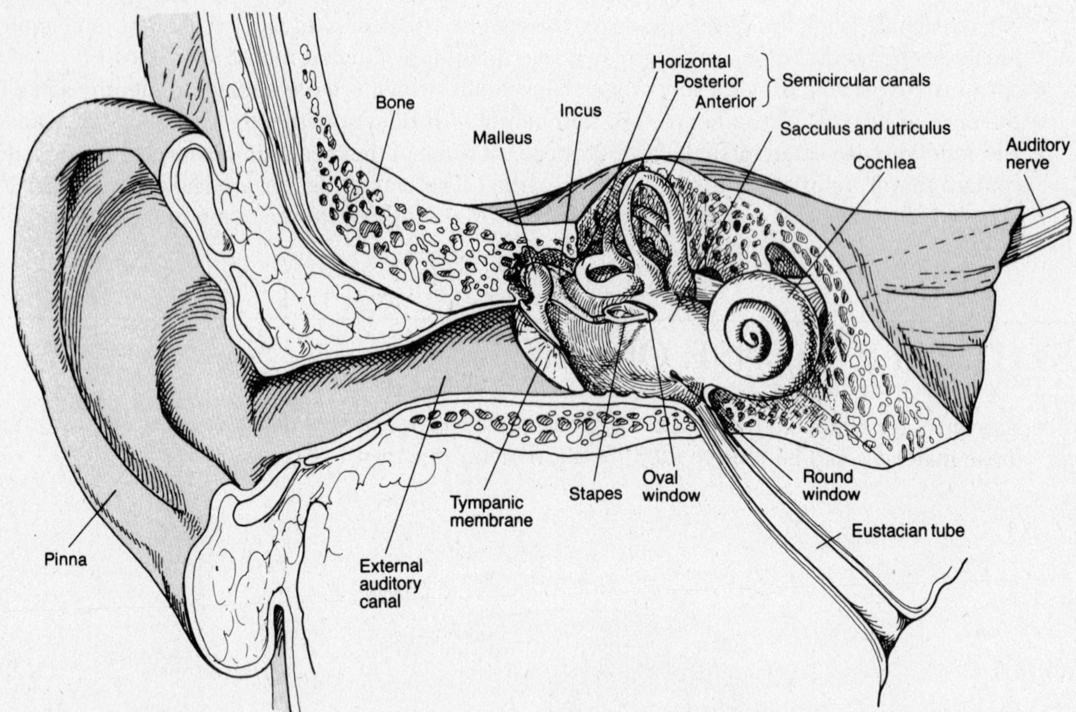

Figure 26-24 Anatomy of the ear.

Sensory Tests

If time permits, perform the following tests on taste, hearing, smell, and touch. The tests demonstrate the sensitivity as well as the limitations of certain senses.

Taste

Different areas on the tongue are sensitive to the four basic tastes: sweet, bitter, sour, and salty. These areas are shown in the taste map in your textbook, but you can make your own map using your classmates as guinea pigs. Your instructor will provide you with the following five types of solutions.

Solution	Taste
5% glucose	sweet
salt water	salt
quinine	bitter
vinegar	sour
water	neutral (control)

- Blindfold a volunteer and place a drop of each type on each of the four regions shown in Figure 26-25. Randomize the order in which you test the five solutions on the four areas. Volunteers should indicate whether they notice any taste for each drop, and if so, what type of taste. During each test the volunteer should keep the mouth open so that the drop is not spread to other parts of the tongue. Rinse the mouth with water between tests. Record your results in Chart 26-1. Mark a plus (+) if a taste is noted, and write the type of taste next to the mark.

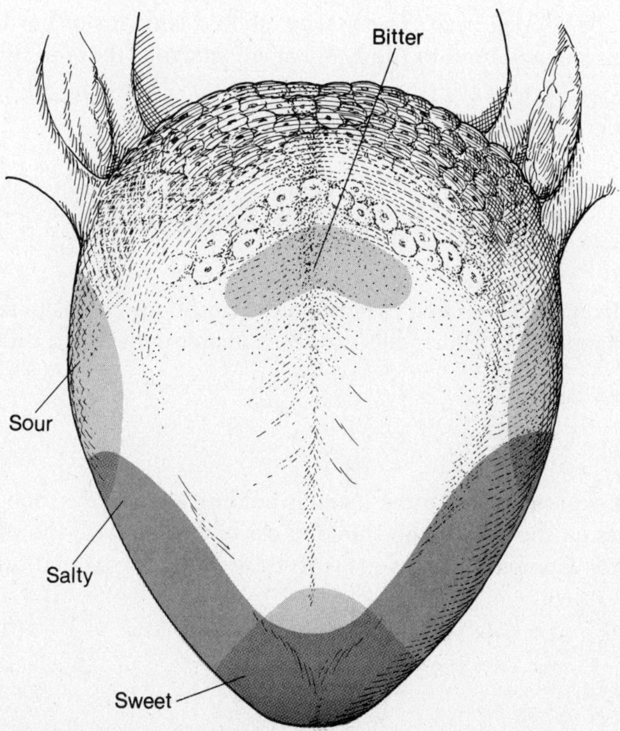

Figure 26-25 Taste areas of the human tongue.

Because individuals may vary in their taste sensitivities, if possible test the five solutions on more than one volunteer.

Chart 26-1 Mapping taste areas on the tongue.

Test solution	Area on tongue 1	2	3	4
Sweet	________	________	________	________
Salt	________	________	________	________
Bitter	________	________	________	________
Sour	________	________	________	________
Water (control)	________	________	________	________

- Use colors or different types of shading to map the sensitive regions of the tongue for each taste.

Hearing

The range of sound frequencies audible to the human ear is remarkable. Another aspect of hearing, however, is spatial location of sound.

- Blindfold one volunteer and have two others stand in various positions around the volunteer. The others should snap their fingers, and the blindfolded person should point to where the sounds appear to be coming from. The listener should keep his or her head on a level plane, even though he or she will tend to tilt it. What advantage is there in tilting the head?

- Have the snappers move closer and closer together until one passes in front of the other. How close must the snappers be before the listener is unable to detect a difference in direction of the snaps?

- Next, repeat the experiment with the listener holding a hand over one ear. Try the test once with the snappers on the side of the shielded ear and again with the snappers on the side of the unshielded ear. Compare the results with those of the two-eared test.

- Comment on the effectiveness of the ear(s) in spatial location of sounds.

Smell

Humans can smell some substances in very small amounts. However, in this test you will compare the ability of the olfactory sense to locate the source of odors. Because odors diffuse quickly in air, this test may have to be performed by only one group before the classroom is saturated with odor that will confuse the subject.

- Blindfold a volunteer and have four people stand at various positions around him or her. One of these people should open a container of ammonia or other strong-smelling solution. As a control, the others should open empty containers. Can the smeller in the middle detect the direction from which the odor is coming?
- Suggest why the source of a sound is so much easier to locate in space than the source of an odor. (Hint: Consider the different mechanisms by which sound and odors travel in air.)

Touch

The human sense of touch is very sensitive to small differences in pressure. Touch receptors are not evenly distributed over the body, however.

- Have a blindfolded volunteer expose the lower portion of the back. Take two pins and gently touch them to points on the skin several centimeters apart. Move them closer and closer until the subject reports that they feel like a single point. (From time to time, touch the subject with only one pin as a control.) Record the results in Chart 26-2.
- Now repeat the experiment on several skin areas elsewhere on the body, including the palm of the hand and the fingertips. Compare the minimum distance for which two points are distinguishable and comment on the concentration of touch receptors on the various parts of the body.

Chart 26-2 Two-touch discrimination.

Body area	Minimum distance for which two points are detectable
Lower back	______________
Palm of hand	______________
Fingertip	______________
Other areas:	______________
__________	______________
__________	______________
__________	______________

The material in this chapter corresponds to Chapters 41–42 in your text.

27 EVOLUTION AND POPULATION GENETICS

The theory of evolution is the cornerstone of biology. In an oft-quoted statement, Theodosius Dobzhansky, one of the foremost geneticists of the 20th century, said, "Nothing in biology makes sense except in the light of evolution." However, modern biologists recognize that there is no single theory of evolution (see the textbook for a discussion of the history of evolutionary ideas).

Population geneticists sometimes define evolution as a change in gene (or allele) frequencies in the **gene pool** of a population over time. **Equilibrium** is defined as the condition in which allele frequencies in a population remain relatively stable from one generation to the next. It is virtually impossible to demonstrate a change in gene frequencies in a real population of organisms during the course of a single laboratory period. However, one can use "bean-bag genetics" models (as in Chapter 11) to telescope time and the passage of generations to demonstrate some important principles of poplation genetics. In these exercises, you will use bean-bag models to simulate genetic equilibrium in the Hardy-Weinberg model, and to simulate the effects of nonrandom mating, genetic drift, and natural selection on gene frequencies.

EXERCISE 27-1 HARDY-WEINBERG EQUILIBRIUM

Objectives To demonstrate genetic equilibrium in a population of organisms as measured in the stability of gene frequencies; to describe the assumptions under which the Hardy-Weinberg law applies.

G. H. Hardy and W. Weinberg worked independently, but their names are forever joined in the biological literature for their discovery and statement of one of the most important principles of population genetics. The Hardy-Weinberg law states that gene frequencies and genotypes in a population of sexually reproducing organisms remain at approximately the same frequencies over time, *if and only if* the following assumptions are true:

1. **Random mating** Males and females pick their mates at random, and no other factors cause mates to be paired nonrandomly.

2. **Large population size** This assumption requires that when measuring gene and genotype frequencies, one is working with a large sample size, in which the laws of probability apply.
3. **No mutations** Alleles themselves do not change from one generation to the next by mutating to a new form.
4. **Isolated population** No new alleles are important from other populations.
5. **No natural selection** Alleles are not eliminated from the population by factors in the environment.

At first glance, these assumptions seem unrealistic because they remove from consideration most of the interesting evolutionary processes in nature. However, they collectively form a null hypothesis, one that is usually rejected when tested with data from the real world. But that is the function of this null hypothesis: When the Hardy-Weinberg law does not hold in a real population, one can infer that evolution has occurred and is occurring. Further studies may also be done to test which of the five assumptions have been violated and what factors cause changes in gene and genotype frequencies.

In this exercise, you will observe gene and genotype frequencies achieve equilibrium in a population in which the Hardy-Weinberg assumptions are true. The assumptions are easily met in a bean-bag model, where you can control mating, population size, and selection. For simplicity's sake, you will look at only a single pair of alleles.

- Work in pairs or small groups. Each group will be given 100 beans (or beads) of two different colors, referred to here as blue and red (other colors may be used). Each bean represents an allele (*b* and *r*), and an organism is represented by a pair of beans (pair of alleles). Place the beans in containers or small piles where they will not be lost. Three genotypes are possible: *bb, br,* and *rr.* The frequency of each *genotype* is represented by a number between 0 and 1. In a population, the frequencies of the three genotypes add up to 1. Frequencies of paired *alleles* are often represented by the symbols of p and q, where $p + q = 1$.
- Start with a population of 50 individuals. Because this is your own hypothetical population, decide upon three genotype frequencies, the only constraints being that they must add up to 1 and that they are represented by whole numbers in a population of 50 (for example, 0.5 for *bb*, 0.3 for *br*, and 0.2 for *rr*). Now, count out 50 pairs of beans that represent this set of genotypes. For the example suggested, this would mean:

  0.5 × 50 = 25 *bb* genotypes

  0.3 × 50 = 15 *br* genotypes

  0.2 × 50 = 10 *rr* genotypes

  Total = 50 genotypes

  The population consists of 100 alleles. Thus, the corresponding allele frequencies would be

  for *b*: (2 × 25 *bb* genotypes) + (1 × 15 *br* genotypes) = 65 *b* alleles, or 0.65

  for *r*: (2 × 10 *rr* genotypes) + (1 × 15 *br* genotypes) = 35 *r* alleles, or 0.35

  Record the initial numbers of genotypes and alleles in your "starting" population in Chart 27-1.
- Now mix the 100 beans (alleles) for this population of 50 in a single container or pile. This represents the gene pool. To simulate random mating, have a student in your group close his or her eyes and reach into the container and pull out two beans, one at a time. Hereafter, this process will be referred to as "randomly drawing" beans. This bean pair represents the genotype of one offspring of the next generation. Note the genotype of the pair on a piece of scratch paper, and replace the beans in the container. Draw 49 more pairs, replacing and mixing the beans after each draw. Keep a tally of the number of the three genotypes on scratch paper, and enter the numbers of genotypes and alleles for this "first" generation of 50 individuals in Chart 27-1.

- Repeat this procedure for two more generations.

Chart 27-1 Hardy-Weinberg equilibrium in gene and genotype frequencies.

Generation	Numbers of				
	Genotypes			Alleles	
	bb	*br*	*rr*	*b*	*r*
Starting	______	______	______	______	______
First	______	______	______	______	______
Second	______	______	______	______	______
Third	______	______	______	______	______

QUESTIONS

What happened to genotype frequencies in going from the starting population to the first generation?

Did allele (gene) frequencies change in successive generations?

How many generations did it take before the equilibrium genotype frequencies were reached?

Would the results have been different if the genotype frequencies were different in the starting generation? Why or why not? (Consult your classmates' data to compare starting generation frequencies.)

- The theoretical equilibrium frequencies of genotypes can be calculated based on allele frequencies. The probability of obtaining a particular genotype by randomly picking two alleles from a population is the product of the frequencies of the two alleles. For example, if the allele *b* is present with frequency p, the frequency of the *bb* genotype will be $p \times p$, or p^2. If allele *r* is present with frequency q, the equilibrium genotype frequencies in a population can be expressed as:

$$p^2 + 2pq + q^2 = 1$$

for genotypes *bb* *br* *rr*

(The product pq is multiplied by 2 because there are two ways to randomly choose this genotype from a population (pick b first, then r; or pick r first, then b; each event occurring with probability pq).

As an example, let the frequency of allele $b = 0.4$ and the frequency of allele $r = 0.6$. Then the probabilities of obtaining the three possible genotypes are:

$$\begin{aligned} \text{expected frequency of } bb &= (0.4 \times 0.4) = 0.16 \\ \text{expected frequency of } rr &= (0.6 \times 0.6) = 0.36 \\ \text{expected frequency of } br &= 2(0.6 \times 0.4) = \underline{0.48} \\ \text{Total} &= 1.00 \end{aligned}$$

- Use the allele frequencies in your starting population to calculate the equilibrium genotype frequencies. Multiply each equilibrium genotype frequency by 50 to get the theoretical, or

Chart 27-2 Chi-square test on Hardy-Weinberg experiment.

Calculated equilibrium	*bb*	*br*	*rr*
Genotype frequencies	________	________	________
Observed counts	________	________	________
Expected counts	________	________	________
Observed − expected	________	________	________

Chi-square calculations:

Note: $\chi^2 = \Sigma \frac{(\text{observed count} - \text{expected count})^2}{\text{expected count}}$

Look up the probability for the calculated value of χ^2 in the table in Chapter 11. $p <$ __________ .

expected count of genotypes in your equilibrium population. Then use these expected counts to do a chi-square test on the **observed counts** in any of the generations except the starting one. (The chi-square test was first discussed in Chapter 11.) Show your calculations in Chart 27-2.

QUESTIONS

Did the observed results differ significantly from those predicted by the Hardy-Weinberg model?

How do you suppose increasing the sample size of alleles (beans) would affect the results?

EXERCISE 27-2 NONRANDOM MATING

Objective To demonstrate the effect of nonrandom mating on change in genotype frequency between generations.

In most plants and animals, nonrandom mating is the rule rather than the exception. Male and female animals may choose their mates on the basis of body size, territory size, or display behavior. Yet even if conscious mate choice by the organisms themselves has little effect, environmental factors may bring together organisms with similar genotypes and phenotypes. In the bean-bag model, nonrandom mating will be simulated by manipulating the pairing of alleles.

- Start with a population of 50 with the equilibrium frequencies of genotypes calculated for the chi-square test in Exercise 27-1. To do this, multiply the three equilibrium frequencies by 50, and count out the appropriate number of genotypes. Assume that the *b* allele is dominant over the *r* allele, so that *bb* and *br* individuals have the same phenotype. (Normally, we would capitalize the dominant allele, but for this example leave *b* lower case.) Record the starting genotype and allele frequencies in Chart 27-3. Next, assume that organisms prefer to mate with other organisms of their own phenotype. In nature such a preference would not be 100 percent effective, but we can simulate "perfect" compliance by taking all the beans for *bb* and *br* individuals and putting them in one container, and putting all the beans for *rr* in another. These two containers represent separate gene pools, in which separation is enforced by nonrandom, preferential mating.
- Simulate the mating of organisms having the same phenotype by drawing pairs of beans from the *bb*/*br* container and tallying the genotypes on a piece of scratch paper. Replace and mix the beans between draws. Also simulate mating in the *rr* container, although all the offspring in this case must be *rr*, because all of the alleles are *r*. Tally the results on scratch paper. The combined results of the *bb*/*br* and *rr* matings represent the new first-generation genotype and allele frequencies. Add the numbers of *bb*, *br*, and *rr* genotypes from the *bb*/*br* container to the number of *rr* genotypes from the *rr* container. Record the combined numbers of genotypes and alleles for the first generation in Chart 27-3.

- Repeat the experiment, but for the gene pool use the new genotype frequencies of the first generation. Count out the appropriate new numbers of genotypes in the first generation (you may need to get more beans from a stock jar), and again separate the *bb* and *br* individuals into one container and the *rr* individuals into another. Tally the genotypes of the second round of matings on scratch paper. Record the combined second-generation results in Chart 27-3.

Chart 27-3 Effects of nonrandom mating on genotype frequency.

	Numbers of				
Generation	Genotypes *bb*	*br*	*rr*	Alleles *b*	*r*
Starting	______	______	______	______	______
First	______	______	______	______	______
Second	______	______	______	______	______

- As in the Hardy-Weinberg experiment, the changes in genotype frequency caused by preferential mating can be modeled mathematically. Treat each container as a separate population. Calculate the predicted frequency of pairing of the two alleles in each container for the starting generation.

From random pairing in the *bb*/*br* container:

predicted *bb* genotype frequency = frequency of *b* × frequency of *b*
predicted *br* genotype frequency = 2(frequency of *b* × frequency of *r*)
predicted *rr* genotype frequency = frequency of *r* × frequency of *r*

- Multiply each predicted frequency by the number of genotypes chosen from the *bb*/*br* container (the number of genotypes is one-half the total number of beans or alleles) to get the **expected count** of genotypes in the first generation. Enter the data in Chart 27-4.

Chart 27-4 Expected count of genotypes from nonrandom pairing.

	Predicted genotype frequency	Number of genotypes chosen from container	Expected count
For *bb*	______	______	______
For *br*	______	______	______
For *rr*	______	______	______

From random pairing in the rr container:

- The *rr* genotype frequency in this container is 1, so you will get the same number of *rr* individuals you started with *from this container alone*. Number of *rr* individuals: ______ .

- Total the expected genotype frequencies for both containers. Add this number to the expected count of *rr* genotypes for the *bb*/*br* container to get the new frequency of *rr* genotypes in the first generation. In Chart 27-5, compare the expected counts to the actual counts you obtained earlier.

Chart 27-5 Comparison of actual and expected counts in first generation.

	Expected genotype frequencies	Observed genotype frequencies
For *bb*	__________	__________
For *br*	__________	__________
For *rr*	__________	__________

Perform a chi-square test of observed versus expected values in this experiment.

Chi-square calculations:

Note: $\chi^2 = \Sigma \frac{(\text{observed count} - \text{expected count})^2}{\text{expected count}}$

Look up the probability for the calculated value of X^2. $p <$ __________

What is the null hypothesis in this experiment?

Is the null hypothesis accepted or rejected in the chi-square test?

QUESTIONS

The null hypothesis in this case is "Nonrandom mating occurs, in which like phenotypes mate only with like phenotypes." Is the null hypothesis rejected?

What would you expect to happen to genotype frequency over a large number of generations?

What do you suppose would happen if *bb* and *br* individuals mated only with *rr* individuals and vice versa? (If time permits, perform this experiment through one or two generations and see if the results match your predictions.)

EXERCISE 27-3 GENETIC DRIFT

Objectives To demonstrate the effects of genetic drift on genotype frequencies; to describe the changes induced in a population's genotypes caused by the splitting off of a small subsample of the population; and to describe why large population size is a necessary requirement for genetic equilibrium.

In the previous exercise, mating behavior separated the population into two breeding units. This separation had an effect on genotype frequencies. In nature, reproductive populations may be split by geographical barriers that develop over a long period of time, or by dispersal of a few organisms to an isolated habitat. An example of the latter is the dispersal of animals and plants to island communities. Natural bottlenecks in population size also can occur when for some reason a population is reduced to a few individuals.

When a small group of pioneer organisms splits off from a larger population, there is potential for significant **genetic drift**—sharp changes in gene frequency caused by the particular mix of genotype frequencies in the small group of pioneers. This effect is sometimes referred to as **sampling error** (although there is no "error" involved). Genetic drift can be simulated by taking a small subsample of pioneers from the starting generation in Exercise 27-1.

- Set up the starting population used in Exercise 27-1 by mixing 50 pairs of beans with the required genotypes in one container. This represents the gene pool source for the pioneers.

Pick out four pairs of beans at random and record their genotypes in Chart 27-6. These pairs represent a population of four pioneers. Replace the beans in the container, and repeat the process for four more pioneer populations. Record the genotypes of the four pioneers in each population in the chart. Then calculate the genotype frequencies in each population. For example, three *bb* genotypes in a population of four individuals represent a frequency of 0.75. Record the genotype frequencies in Chart 27-6.

Chart 27-6 Possible pioneer populations.

Genotypes of four individuals drawn at random from the starting population.

Population 1	Population 2	Population 3	Population 4	Population 5
________	________	________	________	________
________	________	________	________	________
________	________	________	________	________
________	________	________	________	________

Genotype frequencies in each pioneer population.

bb	________	________	________	________	________
br	________	________	________	________	________
rr	________	________	________	________	________

- Compare the frequencies of genotypes in the pioneer populations to those in the starting populations. Explain how the founder effect can produce pioneer populations with genotype frequencies very different from the starting population and each other.

- Genetic drift can cause the **fixation** or **extinction** of alleles in the pioneer population. Fixation occurs when a single allele achieves a frequency of one; extinction occurs when the frequency of an allele drops to zero. Assume you start with a pioneer population of four individuals, with a total of eight alleles in the gene pool, four *b* and four *r*. Simulate this population by mixing four *b* and four *r* beans in a container. Assume that the population will maintain a size of four in each succeeding generation. This time we will determine the genotypes of offspring in a slightly different way than before. Randomly draw out two pairs of beans. Each pair represents two parent individuals. These two individuals will produce two offspring. List the genotypes of this first set of parents in Chart 27-7. Next, to establish the genotypes of their two offspring, use a coin flip or some other randomizing method to determine which of the two alleles is contributed by each parent. For example, assume parent 1 is *bb* and parent 2 is *br*. Parent 1 will then contribute a *b* to each offspring, but parent 2 can contribute *b* or *r*. Flip a coin: If heads, parent 2 contributes a *b* allele; tails, parent 2 contributes an *r* allele. If both parents are genotype *br*, you will need a coin flip for each parent to determine each offspring genotype. Record the genotypes of the first two offspring in Chart 27-7.
- Replace the parent beans in the container and draw two more pairs to represent a second set of parents. Use the same method to determine the genotypes of two offspring, and record the genotypes in the chart. Calculate the allele frequencies in this new generation of four offspring.

- Repeat the entire procedure for a second generation, but, for parents this time, use the genotypes of the four first-generation offspring as the sample of eight beans to draw from. Record the results in Chart 27-7.
- Repeat the procedure once more for a third generation, using the offspring of the second generation as the eight beans to draw from.

Chart 27-7 Fixation and extinction of alleles.

First generation	Genotypes of first set of parents		Genotypes of second set of parents	
	______	______	______	______
	Genotypes of first generation offspring			
	______	______	______	______
	Frequency of allele b =	______		
	Frequency of allele r =	______		
Second generation	Genotypes of first set of parents		Genotypes of second set of parents	
	______	______	______	______
	Genotypes of second generation offspring			
	______	______	______	______
	Frequency of allele b =	______		
	Frequency of allele r =	______		
Third generation	Genotypes of first set of parents		Genotypes of second set of parents	
	______	______	______	______
	Genotypes of third generation offspring			
	______	______	______	______
	Frequency of allele b =	______		
	Frequency of allele r =	______		

QUESTIONS

Is one of the alleles heading for extinction? If so, which one?

Look at your pioneer populations in the previous section. Is the relatively rare allele (with lower frequency of the two alleles b and r) likely to become fixed in any of these? Explain why.

Explain how an allele that is rare in a large population might come to predominate in a small population subject to genetic drift.

EXERCISE 27-4 NATURAL SELECTION

Objectives To demonstrate how selection can cause changes in allele and genotype frequencies in bean-bag models; to describe directional selection and balancing selection in the context of these models; to design a bean-bag experiment to demonstrate frequency-dependent selection.

Because most evolutionary biologists study organisms under natural conditions (or simulated natural conditions), they often refer to natural selection as simply *selection*. An organism is said to be selected over another member of its population if its offspring are more likely to survive and reproduce. The term **fitness** is used to describe the relative reproductive success of organisms in a population. The organism that produces more offspring that survive to reproduce has a higher fitness.

In the bean-bag model for this exercise, you will act as the selective agent by eliminating a certain proportion of each genotype from successive populations. As you will see, selection can have a dramatic effect on gene and genotype frequencies.

A. Directional Selection

Selection often favors one phenotype over another in a given situation. For example, green grasshoppers may survive much better in grassy habitats than red ones of the same species. In this bean-bag model, start with the same equilibrium gene and genotype frequencies that you calculated in Exercise 27-1.

- Count out 50 pairs of beans with the appropriate genotypes and record their numbers as the generation "1 before selection" in Chart 27-8. Now, however, impose an artificial selection regime on the genotypes. Assume that the fitness of *bb* = 1, that is, all the *bb* genotypes survive to reproduce. Assume that the fitness of *br* is 0.8 (80% survive to reproduce) and that the fitness of *rr* is 0 (all of them die before reproducing). This situation may occur in nature when a recessive allele is harmful in the heterozygous state and lethal in the homozygous state. To impose selection on generation 1, multiply the number of beans of each genotype by their respective fitness values to determine the new number of each genotype surviving after selection. Discard the required number of "dead" bean pairs of genotype *br* and *rr* (set them aside in a stockpile). The net effect of this selection regime is that 100% of the *bb* genotypes survive, 20% of the *br* genotypes die, and none of the *rr* genotypes survive. Record the new genotype numbers in generation "1 after selection" in Chart 27-8.
- After "killing off" the required number of *br* and *rr* genotypes, the population will be less than 50. Suppose that the population is capable of asexual or vegetative reproduction to replace

the individuals lost through selection. To reconstitute a new population of 50 (generation 1), add bean pairs (genotypes) in proportion to their frequency in the population after selection.

For example, suppose you start with 10 *bb*, 10 *br*, and 30 *rr* genotypes. After selection, you would have 10 *bb*, 8 *br*, and no *rr* genotypes in a population of 18 individuals. To reconstitute the population to 50, you will need to add 32 bean pairs. In the population of 18 after selection, 10 (55.5%) were *bb*; thus 55.5%, or 18 (in whole numbers), of the 32 new individuals added should be *bb*. The remaining 14 individuals should then be *br*. So the reconstituted generation 1 would consist of 28 *bb* and 22 *br*. Obviously, selection has had a major effect in just one generation.

- Next, simulate mating in generation 1. Mix all the beans for generation 1 after selection in a container and randomly draw 50 pairs (replacing and mixing beans after each draw). Tally the numbers of the three genotypes on scratch paper, and record the result in the chart as generation "2 before selection."
- Again, have selection act on generation 2 by multiplying the genotype counts by the appropriate fitness values, thereby killing off some of the *br* and all of the *rr* genotypes. Calculate the new genotype frequencies and enter the values in Chart 27-8 as generation "2 after selection." Reconstitute the population size to 50 by the same means described above.
- Run through a third generation of selection and record the results.

Chart 27-8 Effects of directional selection on genotype and allele frequencies.

Fitnesses of genotype *bb* = 1.0
br = 0.8
rr = 0

	Numbers of				
Generation	Genotypes			Alleles	
	bb	*br*	*rr*	*b*	*r*
1 before selection	_____	_____	_____	_____	_____
1 after selection	_____	_____	_____	_____	_____
2 before selection	_____	_____	_____	_____	_____
2 after selection	_____	_____	_____	_____	_____
3 before selection	_____	_____	_____	_____	_____
3 after selection	_____	_____	_____	_____	_____

Describe the changes in genotype frequencies as a result of selection.

Describe any changes in allele frequencies.

What would probably happen to allele frequencies over a large number of generations?

Is it likely that the recessive lethal allele (r) would ever be eliminated from the population? Why or why not?

B. Balancing Selection

Suppose that the allele r is fairly rare in a population (perhaps recently a few individuals with the allele migrated into a habitat). And further suppose that in homozygous condition the fitness of genotype rr is very low. But heterozygous organisms (br) have a higher fitness than those homozygous for b. What would happen to the frequency of r?

The condition described is termed **heterozygote advantage** and occurs frequently in nature. It is one form of balancing selection, the process that counteracts the loss of variant alleles that are otherwise selected against. This is a complicated process to model with bean-bag techniques, but the effect of heterozygote advantage on the frequency of a rare allele can be demonstrated.

- For this bean-bag model, assume that the b allele is present in frequency 0.8, and the r allele's frequency is 0.2. Count out 100 beans with these frequencies (80 b, 20 r) and mix them in a container. Randomly draw 50 pairs (replacing and mixing beans between draws) and record the numbers of these genotypes in Chart 27-9 in the row for generation 1.
- Let selection operate. Assume the fitnesses of the genotypes are:

$$\text{fitness of } bb = 0.7$$
$$\text{fitness of } br = 1.0$$
$$\text{fitness of } rr = 0.2$$

These fitnesses reflect heterozygote advantage, that is, br has the highest fitness. Multiply the counts for generation 1 genotypes by their respective fitness values. The resulting numbers represent the population after selection. Divide each count by the total count for all three; these fractions represent the frequencies of the genotypes after selection. Calculate the new allele frequencies after one generation of selection. Record these data in the appropriate spaces in Chart 27-9.

Chart 27-9 Effect of heterozygote advantage on allele frequencies.

Initial frequency of alleles: *b* frequency = 0.8
r frequency = 0.2

Generation 1	Genotype counts		
	bb	*br*	*rr*
	______	______	______
Fitness:	0.7	1.0	0.2
Counts after selection	______	______	______

New allele frequencies:

b frequency = ______

r frequency = ______

How did frequency of the *r* allele change after one generation of selection?

Could the *r* allele ever become very common in this population? Why or why not?

C. Frequency-Dependent Selection

Suppose a seed-eating bird searches in certain habitats where seeds from one species of plant are abundant, until the seeds become hard to find. The bird then switches to a different habitat and searches for seeds of a different plant. The fitnesses of seeds of various species vary as their abundances vary and their susceptibility to predation varies. This phenomenon, termed *frequency-dependent selection*, is another form of balancing selection, and it is probably common in the complex natural world. In addition to predation, interspecific competition also may affect fitness in a frequency-dependent way. For example, plants growing in high-density plots (with many other plants as competitors) may not grow as tall or produce as many seeds as other plants growing in low-density plots.

- Based on the bean-bag models you have already used in this chapter, design a simple experiment that shows the effects of frequency-dependent selection. Use the same types of genotypes and alleles, but set up rules that govern their fitnesses at various densities. For example, if an allele becomes rare (its frequency drops below some arbitrary threshold), its fitness increases. If in later generations its frequency exceeds the threshold, the fitness drops to the original value. Or, in a more complicated case, the fitness might vary inversely with abundance. Try to design an experiment so that you can see an effect within two or three bean-bag generations.

Describe the experiment, the beginning frequencies of the genotypes and alleles, the regime governing fitness variation, and record your data in Chart 27-10.

Chart 27-10 Effect of frequency-dependent selection.

Beginning frequencies of genotypes:

bb	*br*	*rr*
______	______	______

Beginning frequencies of alleles:

b	*r*
______	______

Fitness regime:

Experimental procedure:

Data:

The material in this chapter corresponds to Chapters 44–45 in your text.

28
ECOSYSTEMS AND THE BIOSPHERE

The discipline of **ecology** is concerned with the interrelationships of organisms and their environment. Studies of such relationships vary in scope, from an investigation of the ecology of a small population of dandelions to one dealing with the global productivity of phytoplankton in the oceans. Ecologists have given names to the different functional units:

Ecosystem: a complete life-supporting environment, including living organisms and their physical and chemical environments.

Biosphere: Earth's surface region, including its land, waters, and atmosphere, which support all life on the planet.

Communities: groups of interacting species that share the same general ecosystem or habitat; the term is often used to refer to organisms that function together in an ecosystem, such as "a community of herbivores."

Populations: groups of individuals of the same species that live and interact with each other; this term, like *community,* is often used by ecologists to refer to small and large populations, which are dynamic entities whose growth or decline can be described statistically in terms of natality (per capita birth rate) and mortality (per capita death rate).

Ecologists often study organisms in the field. Field studies may consist of surveys of flora or fauna, monitoring of climatic conditions, or experimental manipulations of organisms or their environment. In field experiments, one factor is often controlled by the experimenter. For example, water may be artificially added to small plots of ground in the desert. Otherwise, nature is allowed to take its course—the amount of sunlight, wind, number of grazing herbivores, and so on, are uncontrolled. Compare this to a laboratory experiment in which the experimenter usually tightly controls *all* factors while varying one experimental factor in a strictly defined way.

This chapter deals with the ecology of a laboratory **microcosm**. A microcosm is a small system extracted from a larger one, but is analogous to the latter in its general constitution and function. In this case, you will be creating "minibiospheres," or miniature closed ecosystems, by sampling and sealing small portions of freshwater pond communities in closed glass containers. You will compare the structure and diversity of the community of pond organisms at the beginning and end of a period, and from these observations you will draw some inferences about the functioning of the larger biosphere.

EXERCISE 28-1 CREATING MINIBIOSPHERES

Objectives To set up four minibiospheres, extracted from a freshwater pond ecosystem, in sealed glass containers; to subject them to a variety of conditions, and to determine how such self-contained microcosms change under the defined conditions.

At first, the idea of creating a miniature biosphere to replicate a natural ecosystem may seem ludicrous. As your textbook explains, the Earth's biosphere is a highly complex system. Large-scale interchanges of chemical compounds between living and nonliving portions of the biosphere involve massive cycles of biologically important elements. These elements are the same ones introduced in Chapter 4 of this manual. They are sometimes referred to as a group with the acronym "**CHNOPS**" (pronounced roughly, "chin-ups"). The letters stand for carbon, hydrogen, nitrogen, oxygen, phosphorus, and sulfur. These elements play vital roles in living organisms; their renewal, or turnover, through the material cycles of the biosphere is vital to the continuance of life. The movement of energy through food chains or webs is also complicated, from **primary producers** (plants, algae, and photosynthetic bacteria) that capture the energy in sunlight to **consumers** (herbivores and carnivores) to **decomposers** (microbial populations that break down dead organic material). To try to bottle up a small microcosm of this vast system would seem absurd.

As it turns out, however, such microcosms are relatively easy to create, though still difficult to understand. In recent years researchers have bottled up small parts of larger ecosystems such as freshwater ponds or coral-reef–sand communities and found that the communities actually thrive inside the **closed ecosystems**. An example of a closed ecosystem is shown in Figure 28-1. Such minibiospheres are materially closed, that is, they are completely sealed off from any interchange of solid, liquid, or gas with the outside world. However, they are energetically open. Sunlight (solar energy) passes through the glass; heat energy is gained or lost depending on the external temperature. The particular minibiosphere shown in Figure 28-1 is an outgrowth of years of work by

Figure 28-1 An Ecosphere™ containing shrimp, algae, and bacteria in a saline solution. (Photograph courtesy Engineering & Research Associates, Tucson, Arizona.)

scientists, and is based on a proven, synthetic "recipe" of organisms and nutrients that is relatively stable. Called an Ecosphere™, this liter-sized glass sphere contains algae, adult shrimp about one centimeter long, various bacteria, and a mixture of nutrients in a saline solution. The company that makes it claims that with proper care (described below) the shrimp will live for several years and the algae and bacteria will survive even longer.

Apparently, then, minibiospheres are stable: Closing up a small portion of a larger ecosystem does not cause the death of the inhabitants. Dr. Clair E. Folsome of the University of Hawaii has been sealing up small samples of coral-reef sand in glass flasks for several decades, and he finds that the living systems achieve some sort of equilibrium and remain healthy for years. A typical Folsome-flask is shown in Figure 28-2. The more aesthetically pleasing Ecospheres were developed from concepts based on Folsome's originals. The Folsome-flask and Ecosphere are, however, different in an important aspect. Folsome-flasks are "pieces" of natural communities, whereas Ecospheres are artificially composed by scientists and are intended to support a particular higher life form, in this case, shrimp. Evidently, the complex CHNOPS cycles that occur in nature also occur in both types of flasks.

Figure 28-3 shows how carbon and oxygen may cycle through the living and nonliving components of an Ecosphere. Note that the algae are the primary producers of organic material (although some photosynthetic bacteria may also contribute to primary production). The algae also produce oxygen via photosynthesis. The shrimp and bacteria use this oxygen in aerobic metabolism. The shrimp function as consumers, grazing on the algae. The bacteria are decomposers, breaking down the fecal pellets of the shrimp, as well as any other dead organic matter. Through their respiratory metabolism, the shrimp and bacteria produce carbon dioxide, which is used by the algae in photosynthesis. These cycles of carbon and oxygen undoubtedly take place in the glass spheres, but exactly how other element cycles work and why the minibiospheres are stable remains a mystery.

In this exercise, you will work in small groups and use simple materials to make several minibiospheres. You will also design an experiment to test the effects of some environmental factors on the life inside the minibiospheres. Because of the amount of time required for this investigation, you will set up the minibiospheres 4–6 weeks before the end of the course. Finally, you will write up the results of your experiment and present them to the class for general discussion, when the findings of other groups can be compared to yours. This is an open-ended experiment: There are

Figure 28-2 Materially closed but energetically open ecosystem of the coral-reef–sand community developed by Dr. C. E. Folsome. Note sampling ports for withdrawing small samples of gas and liquid from 1-liter flask.

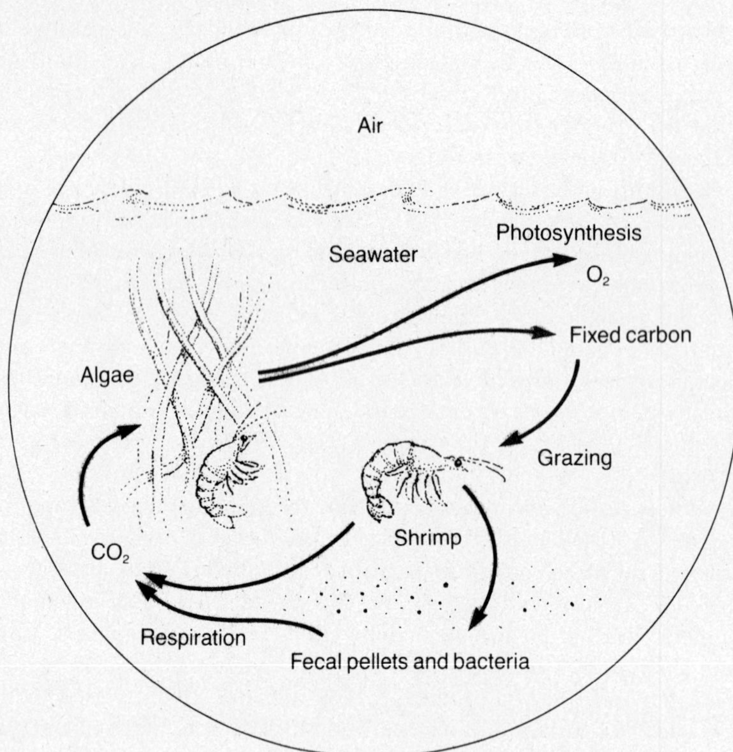

Figure 28-3 Probable cycles of carbon and oxygen within a materially closed ecosystem.

no right or wrong answers. Similarly designed minibiospheres may not yield similar results. Work as carefully as you can and keep detailed and accurate notes about how you prepare and observe the minibiospheres, and your experiment will yield worthwhile results.

- Although you need to plan your experimental design before making the minibiospheres, read the following description of how to set up a minibiosphere under standard conditions. Then you can decide on your experimental methods. The minibiospheres are relatively easy to set up. Work in small groups as directed by your instructor.

  1. Obtain four clean mason jars with screw-top, sealing lids. These sealing caps will be used to close the jars. If too much organic matter is used in the minibiospheres, gas buildup inside may cause them to explode. Therefore, use a nail to poke a hole in each lid, and seal the hole with melted wax. The wax prevents gas exchange and acts as a pressure-release valve.
  2. In each jar place a mixture of pond organisms, either provided by your instructor or collected in the field. Your jar should contain mostly water (about 3/4 full), plus a mixture of primary producers (algae and plants), consumers (snails and insects), and decomposers (bacteria mixed with 20–40 g of mud). Do not include any large animals or plants—the jar should provide a complete niche for each of the organisms in it. Obviously, a large fish or a cluster of many snails will not find the jar a suitably sized habitat.
  3. Let the jars sit on a desk top for the time it takes you to make a census of the organisms in them (up to a few hours).
  4. After the census, close the jars tightly, and place them on a shelf in the laboratory (or in your home or dormitory room) where you can watch their progress. Each group should maintain one jar as a control under standard conditions: indirect sunlight, a temperature range of 15–25°C.

5. During the succeeding 4–6 weeks, write a weekly description (about one-half page) of the appearance of the jar's contents. Note any dramatic changes in abundance of organisms (bacterial blooms, snail mortality, and so on). Although duties in tending the various jars may be split between group members, all members should be aware of the progress of all the jars.

- The four minibiospheres you will make constitute one control and three replicates, which will be subjected to various experimental conditions. Discuss with group members and your instructor what kinds of manipulations to perform on the experimental jars. The following list includes a few factors you might consider. Use your imagination.

1. The effect(s) of direct sunlight, which causes a greenhouse effect inside the jar.
2. The effect of darkness or cold on the minibiosphere.
3. The effect on populations in the jar of a top-heavy food pyramid (many consumers, few primary producers).
4. The effect on consumers of an initial algal "bloom" (dense algal concentrations).
5. The effect on algal and consumer populations of an abundance of mud and associated microbes.
6. The effect on algal productivity of adding a small amount of fertilizer (phosphate or nitrate).

Your instructor may keep one open jar as a nonclosed biosphere for comparison with the groups' closed models.

- A census of the organisms in the ecosystem will be the most difficult task of this exercise. By now, you are aware of the overall diversity of organisms in the living world (Chapters 14–22). However, the diversity of microorganisms in even a small part of a freshwater-pond community can be bewildering. The key to making this census is not to identify each individual organism (a virtually impossible task), but to get some quantitative measurement of the diversity and abundance of organisms at the beginning and the end of the experiment. You may also want to construct a food web representing the general types of consumers, producers, and decomposers in the minibiospheres.

- Your instructor may provide some guidelines for census methods, but you should use your own ingenuity as well. Here are a few suggestions.

1. The jar contains several **microhabitats**. These include the mud surface, buried mud, water column, glass walls of jar, and surfaces of large plants. You may think of other significant microhabitats, but you may opt not to survey them all. For example, you might sample 5 ml of water, centrifuge it for several minutes, and count the organisms that settle out. This would reveal the types and density (per 5 ml) of organisms present. Take at least two samples of each microhabitat you select to monitor. If the two samples are very different, take a third sample to make sure you have a good representation of organisms in each microhabitat.
2. If available, **hemocytometer slides** should be used to count the abundance of microorganisms in your microhabitat samples (normally the slides are used to count blood cells). These slides have a grid area on which organisms should be spread evenly. By counting the number of organisms of various types that occur in a set number of grid squares, you can measure the density of protists. If a hemocytometer slide is not available, densities can be calculated by counting the numbers and types of protists in a randomly chosen microscope field of view at a given magnification.
3. When counting organisms, classify them into broad taxonomic groups, such as green algae, aquatic plants, diatoms, ciliates, amoebae, and insect larvae.

- Measure the pertinent physical parameters of your experimental design. Use a light meter to determine illumination of the jars; also record the temperature regime to which the jars are exposed (minimum and maximum daily temperature). If algal density changes in the jar, you might also use the light meter to measure the opacity of the jar (amount of light passing through).
- Shown on the following pages are sample data sheets, which you can modify for your own experiment. Following the 4–6 weeks of the experiment, repeat the census of organisms in

the minibiosphere using the same methods employed before they were sealed. Use the weekly descriptions and before/after comparisons as data in your report. The report should include the following:

1. *Introduction*. General description of the minibiospheres and the hypotheses your experimental design planned to test in each case.
2. *Methods*. Precise descriptions of the experimental conditions to which each jar was exposed.
3. *Results*. A summary of the raw data from your before/after censuses and weekly descriptions. Do not simply include the raw data sheets. Make graphs or histograms to compare density and diversity (number of different kinds of organisms) before and after the experiment. Supplement quantitative data with a summary of changes noted in your weekly descriptions.
4. *Discussion and conclusions*. Did the experiment reveal anything about the original hypotheses you tried to test? If not, why not? Did any chance events occur that led you to some unexpected insight about the workings of the minibiospheres? What processes such as predation, competition, or temperature shock might account for the changes you observed? Can you suggest any future experiments that would clear up some of the questions left unanswered by your experiment? Finally, did the experiment give you any insight or appreciation into the functioning of the Earth's biosphere?

Experimental Treatment of Minibiospheres

Minibiosphere # ____________

Temperature regime: Min. ____________ Max. ____________

Photoperiod: ____________ hours light ____________ hours dark

Hypotheses to be tested:

Experimental methods:

Sample Data Sheet

Microhabitat sampled ______________

Method of sampling: (pipette, small scoop, etc.) ______________

Type of organism	Density (number in field of view or in area marked by grid lines on slide)
Green algae	______________
Unicells	______________
Filaments	______________
Colonies	______________
Diatoms	______________
Ciliates	______________
Snails	______________
Higher plants	______________
______________	______________
______________	______________
______________	______________
______________	______________
______________	______________
______________	______________

Sample Weekly Description

Minibiosphere # ______________

General description:

Continued on p. 406

Sample Data Sheet (continued)

Description of specific microhabitats:

Mud surface

Buried mud

Water column

Surfaces of higher plants

The material in this chapter corresponds to Chapters 48–49 in your text.

29
ANIMAL BEHAVIOR

Behavior is defined as the actions or reactions of an organism under specified circumstances. At one end of the spectrum are very simple reflex behaviors exhibited by many animals, such as a clam snapping shut when its shell is tapped. At the other end of the spectrum are the complex social behaviors of aggression, altruism, and others discussed in your textbook.

In this chapter, you will conduct experiments on both simple and relatively complex behaviors.* One exercise deals with the stereotyped responses of an organism to various environmental stimuli. The other exercise deals with the more complicated and variable aggressive behavior of a social vertebrate (a freshwater tropical fish). While demonstrating how behavior can be studied in a scientific way, these exercises also show that the more complicated a behavior is, the more it is likely to be affected by a variety of factors that the experimenter has a hard time controlling.

EXERCISE 29-1 REFLEX BEHAVIOR

Objectives To demonstrate the stereotyped behaviors of organisms to particular environmental stimuli; to define a taxis, and to design an experiment to determine which stimuli elicit one or more taxes in an experimental animal.

Animal taxes (singular taxis) are the simple responses of animals moving toward or away from a stimulus. The **tropisms** that you observed in plants (Chapter 25 of this manual) are analogous to the **taxes** of animals. However, instead of being the expression of changes in cell structure caused by hormones that typify plant tropisms, animal taxes are behaviors stimulated by electrochemical activity of the animal's nervous system.

Many organisms exhibit taxes in response to different features in the environment. Common kinds of taxes are **phototaxis** (movement in response to light), **chemotaxis** (movement in response to chemicals produced by the environment or other organisms), and **geotaxis** (movement in response to gravity). A taxis can be categorized as positive (movement *toward* the stimulus) or negative (movement *away from* the stimulus).

- Your instructor will provide you with one or more test organisms (snails, fish, fruit flies, and so on). Under the appropriate circumstances, these organisms exhibit one or more taxes. Your

*Guy Hoelzer of the University of Arizona contributed to the preparation of this chapter.

task will be to observe the organisms under "normal" conditions and to develop hypotheses about their possible taxes. Then you will design a simple experiment to test these hypotheses using the materials and equipment provided by the instructor. This exercise involves all the features of hypothesis development and testing covered in Chapter 1 of this manual. At this point you should be familiar enough with experimental design and the use of controls to design a straightforward experiment to test a clear-cut hypothesis. Use your creativity to formulate the hypothesis as a testable null hypothesis. The only constraints are (a) to use simple equipment and (b) to inflict no undue noxious stimuli on the creatures you are testing.

- Depending on time and animals available, you may test several possible taxes. Perform several replicates of the experiment(s) to be certain of your results. Warning: Some of the animals may exhibit behavior that only *appears* to be a simple taxis, and your experiments may thus "fail" to support your hypothesis. However, this is not failure—report the results of your experiment as best you can. If the results are inconclusive, modify your methods if time permits, or at least suggest how the methods should be modified to test the hypothesis. For each experiment, complete one of the data sheets provided.

Data Sheet for Experiment on Animal Taxes

Animal observed ______________

Observations, potential taxes to be tested

Experimental design (include drawings if helpful):

Results and data analysis:

Conclusion regarding type of taxis and positive or negative response:

Suggestions for further testing or to improve experimental design:

Data Sheet for Experiment on Animal Taxes

Animal observed ______________

Observations, potential taxes to be tested

Experimental design (include drawings if helpful):

Results and data analysis:

Conclusion regarding type of taxis and positive or negative response:

Suggestions for further testing or to improve experimental design:

Data Sheet for Experiment on Animal Taxes

Animal observed ________________

Observations, potential taxes to be tested

Experimental design (include drawings if helpful):

Results and data analysis:

Conclusion regarding type of taxis and positive or negative response:

Suggestions for further testing or to improve experimental design:

EXERCISE 29-2 AGONISTIC BEHAVIOR

Objectives To observe and describe agonistic (aggressive) behavior in male freshwater tropical fish; to describe specific behaviors used by the fish in confrontations with other males and in mock confrontations with their own mirror images; to describe the usefulness of display behavior in determining dominant and subordinate relationships.

Many animals exhibit strong agonistic behavior, or aggression toward members of their own and other species. These agonistic behaviors sometimes demarcate the boundaries of defended territories. Other times the behaviors establish dominance hierarchies. Much of this type of fighting is ritualized, and the combat is broken off before either party inflicts serious damage on the other. Establishing a "winner" without actual violence benefits not only the loser, who lives to fight another day, but also the victor, who can ill afford even small injuries that would hamper it in future agonistic bouts. In effect, both sides win (neither is injured), but the victor wins more (in territory, mating privileges, or social status).

Various species of marine and freshwater fish are excellent subjects for study of agonistic behavior. Territoriality is common in many species, in which males guard feeding areas or nest sites. Dominance hierarchies are also common, in which males establish a "pecking order" of dominance by a series of agonistic encounters between pairs of males. Agonistic behaviors can be elicited in many species by presenting conspecifics (members of the same species) or artificial models to a male. Physical or behavioral cues of one fish act as **releasers** of stylized behavior patterns in the other.

In this exercise, you will observe agonistic behavior in Siamese fighting fish (*Betta splendens*) commonly called Bettas. In a sense, this species is "unnatural" because it has been bred (artificially selected) for its highly aggressive behavior. In fact, contrary to the generalizations made regarding ritualized combat, no more than one male can live in a tank because males fight to the death. In this case, natural selection might have favored the evolution of a less-than-fatal social interaction, but artificial selection by fish hobbyists has favored the reproduction of males that fight to the death. Nevertheless, the specific agonistic behaviors displayed by male Siamese fighting fish are typical of many other fish species.

A. Nonagonistic Behavior

- Work in small groups.
- Your instructor will provide you with a small bowl or fish tank containing a single male Betta. Without unduly disturbing the fish, place a ruler in the tank near the fish and estimate the animal's size to the nearest 0.5 cm. Observe the fish for 5 minutes and take an inventory of its normal behavior patterns. Watch quietly, and try to make no sudden movements that might startle it. Record your observations in Chart 29-1. Make a sketch of the fish in the space provided. In your written notes and sketch, note in particular the following activities or physical features:

1. General levels of activities such as swimming or quietly drifting in midwater
2. General direction of body orientation (deviation of body axis from horizontal)
3. Position and shapes of dorsal, ventral, and caudal fins
4. Motion of pectoral fins
5. Position and movements of gill covers
6. Body coloration
7. Swallowing of air bubbles or creation of floating mats of air bubbles on surface of water

- Whenever possible, quantify the behavior by counting the number of times it occurs in a set time period, or estimate a time budget for certain activities (how much time spent drifting, actively swimming, making bubble mats, and so on).

Chart 29-1 Nonagonistic behavior of *Betta splendens.*

General appearance of fish (size, color):

Sketch of fish showing typical body orientation and fin shapes and positions:

Quantification of behaviors

Behavior	*Description*	*Frequency or time budget*

B. Agonistic Confrontation

- As directed by your instructor, one group will place its fish into a small bowl or jar with a mesh covering and gently lower it into the tank with another group's male. Try to place the new fish on the opposite side of the tank and try not to startle the resident fish in the tank with your own motions. Watch quietly and carefully for 5 minutes. Both groups should focus primarily on the behaviors of their own fish, although the activities of the other group's fish will be obvious as well. Describe any new behaviors not observed during the 5-minute nonagonistic solitary activity recorded earlier. Sketch any significant differences in fin position or motions. Again, quantify behaviors when possible by counting or estimating time budgets. Record your descriptions in Chart 29-2. Compare your observations with those of the other group. Note any differences in the chart.

Chart 29-2 Agonistic confrontation between two male *Betta splendens*.

Size of resident male ________________

Size of introduced male ________________

General notes on activities of your group's male:

New behaviors (not observed during nonagonistic solitary activity):

Sketch of new fin positions or motions:

Quantification of behavior

Behavior	*Description*	*Frequency or time budget*
________	________	________
________	________	________
________	________	________
________	________	________
________	________	________
________	________	________
________	________	________

C. Interspecific Interaction

- So far, we have assumed that the behaviors elicited by male-male confrontation are due to agonistic actions directed at males of the same species. Is this assumption correct? Or is this just a general response to a foreign fish?
- To answer these questions, your instructor will provide you with either female Bettas (much drabber in coloration than males) or comparably sized fish of a different species. Introduce this "neutral" intruder into the tank with your fish, using the same methods as in the previous experiment. Record the behavior of the resident male Betta for 5 minutes in Chart 29-3. What do the results tell you about the behavior during male-male confrontations?

Chart 29-3 Response of male *Betta splendens* to neutral fish presentation.

Type of neutral fish presented ______________________________

General behavior of resident male *Betta* toward intruder:

Quantification of behaviors

Behavior	*Description*	*Frequency or time budget*

D. Mock Confrontation

- Male Bettas are never perfectly matched and many factors (such as size and previous experience) can determine the outcome of a confrontation. However, one can present a male with an evenly matched foe by placing a mirror next to the fish. Perform this experiment by placing a mirror next to the fish but outside the tank. Observe the activities of the fish for 5 minutes and record your observations in Chart 29-4.

Did the behavior of the fish confronting its own image differ from its behavior toward another male? If so, describe the difference in behavior.

What might account for any behavior differences you observed?

Chart 29-4 Response of male Betta to mock confrontation with its mirror image.

General behavior of male toward its mirror image:

Quantification of behaviors

Behavior	*Description*	*Frequency or time budget*

- Describe an experiment using artificial, fishlike models that would determine the exact features of behavior or physical appearance that act as releasers for the agonistic behavior of male Bettas.